# Biological Effects of Low-Frequency Electromagnetic Fields

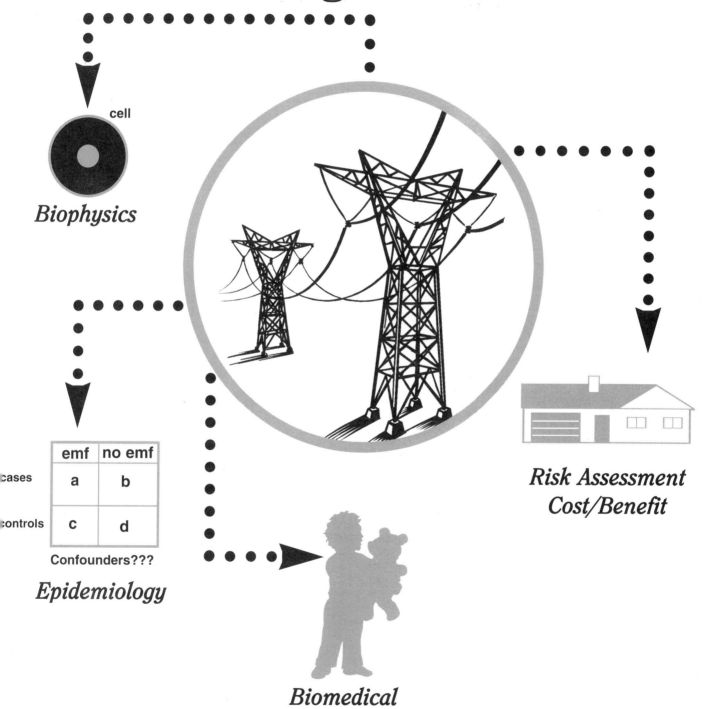

cell

*Biophysics*

| emf | no emf |
|-----|--------|
| cases | a | b |
| controls | c | d |

Confounders???

*Epidemiology*

*Biomedical*

*Risk Assessment Cost/Benefit*

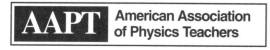

**AAPT** American Association of Physics Teachers

Edited by
D. Hafemeister

612.01442
B 521

**Biological Effects of Low-Frequency Electromagnetic Fields**

© 1998 American Association of Physics Teachers. All rights reserved.

American Association of Physics Teachers
One Physics Ellipse
College Park, MD 20740-3845
www.aapt.org

ISBN 0-917853-89-X

Cover design by Christine Rogers.

# Contents

# Preface

Concern about possible health effects caused by extremely low-frequency electromagnetic fields (EMFs) from power lines has generated a great deal of press coverage, fear, and legal action. The articles in this book explore facts and conclusions from several different fields of study behind this public policy issue.

Physicists long have been skeptical of the 1979 paper that reported a weak association (a correlation) between childhood leukemia and the current capacity of power lines near residences. However, correlations do not prove causality; other factors can correlate with the wire-code designations and "confound" the data. This is particularly true because the EMFs from the powerlines are usually considerably less than the EMFs produced inside the home. It is very difficult for epidemiologists to determine true associations of very small (or zero) effects on relatively rare death modes because confounding affects can confuse the data.

Biophysicists have carried out experiments and theoretical calculations attempting to determine possible EMF mechanisms that might cause cancer. Thus far, this research has not found a viable mechanism, but the biophysics papers contained in this compilation show how some physics interactions might affect biological systems. Some of the evidence gathered in the articles contained in this book indicates that externally induced electrical fields and currents are 1,000 times less than naturally occurring currents from thermal motion.

The main conclusion of my research on this subject can be summed up by the a statement in a study published by the National Academy of Sciences panel: "Based on a comprehensive evaluation of published studies relating to the effects of power-frequency electric and magnetic fields on cells, tissues, and organisms (including humans), the conclusion of the committee is that the current body of evidence does not show that exposure to these fields presents a human-health hazard. Specifically, no conclusive and consistent evidence shows that exposures to residential electric and magnetic fields produce cancer, adverse neurobehavioral effects, or reproductive and developmental effects."

I invite you to read the articles compiled in this book and to come up with a reasonable and scientific conclusion based on the evidence at hand.

David Hafemeister
California Polytechnic State University
San Luis Obispo, CA  93407

*Dr. David Hafemeister led the American Physical Society's Panel on Public Affairs Study on* Powerline Fields and Public Health *in 1995-96. He chaired APS-POPA during 1996-97.*

# RESOURCE LETTER

Roger H. Stuewer, *Editor*
*School of Physics and Astronomy, 116 Church Street*
*University of Minnesota, Minneapolis, Minnesota 55455*

This is one of a series of Resource Letters on different topics intended to guide college physicists, astronomers, and other scientists to some of the literature and other teaching aids that may help improve course content in specified fields. [The letter E after an item indicates elementary level or material of general interest to persons becoming informed in the field. The letter I, for intermediate level, indicates material of somewhat more specialized nature; and the letter A, indicates rather specialized or advanced material.] No Resource letter is meant to be exhaustive and complete; in time there may be more than one letter on some of the main subjects of interest. Comments on these materials as well as suggestions for future topics will be welcomed. Please send such communications to Professor Roger H. Stuewer, Editor, AAPT Resource Letters, School of Physics and Astronomy, 116 Church Street SE, University of Minnesota, Minneapolis, MN 55455.

# Resource Letter BELFEF-1: Biological Effects of Low-Frequency Electromagnetic Fields

David Hafemeister
*Physics Department, California Polytechnic State University, San Luis Obispo, California 93407*

(Received 19 December 1995; accepted 5 April 1996)

This Resource Letter provides a guide to the literature on the interaction of extremely low-frequency electromagnetic field (ELF/EMF) interactions with biological matter, and on the possibility that such interactions could have a harmful effect on human health. Journal articles and books are cited for the following topics: ELF/EMF theoretical interactions with biological cells, organs and organisms, magnetic dipole interactions, sensing by animals, biomedical–biophysical experiments, epidemiology, and litigation–mitigation risk issues. © *1996 American Association of Physics Teachers.*

## I. INTRODUCTION

The interaction of electric and magnetic (EM) fields with matter has been studied by physicists for over a century. Calculations based on the classical equations of Maxwell and the equations of quantum mechanics have long been used to estimate the strengths and characteristics of the EM interactions with condensed matter, molecules, atoms, and particles. Experiments have shown that these equations successfully represent the interactions, thus allowing physicists to use these interactions to investigate the basic properties of matter. The bibliography in this Resource Letter will extend this subject matter into the region of 50 Hz (European) and 60 Hz (U.S.), the extremely low-frequency electromagnetic fields (ELF/EMF) interacting with biological matter.

Physicists are often asked about the potential health hazards of ELF/EMF. In 1979, an epidemiology study by N. Wertheimer and E. Leeper reported an enhanced rate of leukemia for children living near 60-Hz electrical power lines in Denver, CO. This study catalyzed the wide-spread opinion that it is dangerous to live near electrical power lines. However, this study has been widely criticized inasmuch as the assignments of wire configurations (type of nearby power lines) to residences were made subjectively and with the investigators' knowledge as to whether an afflicted child or control had lived there. Furthermore, cumulative data on childhood leukemia has been inconsistent and inconclusive, considered by some to suggest only a weak association with ELF/EMF. By late 1995 there were well over 100 published epidemiological studies in the general scientific literature. These studies fueled public concerns about the possibility that ELF/EMF can promote cancer. In response to this concern, many disciplines are carrying out wide-ranging research programs to determine if there is a positive linkage between ELF/EMF and cancer. In 1991, Congress asked the National Academy of Sciences/National Research Council (NAS/NRC) to evaluate the literature on possible health effects of ELF/EMF. The Academy is expected to report its results in 1996. In addition, the 1992 Energy Policy Act established a $65 M 5-year program on ELF/EMF research, which is being reviewed by the NAS/NRC. A much longer version of this paper can be obtained at http://www.calpoly.edu/~dhafemen.

### A. ELF/EMF source terms

Since the 5000-km wavelength of 60-Hz radiation is much larger than the relevant distances from power lines and appliances, the nonradiative, near-field terms are considerably larger than the radiative terms. In practice, only 1 mW is radiated from a 10-km section of a 60-Hz, 500-MW power line which is only $10^{-12}$ of the transmitted power. To a very good approximation the electric field from a power line is determined from its charge distribution (or its voltage) from Gauss's law while the magnetic field is determined from the current flow with Ampere's law. Since power lines have op-

© 1996 American Association of Physics Teachers     974

posing, separated currents, the electric and magnetic dipole moments per unit length produce EM fields that diminish as the inverse square of the distance.

Several state regulations limit the fields from transmission lines to about 10 kV/m for the $E$ fields and about 200 mG for $B$ fields. (The mG unit is the standard unit for most U.S. regulations and publications in this area. For SI units, 1 $\mu T = 10$ mG, 1 $T = 10^4$ Gauss.) Some city regulations seek to constrain $B$ fields to less than 2 mG, a direction that is supported at the national level by those who believe there are harmful biological effects. There are public guidelines for ELF/EMF at 1000 mG because pacemakers can exhibit abnormal pacing characteristics in 60-Hz fields above that threshold and because of induced body currents.

A typical U.S. home has the Earth's constant magnetic field of about 450 mG and a 60-Hz background magnetic field level (primarily not from power lines) that ranges from 0.5 to 4 mG with an average value of 0.9 mG. Five percent of the homes have fields above 2.9 mG, and 1% are above 6.6 mG. For comparison sake, one study reports that electrical powerline workers experience an average field of 11 mG. Typical transmission power lines produce average fields at distances of 30 and 60 m as follows:

| | $E$ (V/m at 30/60 m) | $B$ (mG at 30/60 m) |
|---|---|---|
| 115 kV | 0.07/0.01 | 1.7/0.4 |
| 230 kV | 0.3/0.05 | 7.1/1.8 |
| 500 kV | 1.0/0.3 | 12.6/3.2 |

As a simple example, a two wire 500 MW transmission line at 500 kV draws 500 A in opposing directions in the two wires. From Ampere's law a single wire of 500 A produces a field of 33 mG at a distance of 30 m. If two opposing currents of 500 A are separated by 4 m, the field will be 4.4 mG (in the plane of the wires). By reducing the separation to 1 m, the field falls to 1.1 mG. At a doubled distance of 60 m, the field from the single conductor is 17 mG and the fields from the paired conductors are 1.1 mG for a 4-m separation and 0.3 mG for 1-m separation. Motor and appliance electrical coils produce either magnetic dipole or quadrupole fields that diminish as the inverse square or cube of the distance, respectively. Average fields at a distance of 30 cm are: color television (7 mG), microwave (4 mG), analog clocks (15 mG), electric razors (20 mG, 100 mG at 15 cm) and hair driers (1 mG, 300 mG at 15 cm).

## B. Electric fields in biological matter

$E$ fields are greatly reduced in biological matter from their values in air external to the body. Since the boundary conditions on Maxwell's equations require the real current density in the body to almost equal the displacement current density outside the body, the 60-Hz electric field from a power line is diminished by seven to eight orders of magnitude inside the human body. This factor reduces the maximum allowable $E$ field of 10 000 V/m at the edge of the right-of-way of a power line to an internal electrical field of only $10^{-3}$ to $10^{-4}$ V/m. A smaller 60-Hz $E$ field of 100 V/m, the same magnitude as the earth's surface field, will produce an $E$ field in the body of about $10^{-5}$ to $10^{-6}$ V/m. These values of internal $E$ fields should be compared to the internal field in the human body from thermally driven charge-density fluctuations in the human body. Since the $E$ field from the charge of a proton at ten Bohr radii is a very considerable $6 \times 10^{+9}$ V/m,

it is not surprising that fluctuations in the electric dipolar fields from Brownian motion can contribute meaningfully. Thermal fluctuations in the electrolyte of the biological resistors cause $E$-field fluctuations that appear as voltage fluctuations. Estimates of the Johnson–Nyquist noise voltages give root-mean-square average $E$-field fluctuations of about $2 \times 10^{-2}$ V/m within the electrolyte of a 20-$\mu$ cell. The fluctuating $E$ fields in the electrolyte are considerably larger than the internal fields of $10^{-6}$ to $10^{-3}$ V/m from power lines.

Since cellular membranes have a much higher electrical resistance than the electrolyte between the cells, there is considerably less current flow through the cellular membranes from external sources. The potential across a cellular membrane is about 50 mV. Since the thickness of a cellular membrane is only 5–10 nm, very large $E$ fields of about $10^7$ V/m are produced in the membrane. Thermal fluctuations in the membrane are of the order of a $\mu$V, considerably less than the potentials of 50 mV across the membrane. As in the case of the cellular electrolyte, the noise fields in the cellular membranes are considerably larger than the ELF $E$ fields induced in the membranes.

If there were any health problems from EM fields, it is generally believed that the $B$ fields, and not the $E$ fields, would be the cause of health problems because the $E$ field is effectively shielded by the human body while the $B$ field is not shielded.

## C. Electric fish

Some animals have specialized organs to sense weak EM fields, a fact that is not relevant to potential health effects. Electric rays and electric eels produce very large electric discharges. The freshwater electric eel whose body is mostly an electric organ generates stunning 2 ms pulses of one ampere at 500 V, for a peak power of almost 500 W and an energy of one Joule per pulse. Whereas these pulsed fields have a low duty cycle, some freshwater fish produce continuous electric fields with amplitudes on the order of 10 V/m, frequencies from dc to 10 kHz, and power on the order of 10 mW. These so called weakly electric fish sense their environment and communicate by modulating and detecting modulations in the electric current through their skin.

Sharks can detect external fields of less than 1 $\mu$V/m at frequencies of the order of 1 Hz with their long electric sensing organs, the Ampullae of Lorenzini. As the shark crosses the earth's $B$ field lines, the Lorentz force induces electric fields in the amupulae that the shark detects and uses for navigation. Sharks also locate prey by sensing electric fields emanating from the prey's muscles and nerves during respiration and movement. Some amphibians, salamanders, and even a mammal, the duck-billed platypus, possess low-frequency electric sensory systems used for detecting weak electric fields generated by their prey's muscle activity. Electrosensory systems are not found in terrestrial animals because the high impedance of air attenuates the electric current and power in the electrostatic field to below detectable levels. At the other end of the spectrum, it takes strong $E$ fields of the order of 10 000 V/m to give humans a tactile sensation, by torquing body hairs that become polarized as they attract static electric charges.

## D. Magnetic fields in biological matter

Power line magnetic fields are often constrained by "prudent avoidance" to about 200 mG at the edge of a right-of-way, but in practice they are usually less than 2 mG for those living near power lines. By applying Faraday's law to this range of 2–200 mG, one obtains $E$ fields of between 4–400 $\mu$V/m. These values are considerably less than the natural Johnson–Nyquist $E$ fields of 0.02 V/m.

Walking in the earth's magnetic field of about 400 mG produces ''electromotive force'' voltages from Faraday's law. Walking in a constant magnetic field does not generate currents, but it is interesting to calculate the $E$ fields generated by walking. By moving very slowly at the rate of 0.1 m/s, an internal $E$ field of 4 $\mu$V/m is developed (corresponding to 2 mG of ELF/EMF). It one runs very fast at 8 m/s (18 mph), an internal $E$ field of 400 $\mu$V/m is developed (corresponding to 200 mG).

Rotations (or twirling) of the human body in the Earth's magnetic field of about 400 mG creates radial electric fields, giving rise to currents in the human body. A tilt of the head of 45 degrees in the slow time of 1.6 seconds will create an electrical field of 4 $\mu$V/m, corresponding to a 60-Hz field of 2 mG. A fast nod in 0.16 seconds creates an electric field of 40 $\mu$V/m, corresponding to a 60-Hz field of 40 mG.

## E. Biogenic magnetic materials

Some bacteria have tightly coupled chains of single domain, superparamagnetic magnetosomes, magnetite ($Fe_3O_4$) or greigite ($Fe_3S_4$) particles, that allow them to magnetically navigate vertically to find food. Chains of many magnetite grains, 50 nm on a side, have been observed in these bacteria. Because the magnetic interaction of these bacterial magnetic chains in the Earth's magnetic field is many times the thermal energy, the bacteria maintain their orientation with respect to the Earth's magnetic field. Since the magnetosome dipole relaxation times are much longer than 1/60 s in water in the earth's magnetic field, the bacteria do not oscillate significantly in 60-Hz fields.

Honey bees navigate by observing changes as small as 0.6% in the Earth's magnetic field (2.5 mG out of 400 mG). Other studies have shown that other animals, such as sea turtles and homing pigeons, can navigate using the Earth's magnetic field as a guide. In order to navigate to precision, it is necessary to have many magnetosomes with a permanent dipole moment which are able to maintain their direction in the Earth's magnetic field while being buffeted by Brownian thermal fluctuations.

Small magnetite crystals with average diameters of 33 nm, in some cases 200 nm, have been reported (but the work has not yet been replicated) in the human brain by using transmission electron microscopy. The level of magnetite is very low, of the order of one part in $10^9$ of the mass of the brain, much less than the magnetite fraction in magnetic bacteria of about 1%. It has not been shown that these magnetic particles are relevant for ELF/EMF and public health. If the magnetosomes are too small, they lack the ability to strongly torque in a weak magnetic field at 60 Hz. If the magnetosomes are large, the magnetite becomes multidomained, and the increased viscous torques dominate. In order to enhance this magnetic interaction it would be necessary to have very long chains of magnetosomes within a cell (which have not been observed) acting coherently. Calculations show that for fields less than 50 mG, viscosity damps out the induced oscillations to amplitudes less than those from thermal fluctuations. It has been conjectured that the large magnetic fields of

a magnetosome next to a cell might affect the flux of calcium ions through its membrane, but this should not be influenced significantly by weak 60-Hz magnetic fields.

## F. Stochastic resonance and squared dependence

Under certain circumstances, the addition of a small amount of input noise to a larger input signal can greatly increase the output signal and the output signal-to-noise ratio. The phenomena has been labeled ''stochastic resonance'' though the process does not involve ordinary resonance. Such stochastic-resonance enhancements have been observed in the mechanoreceptor hair cells of cray fish. It is highly speculative to connect stochastic resonance to predict enhanced ELF/EMF sensitivity in biological matter. Since the addition of a small input signal to a larger input noise does not result in an increased output signal-to-noise ratio, it would not seem that the stochastic resonance phenomena would enhance ELF/EMF sensitivity in biological matter.

Both the EM torque and force are proportional to the first power of the oscillating EM fields. Since the time average of a sine wave is zero, the average energy imparted to a system over many oscillations cannot be proportional to the first power of $E$ or $B$. Since the time average of the sine squared is nonzero, the projected biological effects would be expected to be proportional to the square of the oscillating fields ($E^2$ or $B^2$). This does not rule out a linear dependence for the case of constant or quasi-dc fields as observed at 1–2 Hz for sharks and bees. Since human epidemiology data do not show consistent, meaningful associations with cancer for those living in very high field regions, such as sleeping under electric blankets, working on electrical power lines, or working on electric railways, a squared dependent relationship has not been demonstrated.

## G. Radon near power lines

Henshaw et al.[38] report that naturally occurring radioactive daughters of radon are enhanced near power lines. After the daughters attach themselves to aerosols, the neutral aerosols are attracted by the gradient of the $E$ field toward the power line. Because the contaminated aerosols oscillate with the power frequency, they would tend to plate out more frequently on the skin. The aerosols containing the radioactive radon daughters would also be inhaled into the lungs in a strong enough concentration to cause cancer.

Detractors of this theory respond as follows: Radon concentrations in open air near power lines are very slight. The half-lives of the radon daughters are relatively short, thus making the transition to humans at a distance problematical. Some epidemiology data shows an association with magnetic fields, but essentially none show an association with electric fields. Residences beyond the right-of-way of power lines do not have considerable elevated electric fields. One would expect enhanced lung cancer which is not reported in excess near power lines, rather than the usual suspects of leukemia and brain cancer. Last, one would expect the radioactive aerosols to plate out on the power lines or on the skin in comparison to lung deposition.

## H. Cancer mechanisms

Chemicals, such as unburned carbon, and EM radiation at frequencies above the visible region have sufficient energy to directly initiate cancer. Visible light breaks bonds in the process of photosynthesis but is not usually suspected of causing cancer. The energy of a hydrogen bond is about 0.1 eV and that of a carbon–carbon single covalent bond is 3.6 eV. The photon energy from 60-Hz radiation of $2.5 \times 10^{-13}$ eV is, of course, insufficient to directly break chemical bonds. Thus, new interaction mechanisms would have to be proposed to predict possible health problems from ELF/EMF. It is known that very large EM fields affect membrane permeability and the recombination of ion radicals.

Cancer can be initiated by direct damage to the genetic material of cells (genotoxicity), or it can be promoted by increasing the probability that a genotoxic exposure will cause cancer (epigenetic activity or promotion). Direct cancer effects are exemplified by the breaking of chemical bonds in DNA, while indirect effects could promote the likelihood, severity or speed that cancer might be caused once the DNA bonds had been broken. It is conjectured that ELF/EMF could supply currents, torques, or forces in the body that could enhance the risk of cancer, such as the reduction of melatonin from the pineal gland from the action of ELF/EMF on magnetite in the brain. Or, ELF/EMF could be part of a multistep biological process. In order to clearly establish these conjectures, it is necessary to demonstrate a meaningful combination of positive findings from epidemiology and biomedical–biophysical experiments, which are consistent with a theoretical biophysical mechanism. The stronger the evidence from epidemiology, the lesser the requirement to have a consistent theoretical mechanism in order to take a public policy position, but conversely, weak epidemiology evidence should be treated with great caution.

## I. Epidemiology

By 1995 over 100 additional epidemiological studies have examined various possible associations between public health and ELF/EMF from power lines, appliances and other devices. Most of this literature is concerned with the power-line frequencies of 50 and 60 Hz and magnetic fields in the region of 1–10 mG. Scientific review panels have generally concluded that the combined data show at best a weak association with ELF/EMF and at worst that the findings are mutually inconsistent and inconclusive. Epidemiology examines disease and health in human populations by identifying associations between the occurrence of human diseases and the possible causes of those disease. Because epidemiology searches for correlations between a particular disease and environmental or other factors, it does not directly prove causality because there can be other explanations for correlations. However, when there is, for example, a very strong association between cancer and exposure, such as a strong linear correlation between the amount of additional cancer and the rate of smoking, the epidemiology data and the fact that the smoke contains known carcinogens are considered as the proof of causality. On the other hand, the association between cancers for nonsmoking family members and the rate of smoking in the home is quite weak. This epidemiology data has been accepted by the regulatory process as significant because of the strength of the other evidence (experiments and mechanisms). The tobacco industry and others consider this conclusion as political, based on weak data.

Because less than robust epidemiology data can be misinterpreted, Sir Austin Bradford Hill in his Presidential Address to the Section of Occupational Medicine at the Royal Society of Medicine (U.K.) presented a list of suggested cri-

teria by which to judge whether an association was indeed causal. The criteria list is not necessarily all-encompassing, but it gives very useful benchmarks.

(1) Strength: Is there a strong correlation between disease and ELF/EMF fields?
(2) Consistency: Have the same results been obtained by different researchers in different locations?
(3) Specificity: Does ELF/EMF produce the same types of cancer in similar proportions to other groups similarly exposed?
(4) Temporality: Since there is a latency period for cancer, are the measurements of ELF/EMF in the present the same as in the past?
(5) Biological gradient: Do higher ''doses'' of ELF/EMF cause more cancer than lower doses? Is there an approximate proportionality of risk and dose, as in the case of the probability of additional lung cancer and the number of cigarettes smoked per day?
(6) Plausibility: Does the biological data on conjectured cancer promotion by ELF/EMF converge on a plausible, consistent biological–biophysical mechanism?
(7) Coherence: One should expect coherence between the data and the mechanism. In general, most mechanisms that attempt to connect ELF/EMF and cancer would predict that enhanced exposures of ELF/EMF would enhance cancer rates.
(8) Experiment: Are the various in vitro (cells in culture) and in vivo (complete living systems) experiments consistent among themselves and with a theoretical mechanism?
(9) Analogy: Is the connection between ELF/EMF and cancer analogous to situations where the proof is more substantial. Does one have to have ''new'' physics to understand this connection?

Review panels have concluded that Hill's criteria do not lead to a link between ELF/EMF and cancer. The scientific panels that have reviewed the ELF/EMF epidemiology data have separated the results by the type of cancer. For example, recently three studies of ELF/EMF on electrical workers have appeared. The 1993 California study reported no association with either leukemia or brain cancer. The 1993 Canadian–French study reported an association with leukemia and astrocytoma, out of the 32 cancer types studied. Because these studies do not make corrections for multiple comparisons, one would expect a study of this many different types of cancer to produce 1 or 2 ''significant'' correlations even if there were no real associations, that is 1 or 2 ''false positives.'' (In addition, this study suffers from internal inconsistencies.) By contrast, the 1995 Savitz/Loomis study reported no association with leukemia, but they reported an association with brain cancer with weak statistics.

For these epidemiology studies, it is necessary to estimate the individual ELF/EMF doses. In the best epidemiological experiments, the magnetic doses have been measured for the electrical workers, but there are limits to these estimates. It is unclear whether the exposure metric should be the product of magnetic field strength times the duration of exposure, or proportional to the square of the field as dictated by basic physics (neglecting nonlinear cellular mechanisms), or the direction and magnitudes between ELF and Earth $B$ fields, or the harmonic content, or a frequency window.

## J. Biophysics and medical-physics experiments

Many types of experiments have been carried out to examine the possible interaction of ELF/EMF and biological matter, such as: (a) direct effects (heating, induced electric current, energy of charged molecules, excitation of molecules, changes in membrane potential); (b) direct forces on electric charges or electric moments; (c) resonant interactions (ion cyclotron or paramagnetic resonance); (d) torques on magnetic moments; (e) free-radical chemistry; (f) temporal average or spatial intensification of weak ELF/EMF waves. There have been many positive and negative findings from *in vivo* and *in vitro* experiments with ELF/EMF. Usually the researchers with positive findings do not claim a causal connection between cancer and ELF/EMF, but rather that the data is part of the findings that might make such a connection possible. The scientific review panels and review articles have pointed out the continuing problem with replicating experimental results on cells and animals. This failure to find positive links between ELF/EMF and cancer is consistent with those who say that such health effects should be very unlikely because ELF/EMF forces ($10^{-10}$ pN at 100 mG) are much less than both typical biological forces (5 pN myosin muscle molecule) and background forces from thermal oscillations ($10^{-9}$ pN). Because biological systems are very complex, this argumentation cannot be considered to be a sufficient proof of no health effects, but it is a very strong guideline.

## K. Mitigation, litigation, regulation, and cost/benefit

In a rational world, risks to human life would be reduced by prioritized spending on mitigation that ranked all the choices in terms of money per life saved (or money per year of life saved), including estimates for benefits to the natural world. Since the ELF/EMF issue should be joined with other risks in society, it is useful to conclude with some broader topics. Thus, society is concerned with relative rates of risk reduction and costs of mitigation. Cost estimates by the U.S. General Accounting Office for ELF/EMF mitigation from power lines, not covering appliances, have been substantial. Some of GAO's estimates are: $2 million/mile to bury transmission lines in fluid-filled steel pipes to reduce magnetic fields by 99%, $200 billion to bury transmission lines nationwide near homes with fields greater than 1 mG, $250 billion to reduce average exposure to less than 2 mG from all transmission and distribution lines. After an examination of the data described in this review, in 1995 the American Physical Society concluded: ''No plausible biophysical mechanisms for the systematic initiation or promotion of cancer by these power line fields have been identified. Furthermore, the preponderance of the epidemiological and biophysical/biological research findings have failed to substantiate those studies which have reported specific adverse health effects from exposure to such fields. While it is impossible to prove that no deleterious health effects occur from exposure to any environmental factor, it is necessary to demonstrate a consistent, significant and causal relationship before one can conclude that such effects do occur. From this standpoint, the conjectures relating cancer to power line fields have not been scientifically substantiated.''

## ACKNOWLEDGMENTS

I would like to thank Robert Adair, David Bodansky, Aviva Brecher, Richard Frankel, Robert Goldberg, John Moulder and Brian Rasnow for comments on the draft manuscript.

## II. JOURNALS

A wide variety of journals, world wide web sites, and internet newsgroups cover ELF/EMF topics.

*Advances in Electromagnetic Fields in Living Systems*
*American Journal of Epidemiology*
*British Medical Journal*
*Bioelectromagnetics*
*Biophysical Journal*
*Cancer Causes and Control*
*Epidemiology*
*EPRI Journal*
*Health Physics*
*Journal of Comparative Physiology*
*Journal of Experimental Biology*
*Journal of Theoretical Biology*
*IIIE Transactions on Biomedical Engineering*
*Mutation Research*
*Nature*
*Physical Review*
*Proceedings of the National Academy of Sciences*
*Proceedings of the Society of Experimental Biology and Medicine*
*Radiation Research*
*Science*

### A. ELF/EMF periodicals

*EMF Keeptrack*
*EMF Health and Safety Digest*
*EMF Health Report*
*EMF News*
*Microwave News*

### B. World Wide Web

*EMF-Link* (http://infoventures.com)
*Frequently Asked Questions on Powerlines and Cancer* (http://www.cis.ohio/state.edu/hypertext/faq/usenet/static-field-cancer-FAQ/)
National Cancer Institute/National Institute of Health (gopher://gopher.nih.gov/11/clin/cancernet and http://www.os.dhss.gov)

### C. Newsgroups

bionet.emf-bio
sci.med.phys
sci.physics.electromag

### D. Hot lines

Environmental Protection Agency (1-800-363-2383)
National Institute of Environmental Health Science (1-800-643-4794)
National Institute of Occupational Safety and Health (1-800-356-4674)

## III. CONFERENCE PROCEEDINGS

The scientific review panels listed below conclude that ELF/EMF is not a public health problem. Conference proceedings usually do not come to a conclusion nor do they include an economic dimension.

**1. Health Effects of Low Frequency Electric and Magnetic Fields**, Presidential Committee on Interagency Radiation Research and Policy Coordination (Oak Ridge Associated Universities, Oak Ridge, TN, June 1992). (I)
**2. Report of an Advisory Group on Non-ionizing Radiation**, National Radiological Protection Board (United Kingdom), Electromagnetic Fields and the Risk of Cancer Vol. 3 (1992). (I)
**3. Electromagnetic Fields: Biological Interactions and Mechanisms**, edited by M. Blank, Adv. Chem. **250** (1995). (I)
**4. Biological Effects of Electric and Magnetic Fields (Vol. 1. Sources and Mechanisms: Vol. 2, Beneficial and Harmful Effects)**, D. O. Carpenter and S. Ayrapatyan (Academic, San Diego, CA, 1994). (I)
**5. Extremely Low Frequency Electromagnetic Fields: The Question of Cancer**, edited by B. W. Wilson, R. G. Stevens, and L. E. Anderson (Battelle, Columbus, OH, 1990). (I)

## IV. TEXTBOOKS AND EXPOSITIONS

The following is a wide-ranging collection of summaries of ELF/EMF issues.

**6. Health and Low-Frequency Electromagnetic Fields**, W. R. Bennett (Yale U. Pr., New Haven, CT, 1994). A discussion of the ELF/EMF issues that were considered by the Oak Ridge interdisciplinary panel of scientists. (I)
**7. CRC Handbook of Biological Effects of Electromagnetic Fields**, 2nd ed., edited by C. Polk and E. Postow (CRC, Boca Raton, FL, 1996), Review chapters on ELF/EMF. (I)
**8. Phantom Risk: Scientific Inference and the Law**, edited by K. R. Foster, D. E. Bernstein, and P. W. Huber (MIT, Cambridge, MA, 1993). A summary of the various risks that society is concerned about. (I)
**9. Power Frequency Magnetic Fields and Public Health**, edited by W. F. Horton and S. Goldberg (CRC, Boca Raton, FL, 1995). Discusses in detail the ELF fields from power lines and appliances and the approaches that would be needed to mitigate them if ELF/EMF were a serious problem. (I)
**10. Radio-Frequency and ELF Electromagnetic Energies: A Handbook for Health Professionals**, edited by R. T. Hitchcock (Van Nostrand Reinhold, NY, 1995). (I)
**11.** "Cancer and Power Lines," W. R. Bennett, Phys. Today **47**, 23–29 (April 1994), and letters, Phys. Today **48**, 13–15, 71–73 (January 1995). A good discussion of the basic physics involved with ELF/EMF. (I)
**12.** "Biological Effects of Power-Frequency Fields as They Relate to Carcinogenesis," J. E. Moulder and K. R. Foster, Proc. Soc. Exp. Biol. Med. **209**, 309–324 (1995). An excellent survey and interpretation of the totality of the biomedical–biophysical data. (I)
**13.** "Electromagnetic Fields and Power Lines," W. R. Bennett, Science Med. **1**, 68–77 (July/August 1995). (I)
**14.** "Today's View of Magnetic Fields," T. S. Perry, IEEE Spectrum **31**, 14–23 (December 1994). A compilation of epidemiology data, but it fails to subdivide the data by the types of cancer involved. (E)

Two booklets give a great deal of information on ELF/EMF:

**15. Fields from Electric Power**, M. G. Morgan (Dept. Engineering and Public Policy, Carnegie Mellon, Pittsburgh, PA, 1995). (E)
**16. Questions and Answers About EMF: Electric and Magnetic Fields Associated with the Use of Electric Power** (Nat. Instit. Envir. Health Sci. and U.S. Dept. Energy, 1995). (E)

Three journalists, Paul Brodeur, who sensationalized ELF/EMF, and Gary Taubes and Jon Palfreman, who respond, give differing views on ELF/EMF.

**17. The Great Power-Line Cover-Up: How the Utilities and the Government Are Trying to Hide the Cancer Hazard Posed by Electromagnetic Fields**, P. Brodeur (Little Brown, Boston, MA, 1995). (E)
**18.** "Fields of Fear," G. Taubes, Atl. Mon. **274**, 94–108 (November 1994). (E)
**19.** "Apocalypse Not," J. Palfreman, Tech. Rev. **99** (3), 24–33 (April 1996). (E)

## V. CURRENT RESEARCH TOPICS

### A. Theory of ELF/EMF interactions with biological matter

The basic physics of ELF/EMF is discussed in this set of papers with the general conclusion from the physics community that the ELF/EMF interaction energies and forces are less than those from thermal fluctuations in the body.

**20.** "Catalogue of Electromagnetic Environment Measurements, 30–300 Hz," J. Randa *et al.*, IEEE Trans. Electromagn. Compat. **37** (1), 26–33 (February 1995). (A)
**21.** "Constraints on Biological Effects of Weak Extremely-Low-Frequency Electromagnetic Fields," R. K. Adair, Phys. Rev. A **43**, 1039–1049 (1991). (A)
**22.** "Comment on 'Constraints on Biological Effects of Weak Extremely-Low-Frequency Electromagnetic Fields,'" J. L. Kirschvink, Phys. Rev. A **46**, 2178–2184 (1992). (A)
**23.** "Reply to 'Comment on 'Constraints on Biological Effects of Weak Extremely-Low-Frequency Electromagnetic Fields''" R. K. Adair, Phys. Rev. A **46**, 2185–2187 (1992). (A)
**24.** "The Response of Living Cells to Very Weak Electric Fields: The Thermal Noise Limit," J. C. Weaver and R. D. Astumian, Science **247**, 459–462 (1990). (A)
**25.** "Some Engineering Models for Interactions of Electric and Magnetic Fields with Biological Systems," F. S. Barnes, Bioelectromagnetics Supplement **1**, 67–85 (1992). (A)
**26.** "Biological response to Weak 60-Hz Electric and Magnetic Fields Must Vary as the Square of the Field Strength," R. K. Adair, Proc. Nat. Acad. Sci. **91**, 9422–9425 (1995). (A)
**27.** "A model for the acute electrosensitivity of cartilaginous fishes," W. F. Pickard, IEEE Trans. Biomed. Eng. **35**, 243–249 (1988). (A)
**28.** "Rectification and signal averaging of weak electric fields by biological cells," R. D. Austumian, J. C. Weaver, and R. K. Adair, Proc. Nat. Acad. Sci. **92**, 3740–3743 (1995).

### B. Magnetic dipole interactions

The discovery of chains of magnetosomes in bacteria has stimulated interest in searching for magnetic structures in higher animals.

**29.** "Magnetic Guidance of Organisms," R. B. Frankel, Annu. Rev. Biophys. Bioeng. **13**, 85–103 (1984). (A)
**30. Iron Biominerals**, edited by R. B. Frankel and R. P. Blakemore (Plenum, New York, 1991). (A)
**31.** "Electron Microscopic Studies of Magnetosomes in Magnetotatic Bacteria," D. A. Bazylinski, A. J. Garratt-Reed, and R. B. Frankel, Microsc. Res. Technol. **27**, 389–401 (1994). (A)

Kirschvink's group has reported the discovery of very dilute magnetite in human brains, but this work has yet to be replicated. They also are concerned that some of the "positive" ELF/EMF experiments in unclean facilities might be caused by magnetite impurities in samples.

**32.** "Magnetite biomineralization in the Human Brain," J. L. Kirschvink, A. Kobayashki-Kirschvink, and B. J. Woodford, Proc. Nat. Acad. Sci. **89**, 7683–7687 (1992). (A)
**33.** "Magnetic Material in the Human Hippocampus," J. R. Dunn, *et al.*, Brain Res. Bull. **36**, 149–153 (1995). (A)
**34.** "Ferromagnetism and EMFs," A. K. Kobayashi, J. L. Kirschvink, and M. H. Nesson, Nature **374**, 123 (1995). (I)

Basic physics calculations show that it is very unlikely that ELF/EMF could meaningfully interact with chains of magnetosomes under reasonable conditions.

**35.** "Constraints of Thermal Noise on the Effects of Weak Fields Acting on Biological Magnetite," R. K. Adair, Proc. Nat. Acad. Sci. **91**, 2925–2929 (1994).
**36.** "Effects of ELF Magnetic Fields on Biological Magnetite," R. K. Adair, Bioelectromagnetics **14**, 1–4 (1993). (A)
**37.** "Effects of Extremely-Low-Frequency Magnetic Fields on Biological Magnetite," C. Polk, Bioelectromagnetics **15**, 261–270 (1994). Polk states that it is plausible to expect some biological interactions at the 20 mG level. (A)

## C. Radon near power lines

38. "Enhanced Deposition of Radon Daughter Nuclei in the Vicinity of Power Frequency Electromagnetic Fields," D. L. Henshaw, A. N. Ross, A. P. Fews, and A. W. Preece, Int. J. Rad. Biol. **69**, 25–38 (1996). See text for a discussion of the radon issue. (A)

## D. Stochastic resonance

It is unlikely that stochastic resonance can significantly entrain the thermal noise of the body, but it has been observed in biological mechanical systems.

39. "Stochastic Resonance and the Benefits of Noise: from Ice Ages to Crayfish to SQUIDS," K. Wiesenfeld and F. Moss, Nature **373**, 33–36 (1995). (I)
40. "Theory of Stochastic Resonance," B. McNamara and K. Wisenfeld, Phys. Rev. A **39**, 4854–4869 (1989). (A)
41. "The Benefits of Background Noise," F. Moss and K. Wiesenfeld, Sci. Am. **273**, 66–69 (August 1995). (E)

## E. Animals sensing ELF/EMF

Animals can sense $E$ fields less than 1 $\mu$V/m, $B$ field differences of less than 1 mG, and currents from their electrical organs to find food. These unique sensory abilities do not implicate public health from ELF/EMF.

42. "Honeybees Can Be Trained to Respond to Very Small Changes in Geomagnetic Field Intensity," M. M. Walker and M. E. Bitterman, J. Exp. Biol. **145**, 489–494 (1989). (A)
43. "Acquisition of Magnetic Directional Preference in Hatchling Loggerhead Sea Turtles," K. Lohmann, J. Exp. Biol. **190**, 1–8 (1994). (A)
44. "Electroreception and the Compass Sense of Sharks," M. Paulin, J. Theor. Biol. **174**, 325–339 (1995). (A)
45. "Electrosensory Organisms," J. Bastian, Phys. Today **47**, 30–37 (February 1994). (E)
46. "Phase and Amplitude Maps of the Electric Organ Discharge of the Weakly Electric Fish, Apteronotus, Leptorhynchus," B. Rasnow, C. Assad, and J. M. Bower, J. Comp. Physiol. A **172**, 481–491 (1993). (A)
47. "Interactions in the flexible orientation system of a migratory bird," K. P. Able and M. A. Able, Nature **375**, 230–232 (1995). Sparrows have a migratory magnetic compass and a star compass, updating with visual cues from the sky at sunset. (A)
48. "Interaction of apical and basal membrane ion channels underlies electroreception in ampullary epithelia of skates," J. Lu and H. M. Fishman, Biophys. J. **67**, 1525–1533 (1994). (A)

## F. Paramagnetic/cyclotron resonance

It is difficult to understand how cyclotron resonance could exist in liquids since they have high collision rates.

49. "Kinematics of Channelized Membrane Ions in Magnetic Fields," A. R. Liboff and B. R. McLeod, Bioelectromagnetics **9**, 39–51 (1988). (A)
50. "On the Cyclotron Resonance Model of Ion Transport," J. Sandweiss, Bioelectromagnetics **11**, 203–205 (1990). (A)

Some interesting, but unreplicated data on paramagnetic resonance follows, along with theoretical articles that disagree with the work.

51. "Clarification and Application of an Ion Parametric Resonance Model for Magnetic Field Interactions with Biological Systems," J. P. Blanchard and C. F. Blackman, Bioelectromagnetics **15**, 217–238 (1994). (A)
52. "Empirical Test of an Ion Parametric Resonance Model for Magnetic Field Interactions with PC-12 Cells," C. F. Blackman, J. P. Blanchard, S. G. Benane, and D. E. House, Bioelectromagnetics **15**, 239–260 (1994). (A)
53. "Criticism of Lednev's Mechanism for the Influence of Weak Magnetic Fields on Biological Systems," R. K. Adair, Bioelectromagnetics **13**, 231–235 (1992). (A)

## G. Further biomedical–biophysical experiments

The first reference below by Goodman et al., is a review of the biomedical–biophysical data from those who claim to see an effect from ELF/EMF. In the second paper, Valberg points out that many ELF/EMF experiments have failed replication tests. He suggests experimental procedures to clarify experimental categorizations. This section concludes with 20 biomedical–biophysical experiments using ELF/EMF. Also, see Ref. 12 by Moulder, who discusses these kinds of ELF/EMF experiments.

54. "Effects of Electromagnetic Fields on Molecules and Cells," E. M. Goodman, B. Greenbaum, and M. T. Marron, Int. Rev. Cytol. **158**, 279–338 (1995).
55. "Designing EMF Experiments: What is Required to Characterize Exposure?," P. A. Valberg, Bioelectromagnetics **16**, 396–401 (1995). (I)
56. "Effect of Low-level, 60-Hz Electromagnetic Fields on Human Lymphoid Cells: I. Mitotic Rate and Chromosome Breakage in Human Peripheral Lymphocytes," M. M. Cohen et al., Bioelectromagnetics **7**, 415–423 (1986). (A)
57. "Exposure of Mammalian Cells to 60-Hz Magnetic or Electric Fields: Analysis for DNA Single-strand Breaks," J. A. Reese et al., Bioelectromagnetics **9**, 237–247 (1988). (A)
58. "Effects of 50-Hertz EM Fields on Proliferation and on Chromosomal Aberrations in Human Peripheral Lymphocytes Untreated and Pretreated with Chemical Mutagens," M. Rosenthal and G. Obe, Mutat. Res. **210**, 329–335 (1989). (A)
59. "Exposure of Mammalian Cells to 60-Hz Magnetic or Electric Fields: Analysis of DNA Repair of Induced, Single-strand Breaks" M. E. Frazier, et al., Bioelectromagnetics **11**, 229–234 (1990). (A)
60. "Reproductive Integrity of Mammalian Cells Exposed to Power-frequency Electromagnetic Fields," G. K. Livingston et al., Environ. Molec. Mutat. **17**, 49–58 (1991). (A)
61. "Effect of 60-Hz Magnetic Fields on Ultraviolet Light-induced Mutation and Mitotic Recombination in Saccharomyces Cerevisiae," D. D. Ager and J. A. Radul, Mutat. Res. **283**, 279–286 (1992). (A)
62. "Electric and/or Magnetic Field Effects on DNA Structure and Function in Cultured Human Cells," M. Fiorani et al., Mutat. Res. **282**, 25–29 (1992). (A)
63. "Effects of Magnetic Fields on Mammary Tumor Development Induced by 7,12-dimethylbenz(a)anthracene in Rats," M. Mevissen et al., Bioelectromagnetics **14**, 131–143 (1993). (A)
64. "Exposure of Rats of a 50-Hz, 30-mT Magnetic Field Influences Neither the Frequencies of Sister-chromatid Exchanges nor Proliferation Characteristics of Cultured Peripheral Lymphocytes," M. Mevissen et al., Mutat. Res. **302**, 39–44 (1993). (A)
65. "Reproductive and Teratologic Effects of Electromagnetic Fields," R. L. Brent et al., Reproduc. Toxicol. **7**, 535–580 (1993). (A)
66. "Tumor Promotion in a Breast Cancer Model by Exposure to a Weak Alternating Magnetic Field," W. Loscher et al., Cancer Lett. **71**, 75–81 (1993). (A)
67. "Intermittent 50-Hz Magnetic Field and Skin Tumor Promotion in Sencar Mice," A. Rannug et al., Carcinogenesis **15**, 153–157 (1994). (A)
68. "Effects of Weak Alternating Magnetic Fields on Nocturnal Melatonin Production and Mammary Carcinogenesis in Rats," W. Loscher et al., Oncology **51**, 288–295 (1994). (A)
69. "Cytological Effects of 50 Hz Electromagnetic Fields on Human Lymphocytes in Vitro," A. Antonopoulos et al., Mutat. Res. **346**, 151–157 (1995). (A)
70. "A Histopathological Study of Alterations in DMBA-induced Mammary Carcinogenesis in Rats with 50 Hz, 100 $\mu$T Magnetic Field Exposure," A. Baum et al., Carcinogenesis **16**, 119–125 (1995). (A)
71. "No Effect of 60 Hz Electromagnetic Fields on MYC or Beta-actin Expression in Human Leukemic Cells," A. Lacy-Hulbert et al., Rad. Res. **144**, 9–17 (1995). (A)
72. "Dominant Lethal Studies in Male Mice after Exposure to a 50 Hz Magnetic Field," C. I. Kowalczuk et al., Mutat. Res. **328**, 229–237 (1995). (A)
73. "A 60-Hz Magnetic Field Increases the Incidence of Squamous cell Carcinomas in Mice," J. McLean et al., Cancer Lett. **92**, 121–125 (1995). (A)
74. "Short Exposures to 60 Hz Magnetic Fields Do Not Alter MYC Expression in HL60 or Daudi cells," J. D. Saffer and S. J. Thurston, Rad. Res. **144**, 18–25 (1995). (A)
75. "Melatonin and Puberty in Female Lambs Exposed to EMF: a Replicate Study," J. M. Lee et al., Bioelectromagnetics **16**, 119–123 (1995). (A)
76. "Therapeutic Applications of Low Frequency Electric and Magnetic

Fields," C. Polk, Adv. Electromagn. Fields Living Syst. **1**, 129–153 (1994). Large magnetic fields that change very quickly cause large internal currents that may aid bone growth. (A)

77. "Single Myosin Molecule Mechanics: Piconeutron Forces and Nanometre Steps," J. T. Finer, R. M. Simmons, and J. A. Spudich, Nature **368**, 113–119 (1994). (A)

### H. Epidemiology

78. "The Environment and Diseases: Association and Causation," A. B. Hill, Proc. R. Soc. Med., Sec. Occup. Med. **58**, 295–300 (1965). Criteria to base conclusions. (I)
79. **Modern Epidemiology**, K. J. Rothman (Little Brown, Boston, 1986). (A)
80. **Fundamentals of Epidemiology (Parts I and II)** (Electric Power Research Institute, Palo Alto, CA, 1993). Basic facts. (I)
81. "Epidemiology Faces its Limits," G. Taubes, Science **269**, 164–169 (1995). (E)
82. "Weak Magnetic Fields: A Cancer Connection?" K. R. Foster in Ref. 8. A nice discussion on epidemiology associations. (I)
83. "Are Stray 60 Hz Electromagnetic Fields Associated with the Distribution and Uses of Electrical Power a Significant Cause of Cancer," J. D. Jackson, Proc. Nat. Acad. Sci. **89**, 3508–3510 (1992). Electrical use rises considerably while childhood cause cancer remains relatively constant. (I)
84. **Surveillance, Epidemiology, and End Results (SEER)** (National Cancer Institute, Washington, DC, 1995). The cancer facts needed for analysis. (A)

### I. Childhood Leukemia Studies

85. "Residential Proximity to Electricity Transmission and Distribution Equipment and Risk of Childhood Leukemia, Childhood Lymphoma, and Childhood Nervous System Tumors: Systematic Review, Evaluation, and Meta-Analysis," E. P. Washburn et al., Cancer Causes and Control **5**, 299–309 (1994). A nice summary of the childhood cancer data. (A)
86. "Electrical Wiring Configurations and Childhood Cancer," N. Wertheimer and E. Leeper, Am. J. Epidemiology **109**, 273–284 (1979). (A)
87. "Case-Control Study of Childhood Cancer and Exposure to 60-Hz Magnetic Fields", D. A. Savitz et al., Am. J. Epidemiol. **128**, 21–38 (1988). (A)
88. "Exposure to Residential Electric and Magnetic Fields and Risk of Childhood Leukemia," Am. J. Epidemiol. **134**, 923–937 (1991). (A)
89. "Magnetic Fields and Cancer in Children Residing Near Swedish High-Voltage Power Lines," M. Feychting and A. Ahblom, Am J. Epidemiol. **138**, 467–480 (1993). Letter and reply, R. Wilson and A. Shlyakhter, Am. J. Epidemiol. **141**, 378–379 (1995). (A)
90. "Residence near High Voltage Facilities and Risk of Cancer in Children," J. H. Olsen, A. Nielson, and R. Schulgen, Brit. Med. J. **307**, 891–895 (1993). (A)
91. "Risk of Cancer in Finnish Children Living Close to Power Lines," P. K. Verkasalo et al., Brit. Med. J. **307**, 895–899 (1993). (A)
92. "Childhood Cancer in Relation to Indicators of Magnetic Fields from Ground Current Sources," N. Wertheimer, D. A. Savitz, and E. Leeper, Bioelectromagnetics **16**, 86–96 (1995). (A)

### J. High field studies

The large fields of the order of 100 mG from older electric blankets (before twisted pair wires) and electrical train workers (30 mG) fail to show effects one would expect if the biological coupling was proportional to either the field or the square of the field (Ref. 26).

93. "Magnetic Field Exposure from Electric Appliances and Childhood Cancer," D. A. Savitz, E. M. John, and R. C. Kleckner, Am. J. Epidemiol. **131**, 763–773 (1990). (A)
94. "Leukemia and Brain Tumors in Norwegian Railway Workers, A Nested Case Control Study," T. Tynes, H. Jynge, and A. I. Vistnes, Am. J. Epidemiol. **137**, 645–653 (1994). (A)

### K. Utility employee studies

A study of utility power-line workers reported average fields of about 11 mG. In spite of the higher field values, the epidemiology from the utility studies appears to be inconsistent and inconclusive.

95. "Magnetic Field Exposure in Relation to Leukemia and Brain Cancer Mortality among Electrical Utility Workers," D. Savitz and D. Loomis, Am. J. Epidemiol. **141**, 123–134 (1995). (A)
96. "Cohort and Nested Case-Control Studies of Hematopoietic Cancers and Brain Cancer Among Electrical Utility Workers," J D. Sahl, M. A. Kelsh, and S. Greenland, Epidemiology **4**, 104–114 (1993). (A)
97. "Cancer risks associated with occupational exposure to magnetic fields among electricity utility workers in Ontario and Quebec, Canada, and France," G. Theriault et al., Am. J. Epidemiol. **139**, 550–572 (1994) and **140**, 805–820 (1994). (A)
98. "Magnetic Field Exposure Among Utility Workers," T. D. Bracken et al., Bioelectromagnetics **16**, 216–226 (1995). (A)
99. "Utility Workers and EMF Health Risks," T. Moore, EPRI J. **20**, 6–17 (March/April 1995). (A)

### L. Mitigation, litigation, and prudent avoidance

The diverse costs of ELF/EMF are reported to be over $1 billion/year. Some aspects of these issues are described below.

100. "Containing the Costs of the EMF Problem," H. K. Florig, Science **257**, 468–469, 488, 490, 492 (1992). Present costs of $1 billion/year. (E)
101. **Electromagnetic Fields: Federal Efforts to Determine Health Effects Are Behind Schedule** (General Accounting Office, GAO/RCED-94-115, Washington, DC, 1994). Potential costs of more than $250 billion. (E)
102. "Interim Guidelines on Limits of Exposure to 50/60 Hz Electric and Magnetic Fields" (International Nonionizing Radiation Committee of the International Radiation Protection Association), H. P. Jammet, et al., Health Phys. **58**, 113–122 (1990). Approved in 1993. (E)
103. **Biological Effects of Power Frequency Electric and Magnetic Fields: Background Paper**, I. Nair, M. G. Morgan, and H. K. Florig (Office of Technology Assessment, Washington, D.C., OTA-B1-E53, 1989). (I)
104. "60 Hz Electromagnetic Fields: Problems in Risk Assessment and Policy Response," G. Morgan, Phys. Soc. **19**, 10 (Oct. 1990), and "Prudent Avoidance," Public Utility Fortnightly, March 15, 1992. (E)
105. "The Imprudence of Prudent Avoidance," D. Hafemeister, Phys. Soc. **24** (3), 9–11 (July 1995). (E)
106. "Electromagnetic Fields: Physics, Biology and Law," E. Gerjuoy, Jurimetrics **35**, 55–75 (1994). (E)
107. "Brief of Amici Curiae Robert K. Adair, et al.," San Diego Gas & Electric Co. vs. Orange Country Superior Court and Martin Covalt, et al., Supreme Court of California, 1995. (A)

### M. Risk in general

The following references would help to prioritize spending for reducing health risks.

108. *Of Acceptable Risk: Science and the Determination of Safety*, W. W. Lowrance (Kaufmann, CA, 1976). (E)
109. "Perception in Risk," P. Slovic, Science **236**, 280–285 (1987). (I)
110. "Risk Analysis and Management," M. G. Morgan, Sci. Am. **269**, 32–42 (July 1993). (E)
111. "Societal Risk versus Technological Risk," C. Starr, Science **165**, 1232–1238 (1969). (E)
112. "Energy Hazards: What to Measure, What to Compare," J. P. Holdren, Tech. Rev. **85**, 33–38, 74–75 (April 1982). (E)

Reprinted with permission from *Possible Health Effects of Exposure to Residential Electric and Magnetic Fields*. Copyright 1997 by the National Academy of Sciences. Courtesy of the National Academy Press, Washington, D.C.

# *Possible Health Effects of Exposure to*
# RESIDENTIAL ELECTRIC AND MAGNETIC FIELDS

Committee on the Possible Effects of
Electromagnetic Fields on Biologic Systems

Board on Radiation Effects Research

Commission on Life Sciences

National Research Council

## Executive Summary

### CHARGE TO THE COMMITTEE

Public concern regarding possible health risks from residential exposures to low-strength, low-frequency electric and magnetic fields produced by power lines and the use of electric appliances has generated considerable debate among scientists and public officials. In 1991, Congress asked that the National Academy of Sciences (NAS) review the research literature on the effects from exposure to these fields and determine whether the scientific basis was sufficient to assess health risks from such exposures. In response to the legislation directing the U.S. Department of Energy to enter into an agreement with the NAS, the National Research Council convened the Committee on the Possible Effects of Electromagnetic Fields on Biologic Systems. The committee was asked "to review and evaluate the existing scientific information on the possible effects of exposure to electric and magnetic fields on the incidence of cancer, on reproduction and developmental abnormalities, and on neurobiologic response as reflected in learning and behavior." The committee was asked to focus on exposure modalities found in residential settings. In addition, the committee was asked to identify future research needs and to carry out a risk assessment insofar as the research data justified this procedure. Risk assessment is a well-established procedure used to identify health hazards and to recommend limits on exposure to dangerous agents.

### CONCLUSIONS OF THE COMMITTEE

Based on a comprehensive evaluation of published studies relating to the effects of power-frequency electric and magnetic fields on cells, tissues, and

*1*

organisms (including humans), the conclusion of the committee is that the current body of evidence does not show that exposure to these fields presents a human-health hazard. Specifically, no conclusive and consistent evidence shows that exposures to residential electric and magnetic fields produce cancer, adverse neurobehavioral effects, or reproductive and developmental effects.

The committee reviewed residential exposure levels to electric and magnetic fields, evaluated the available epidemiologic studies, and examined laboratory investigations that used cells, isolated tissues, and animals. At exposure levels well above those normally encountered in residences, electric and magnetic fields can produce biologic effects (promotion of bone healing is an example), but these effects do not provide a consistent picture of a relationship between the biologic effects of these fields and health hazards. An association between residential wiring configurations (called wire codes, defined below) and childhood leukemia persists in multiple studies, although the causative factor responsible for that statistical association has not been identified. No evidence links contemporary measurements of magnetic-field levels to childhood leukemia.

## STUDY FINDINGS

### Epidemiology

Epidemiologic studies are aimed at establishing whether an association can be documented between exposure to a putative disease-causing agent and disease occurrence in humans. The driving force for continuing the study of the biologic effects of electric and magnetic fields has been the persistent epidemiologic reports of an association between a hypothetical estimate of electric- and magnetic-field exposure called the wire-code classification and the incidence of childhood leukemia. These studies found the highest wire-code category is associated with a rate of childhood leukemia (a rare disease) that is about 1.5 times the expected rate.

A particular methodologic detail in these studies must be appreciated to understand the results. Measuring residential fields for a large number of homes over historical periods of interest is logistically difficult, time consuming, and expensive, so epidemiologists have classified homes according to the wire code (unrelated to building codes) to estimate past exposures. The wire-code classification concerns only outdoor factors related to the distribution of electric power to residences, such as the distance of a home from a power line and the size of the wires close to the home. This method was originally designed to categorize homes according to the magnitude of the magnetic field expected to be inside the home. Magnetic fields from external wiring, however, often constitute only a fraction of the field inside the home. Various investigators have used from two (high and low) to five categories of wire-code classifications. The following conclusions were reached on the basis of an examination of the epidemiologic findings:

• Living in homes classified as being in the high wire-code category is associated with about a 1.5-fold excess of childhood leukemia, a rare disease.

• Magnetic fields measured in the home after diagnosis of disease in a resident have not been found to be associated with an excess incidence of childhood leukemia or other cancers.

The link between wire-code rating and childhood leukemia is statistically significant (unlikely to have arisen from chance) and is robust in the sense that eliminating any single study from the group does not alter the conclusion that the association exists. How is acceptance of the link between wire-code rating and leukemia consistent with the overall conclusion that residential electric and magnetic fields have not been shown to be hazardous? One reason is that wire-code ratings correlate with many factors—such as age of home, housing density, and neighborhood traffic density—but the wire-code ratings exhibit a rather weak association with measured residential magnetic fields. More important, no association between the incidence of childhood leukemia and magnetic-field exposure has been found in epidemiologic studies that estimated exposure by measuring present-day average magnetic fields.

• Studies have not identified the factors that explain the association between wire codes and childhood leukemia.

Because few risk factors for childhood leukemia are known, formulating hypotheses for a link between wire codes and disease is very difficult. Although various factors are known to correlate with wire-code ratings, none stands out as a likely causative factor. It would be desirable for future research to identify the source of the association between wire codes and childhood leukemia, even if the source has nothing to do with magnetic fields.

• In the aggregate, epidemiologic evidence does not support possible associations of magnetic fields with adult cancers, pregnancy outcome, neurobehavioral disorders, and childhood cancers other than leukemia.

The preceding discussion has focused on the possible link between magnetic-field exposure and childhood leukemia because the epidemiologic evidence is strongest in this instance; nevertheless, many epidemiologists regard such a small increment in incidence as inherently unreliable. Although some studies have presented evidence of an association between magnetic-field exposure and various other types of cancer, neurobehavioral disorders, and adverse effects on reproductive function, the results have been inconsistent and contradictory and do not constitute reliable evidence of an association.

## Exposure Assessment

The purpose of exposure assessment is to determine the magnitudes of electric and magnetic fields to which members of the population are exposed.

The electromagnetic environment typically consists of two components, an electric field and a magnetic field. In general, for time-varying fields, these two fields are coupled, but in the limit of unchanging fields, they become independent. For frequencies encountered in electric-power transmission and distribution, these two fields can be considered independent to an excellent approximation. For extremely-low-frequency fields, including those from power lines and home appliances and wiring, the electric component is easily attenuated by metal elements in residential construction and even by trees, animals, and people. The magnetic field, which is not easily attenuated, is generally assumed to be the source of any possible health hazard. When animal bodies are placed in a time-varying magnetic field (as opposed to remaining stationary in the earth's static magnetic field), currents are induced to flow through tissues. These currents add to those that are generated internally by the function of nerve and muscle, most notably currents detected in the clinically useful electroencephalogram and the electrocardiogram. The currents produced by nerve and muscle action within the body have no known physiologic function themselves but rather are merely a consequence of the fact that excitable tissue (such as nerve and muscle) generate electric currents during their normal operation.

General conclusions from the review of the literature involving studies of exposure assessment and the physical interactions of electric and magnetic fields with biologic systems are the following:

• Exposure of humans and animals to external 60-hertz (Hz) electric and magnetic fields induces currents internally.

The density of these currents is nonuniform throughout the body. The spatial patterns of the currents induced by the magnetic fields are different from those induced by the electric fields. Electric fields generally are measured in volts per meter and magnetic fields in microtesla ($\mu$T) or milligauss (mG) (1 $\mu$T = 10 mG).

• Ambient levels of 60-Hz (or 50-Hz in Europe and elsewhere) magnetic fields in residences and most workplaces are typically 0.01-0.3 $\mu$T (0.1-3 mG).

Higher levels are encountered directly under high-voltage transmission lines and in some occupational settings. Some appliances produce magnetic fields of up to 100 $\mu$T (1 G) or more in their vicinity. For comparison, the static magnetic field of the earth is about 50 $\mu$T (500 mG). Magnetic fields of the magnitude found in residences induce currents within the human body that are generally much smaller than the currents induced naturally from the function of nerves and muscles. However, the highest field strengths to which a resident might be exposed (those associated with appliances) can produce electric fields within a small region of the body that are comparable to or even larger than the naturally occurring fields, although the magnitude of the largest locally induced fields in the body is not accurately known.

• Human exposure to a 60-Hz magnetic field at 0.1 $\mu$T (1 mG) results in the maximum current density of about 1 microampere per square meter ($\mu$A/m$^2$).

The endogenous current densities on the surface of the body (higher densities occur internally) associated with electric activity of nerve cells are of the order of 1 mA/m². The frequencies associated with those endogenous currents within the brain range from less than 1 Hz to about 40 Hz, the strongest components being about 10 Hz. Therefore, the typical externally induced currents are 1,000 times less than the naturally occurring currents.

• Neither experimental nor theoretic data on locally induced current densities within tissues and cells are available that take into consideration the local variations in the electric properties of the medium.

Because the mechanisms through which electric and magnetic fields might produce adverse health effects are obscure, the characteristics of the electric or magnetic fields that need to be measured for testing the linkage of these fields to disease are unclear. In most studies, the root-mean-square (rms) strength of the field, an average field-strength parameter, has been measured on the assumption that this measurement should relate to whatever field characteristics might be most relevant. As noted earlier, wire-code categories have been used in many epidemiologic studies as a surrogate measurement of the actual exposure.

• Exposure levels of electric fields and other characteristics of magnetic fields (harmonics,[1] transients,[2] spatial, and temporal changes) have received relatively little attention.

Very little information is available on the ambient exposure levels to environmental electric fields other than the rms measurements of field strength. Those might vary from 5 to 10 volts per meter (V/m) in a residential setting to as high as 10 kilovolts per meter (kV/m) directly under power transmission lines. Likewise magnetic-field exposures are generally characterized only in terms of their rms field strengths with little or no information on such characteristics as the frequency and magnitude of transients and harmonics. Residential exposures to power-frequency electric and magnetic fields are generally on the order of a few milligauss.

• Indirect estimates of human exposure to magnetic fields (e.g., wiring configuration codes, distance to power lines, and calculated historical fields) have been used in epidemiology.

These estimates of magnetic fields correlate poorly with spot measurements of residential 60-Hz magnetic fields, and their reliability in representing other characteristics of the magnetic field has not been established. Because of the many factors that affect exposure levels, great care must be taken in establishing electric- and magnetic-field exposures.

• Unless exposure systems and experimental protocols meet several essential requirements, artifactual results are likely to be obtained in laboratory animal and cell experiments.

---

[1]Signals of $nf_0$, where $n$ is an integer and $f_0$ is the fundamental frequency. For example, the higher harmonics of a 60-Hz signal will be 120 Hz, 180 Hz, 240 Hz, and so forth.

[2]Short-duration signals containing a range of frequencies and appearing at irregular time intervals.

Many of the published studies either have used inferior exposure systems and protocols or have not provided sufficient information for their evaluation.

### In Vitro Studies on Exposure to Electric and Magnetic Fields

The purpose of studies of in vitro systems is to detect effects of electric or magnetic fields on individual cells or isolated tissues that might be related to health hazards. The conclusions reached after evaluation of published in vitro studies of biologic responses to electric- and magnetic-field exposures are the following:

• Magnetic-field exposures at 50-60 Hz delivered at field strengths similar to those measured for typical residential exposure (0.1-10 mG) do not produce any significant in vitro effects that have been replicated in independent studies.

When effects of an agent are not evident at low exposure levels, as has been the case for exposure to magnetic fields, a standard procedure is to examine the consequences of using higher exposures. A mechanism that relates clearly to a potential health hazard might be discovered in this way.

• Reproducible changes have been observed in the expression of specific features in the cellular signal-transduction pathways for magnetic-field exposures on the order of 100 $\mu$T and higher.

Signal-transduction systems are used by all cells to sense and respond to features of their environments; for example, signal-transduction systems can be activated by the presence of various chemicals, hormones, and growth factors. Changes in signal transduction are very common in many experimental manipulations and are not indicative per se of an adverse effect. Notable in the experiments using high magnetic-field strengths is the lack of other effects, such as damage to the cell's genetic material. With even higher field strengths than those, a variety of effects are seen in cells.

• At field strengths greater than 50 $\mu$T (0.5 G), credible positive results are reported for induced changes in intracellular calcium concentrations and for more general changes in gene expression and in components of signal transduction.

No reproducible genotoxicity is observed, however, at any field strength. Again, effects of the sort seen are typical of many experimental manipulations and do not indicate per se a hazard. Effects are observed in very high field-strength exposures (e.g., in the therapeutic use of electromagnetic fields in bone healing).

The overall conclusion, based on the evaluation of these studies, is that exposures to electric and magnetic fields at 50-60 Hz induce changes in cultured cells only at field strengths that exceed typical residential field strengths by factors of 1,000 to 100,000.

### In Vivo Studies on Exposure to Electric and Magnetic Fields

Studies of in vivo systems aim to determine the biologic effects of power-frequency electric and magnetic fields on whole animals. Studies of individual cells, described above, are extremely powerful for elucidating biochemical mechanisms but are less well suited for discovering complicated effects that could be related to human health. For such extrapolation, animal experiments are more likely to reveal a subtle effect that might be relevant to human health. The obvious experiment is to expose animals, say mice, to high levels of electric or magnetic fields to observe whether they develop cancer or some other disease. The experiments of this sort that have been done have demonstrated no adverse health outcomes. Such experiments by themselves are inadequate, however, to discount the possibility of adverse effects from electric and magnetic fields, because the animals might not exhibit the same response and sensitivities as humans to the details of the exposure. For that reason, a number of animal experiments have been carried out to examine a large variety of possible effects of exposure. On the basis of an evaluation of the published studies in this area, the committee concludes the following:

• There is no convincing evidence that exposure to 60-Hz electric and magnetic fields causes cancer in animals.

A small number of laboratory studies have been conducted to determine if any relationship exists between power-frequency electric- and magnetic-field exposure and cancer. In the few studies reported to date, consistent reproducible effects of exposure on the development of various types of cancer have not been evident. One area with some laboratory evidence of a health-related effect is that animals treated with carcinogens show a positive relationship between intense magnetic-field exposure and the incidence of breast cancer.

• There is no evidence of any adverse effects on reproduction or development in animals, particularly mammals, from exposure to power-frequency 50- or 60-Hz electric and magnetic fields.

• There is convincing evidence of behavioral responses to electric and magnetic fields that are considerably larger than those encountered in the residential environment; however, adverse neurobehavioral effects of even strong fields have not been demonstrated.

Laboratory evidence clearly shows that animals can detect and respond behaviorally to external electric fields on the order of 5 kV/m rms or larger. Evidence for animal behavioral response to time-varying magnetic fields, up to 3 $\mu$T, is much more tenuous. In either case, general adverse behavioral effects have not been demonstrated.

• Neuroendocrine changes associated with magnetic-field exposure have been reported; however, alterations in neuroendocrine function by magnetic-field exposures have not been shown to cause adverse health effects.

The majority of investigations of magnetic-field effects on pineal-gland function suggests that magnetic fields might inhibit nighttime pineal and blood melatonin concentrations; in those studies, the effective field strengths varied from 10 $\mu$T (0.1 G) to 5.2 mT (52 G). The experimental data do not compellingly support an effect of sinusoidal electric field on melatonin production. Other than the observed changes in pineal function, an effect of electric and magnetic fields on other neuroendocrine or endocrine functions has not been clearly shown in the relatively small number of experimental studies reported.

Despite the observed reduction in pineal and blood melatonin concentrations in some animals as a consequence of magnetic-field exposure, studies of humans provide no conclusive evidence to date that human melatonin concentrations respond similarly. In animals with observed melatonin changes, adverse health effects have not been shown to be associated with electric- or magnetic-field-related depression in melatonin.

• There is convincing evidence that low-frequency pulsed magnetic fields greater than 5 G are associated with bone-healing responses in animals.

Although replicable effects have been clearly demonstrated in the bone-healing response of animals exposed locally to magnetic fields, the committee did not evaluate the efficacy of this treatment in clinical situations.

Reprinted with permission from *MIT's Technology Review Magazine*, copyright 1998.

# Apocaly

Years of scientific research
have yielded no convincing evidence that
magnetic fields produced by electric power lines
cause adverse health effects.

ILLUSTRATIONS BY MAXINE BOLL-HUGHES

# pse Not BY JON PALFREMAN

W ITH some 2 million miles of power lines carrying electricity from generating stations to homes and businesses across the United States, utilities go to great lengths—stringing wires on high towers, burying them underground, and fencing in substations—to avoid accidental electrocutions. But some concerned citizens, journalists, and scientists have warned for more than 15 years of a more pernicious danger emanating from power lines: electromagnetic fields. A charged particle in motion (like an electron flowing in a wire) produces an electric and magnetic field, so a person standing underneath a power line is exposed to both. While the electric field can hardly penetrate skin, much less the walls of houses, a magnetic field will pass through just about anything and can permeate a human body as if it were free space. Thus, a broad consensus has developed that, if the electromagnetic radiation from power lines is dangerous, the magnetic fields must be doing the damage.

This was indeed the hypothesis of Nancy Wertheimer and Ed Leeper in 1979 when they published the first epidemiological study linking electromagnetic fields to childhood cancers. Wertheimer, a psychologist who now works with the Department of Preventive Medicine at the University of Colorado, and Leeper, a retired physicist, compiled a list of 344 children in the Denver area who had died of any form of cancer from 1950 through 1973 and compared them with children without cancer randomly selected from birth records. To estimate exposure to magnetic fields, they ranked the children's homes as a function of their distance from a substation or power line and the configuration and thickness of the wires near them. The results showed that, at the homes ranking highest—that is, likely to be immersed in the strongest magnetic fields—children died of cancer at about three times the rate of those residing in homes that ranked the lowest.

Since Wertheimer and Leeper's study, scientists have conducted some four dozen other epidemiological studies investigating these effects. About two-thirds have been occupational studies of workers such as cable splicers whose job potentially exposes them to strong magnetic fields. The rest are residential studies, investigating whether people living near power lines or substations face increased risk. Many of the scientists participating in these studies have claimed to find positive correlations between estimates of magnetic-field exposure and disease.

The popular media have also carried reports of clusters of cancers and other diseases allegedly caused by power lines and substations. In widely read articles in the *New Yorker*, for instance, environmental journalist Paul Brodeur wrote about a high incidence of cancers among the residents of Meadow Street in Guilford, Conn., who lived near a substation, and about an elementary school in Fresno, Calif., also located near a substation, where 15 teachers and staff members had developed cancer.

These cancer clusters and their alleged association with substations and power lines hit home: many people reading such accounts identified with the citizens and wondered about the power lines on their streets. With so much smoke, they concluded, there must be a fire. Something must be going on. Yet these numerous studies have failed to satisfy any of the

JON PALFREMAN *is an award-winning senior producer at* WGBH, *Boston's public television station, where he specializes in issues at the intersection of medicine and politics. This article is based in part on material he and his colleagues gathered for the* Frontline *program "Currents of Fear."*

basic criteria, established in 1965 by the British epidemiologist Sir Austin Bradford Hill, for convincingly demonstrating cause and effect.

## BIOLOGICAL IMPLAUSIBILITY

Among other things, the so-called Hill criteria declared that any proposed association between an environmental agent and disease should have a biologically plausible link. While acknowledging that this criterion is limited by the "biological knowledge of the day," Hill maintained that researchers must try to offer a reasonable

hypothesis of how a proposed health effect could occur.

Given what we already know about the interaction of electromagnetic fields with living tissue, it seems unlikely that magnetic fields from power lines could cause cancer or other diseases. "There's probably nothing on earth, or in the universe, that we understand as well as electromagnetic fields and the interaction of electromagnetic fields with matter, including biological matter," says Robert Adair, a physicist at Yale. These interactions, he says, make up "all of chemistry and almost all of biology, excepting a few gravitational effects."

Adair is one of a growing group of physicists who have felt compelled to participate in the electromagnetic field debate. A few years ago, Adair and his Yale colleague physicist William Bennett found that the more they studied the area, the more skeptical they became. What makes the connection seem most improbable to Bennett is what he calls the "absolutely minuscule" strength of the magnetic fields in question.

Magnetic fields are measured in milligauss (thousandths of a gauss). The fields recorded in most homes, even ones near power lines, are of the order of a few milligauss at most. Even standing directly under most power lines, one is typically exposed to only 50 milligauss or less. Yet, as every school child knows, we live in the earth's magnetic field. This field in North America averages about 500 milligauss.

While this fact alone makes it sound as though electromagnetic fields from power lines would certainly be lost against this magnetic backdrop, the earth's magnetic field is relatively static. The magnetic field associated with power lines, on the other hand, is normally so-called alternating current (AC), vibrating to and fro some 60 times per second. Some people argue this is the critical difference. As Brodeur puts it, "When you're standing underneath the power lines, every cell in your brain and body is entrained to the rhythm."

But according to Adair, despite the image of every cell in one's body moving back and forth 60 times a second, the effect is minuscule compared with temperature-induced oscillations that occur all the time—an effect with a magnitude thousands of times larger. "It's completely lost in the noise," Adair says. "The fact that we live at 98 degrees Fahrenheit means everything is always oscillating, bouncing back and forth because of thermal effects." Comparing the cell vibrations caused by power lines' electromagnetic fields to those caused by temperature fluctuations, Adair likens them to damage your cat might do to a tree by breathing on it in the middle of a windstorm.

Since the field is so weak, Bennett and Adair, like many other scientists, find it hard to see how it might cause cancer. Cancer is usually caused when very energetic radiation, or some chemical agent, directly breaks or rearranges DNA. But the forces holding DNA molecules together are millions of times larger than any force that electromagnetic fields from power lines could produce.

Participants on both sides of the debate generally agree that the electromagnetic fields emanating from power lines and electrical appliances do not have enough energy to initiate cancer. But some critics argue that electromagnetic fields from power lines might promote an existing cancer or perhaps affect the immune system in a novel way. Some proponents of this view, for example, argue there might be mechanisms in the human body capable of amplifying the signal so it can be heard above the background thermal noise. Such "hardware" has been discovered in sharks that can detect 60 Hz magnetic fields, but not yet in humans. Other scientists, like A.R. Liboff, a physicist at Michigan-based Oakland University, argue that there might be a resonant "window" effect whereby human cells are especially responsive to a frequency range that includes 60 Hz. To account for the power systems in Europe, where some epidemiological findings have come from, however, this window must necessarily include 50 Hz as well.

Bennett and Adair, together with the overwhelming majority of physicists, dismiss these theories outright. The 45,000-member American Physical Society, for instance, released a report on electromagnetic fields last May arguing that cancer fears were unfounded and lending little credence to the resonance hypotheses. But, as Hill stressed, biological plausibility is merely one of several factors that can establish a link between an environmental agent and disease. By itself, the lack of a plausible electromagnetic field-disease hypothesis is not enough to sink the possibility of a connection.

## BULLET-PROOF STUDIES

According to the Hill criteria, researchers can also reveal a link between environmental factors and disease by using controlled procedures in the laboratory. For instance, it is widely agreed that exposure to AC electromagnetic fields in excess of 2,000 gauss—millions of times larger than those implicated in the epidemiological studies—can excite nerves. But early research suggesting that AC magnetic fields could adversely affect the development of chick embryos has not been borne out in subsequent studies and, in general, experiments reporting effects at fields lower than about 5 gauss have not been replicated.

Three years ago, a $65 million federal program operating under the auspices of the National Institute of Environmental Health Sciences began sponsoring a series of carefully designed laboratory studies, funding multiple versions of all the research to increase the likelihood that any findings would be independently replicated. As a key piece of this program, the Illinois Institute of Technology constructed, deep under the streets of Chicago, the world's largest facility designed to expose rodents to electromagnetic fields. Built almost entirely of nonmetallic materials (so not to interfere with the magnetic fields) and containing state-of-the-art monitoring equipment, the $9 million facility is capable of exposing 3,000 rodents at a time to measured doses of magnetic fields ranging from 20 milli-

**M**any people inferred from media accounts of the controversy that with so much smoke, there must be fire.

*Biological Effects of Low-Frequency Electromagnetic Fields*

gauss to 10,000 milligauss—thousands of times the average exposure in most homes. Project leader David McCormick says he wanted a facility capable of producing "bullet-proof studies." And indeed, it appears everything imaginable has been controlled for: the earth's magnetic field in all the rooms has been mapped extensively; temperature, humidity, noise, and light levels are all controlled and monitored continuously lest they confound the results; and every year the National Institute of Standards and Technology checks the lab equipment's calibration.

By last spring, McCormick's group had completed five studies. In one, involving a total of 3,000 rodents, the team investigated whether magnetic fields such as those from power lines caused fetal abnormalities. Pathologists examined the animals' skeletons, heads, and visceral organs. According to McCormick, the results came up completely negative. "We found no adverse effects from the magnetic fields at all," he says.

The group also conducted a reproductive study in which they bred animals continuously exposed to magnetic fields. McCormick's team examined 12 sets of litters over three generations and looked at a variety of outcomes: the number of successful pregnancies, the number of litters delivered, the number of pups per litter, and several other parameters such as birth weight to assess the health of the pups once they were delivered. Again, as McCormick explains, "That study demonstrated no effects of the magnetic fields on reproductive performance in either sex."

To test the hypothesis that magnetic fields could promote an existing cancer, McCormick used two strains of transgenic mice genetically engineered to predispose them to lymphomas. McCormick exposed the transgenic mice to measured intensities of magnetic fields and compared them with an unexposed control group. The result was unambiguous—no evidence appeared that the magnetic fields had stimulated the development of lymphoma in either strain of mice. Similarly, McCormick's team was unable to demonstrate that electromagnetic fields caused any consistent effect on the animals' immune systems.

McCormick's laboratory is still conducting a study in which rats will spend two years—essentially their whole lives—exposed to a magnetic field to test for chronic long-term effects. The results won't be known until later this year.

Proponents of the electromagnetic field-disease hypothesis rightly argue that one should not rely on McCormick's results until they are replicated. Such studies are under way in the United States, Canada, and Scandinavia. But the thrust of the most recent—and most thorough—experimental evidence is unmistakable. McCormick's work is just the latest of a series of whole-animal studies that have failed to find any health effects from electromagnetic fields.

But whole-animal experiments, such as those undertaken by McCormick's group, are just one approach to unlocking the mysteries of magnetic fields. One provocative possibility, also the target of federal research funding, is that exposure to magnetic fields might somehow affect the cancer-causing genes called oncogenes. Research by Reba Goodman and Ann Henderson, molecular biologists at New York's Columbia University and Hunter College, respectively, had claimed just this: that the fields might be capable of stimulating a particular cancer gene known as the MYC oncogene, increasing its activity and perhaps its likelihood of causing cancer.

Two groups—one at Cambridge University in Eng-

No one has found a biologically plausible link between electro-magnetic fields and cancer.

land and one at the Battelle Pacific Northwest Laboratories (PNL) in Washington—were intrigued enough to try to replicate these results. In his attempts, Jeffrey Saffer, a molecular biologist at PNL, controlled for factors such as temperature, humidity, noise, and vibrations by placing batches of human cells into two identical test chambers. Then, in each trial, he randomly assigned one chamber to receive exposure from 60 Hz magnetic fields. Next he analyzed the samples to see if there were any differences. The whole procedure was conducted blind to eliminate potential investigator bias.

When Saffer's first results failed to detect any effect, he repeated the experiment dozens of times, changing parameters such as field intensities, serum types and concentrations, and the type of cell culture. But despite these efforts, nothing worked. Finally, Saffer took an unusual step; he went to the laboratory of Reba Goodman and repeated the experiment using her cells, culture vessels, and exposure system. His result was the same. As Saffer puts it, "We were unable to find evidence for a change in MYC expression due to the magnetic field."

Saffer concluded that the effects reported by Henderson and Goodman probably resulted from inadequate experimental controls. (A full account of Saffer's work appeared in the October 1995 edition of the journal *Radiation Research* along with a report from the team in Cambridge, England, that also tried—and failed—to replicate the effect.)

Although other studies here and abroad have reported negative results as well, some critics argue that electromagnetic fields might affect human beings in ways that these experiments are failing to pick up. Public policy, they further argue, should not be determined in the laboratory but rather with reference to the many epidemiological studies investigating the link between 60-Hz magnetic fields and disease in humans.

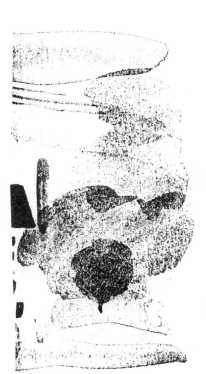

## STRENGTH, CONSISTENCY, AND SPECIFICITY

According to the Hill criteria, epidemiology alone can establish a causal connection even in the absence of biological plausibility or laboratory evidence, provided any association possesses the qualities of strength, consistency, and specificity.

A notable case of strength occurred, for instance, when workers exposed to vinyl chloride were found to contract a rare form of liver cancer at a rate some 200 times normal. Another clear modern example is the link between smoking and lung cancer. In his work with the epidemiologist Sir Richard Doll, Hill found that a person who smokes a pack of cigarettes per day is 14 times more likely to develop lung cancer than a nonsmoker. Moreover, Doll and Hill found that this number—the so-called risk ratio—increased as the dose grew. Smokers who consumed two packs a day, for instance, faced a significantly greater risk. This effect—a so-called dose-response in which more is worse—Hill argued, was also strong evidence of causality.

In the extensive search for a connection between electromagnetic fields and adverse health effects, though, even those studies that have found a link have risk ratios that hover between 1 and 2. Such low ratios might signal a real effect yet to be isolated, but they might also simply reveal statistical noise. Despite some 15 years of

research on this topic, both possibilities "still remain viable," according to David Savitz, an epidemiologist at the University of North Carolina.

Traditionally, evidence of an effect increases as scientific studies improve, but that doesn't seem to have happened in this area. Some of the most recent and sophisticated studies, such as two large-scale investigations of pregnant women who use electric blankets, another source of exposure to electromagnetic fields that has caused concern, have yielded negative results.

But because no single study can be relied on as definitive, Hill wisely noted that consistency can help establish an epidemiological link. In the case of smoking, for example, hundreds of studies have reproduced what Doll and Hill found for lung cancer, revealing risk ratios in the range of 10 to 30.

Proponents of the hypothesis that electromagnetic fields cause cancer acknowledge the lack of strength in the association but argue that an unmistakable trend exists. As David Carpenter, dean of the School of Public Health at the State University of New York (SUNY) at Albany, puts it, "while I admit that the proof is not 100 percent, there is consistency in correlation between leukemia and brain tumors and exposure to magnetic fields both in residential and occupational settings."

But is there really a consistent trend? In the past few years, several very large occupational studies have been published attempting to link electromagnetic-field exposure to disease. One 1994 study of Canadian workers, led by Gilles Theriault at McGill University, found a small association with leukemia but no link with brain cancer. Another study by David Savitz and colleagues at the University of North Carolina found no link with leukemia but a small association with brain cancer. Research by Jack Sahl at the UCLA School of Public Health in 1993 found nothing at all. The picture is also inconsistent for specific diseases like childhood leukemia. Savitz found a weak association, but other researchers, such as M.P. Coleman at the International Agency for Research on Cancer, did not. An earlier study in 1986 by L. Tomenius, former medical officer for the county of Stockholm, Sweden, even found an inverse correlation (implying electromagnetic fields offer protection against leukemia).

In fact, these study findings aren't just inconsistent, they also lack specificity. In his criteria, Hill emphasizes that actual epidemiological links must be specific: a particular kind of disease associated with a particular exposure offers a strong argument in favor of causation. Less compelling, on the other hand, are findings claiming that a whole range of diseases are linked to a diverse set of exposures. Judged in this light, the studies of electromagnetic fields and health effects have revealed few such specific links. Childhood leukemia and adult brain cancer have been implicated in several studies while others cite weak evidence for a range of ailments including adult leukemia, eye cancer, central nervous system tumors, neuroblastomas, meningiomas, lung cancer, male breast cancer, female breast cancer, Alzheimer's, and Parkinson's disease.

So what about the reported "clusters" of disease that are purported to be related to exposure to electromagnetic fields? One thing virtually all epidemiologists agree on is that, while clusters of disease may point to fruitful topics of study, their existence alone is not scientifically valid as a method to prove a connection between an environmental agent and disease. Epidemiologists like to tell their students the cautionary tale of the Texas sharpshooter, who fires bullets at the side of a barn and then draws in the target afterward to maximize his number of bulls' eyes. The point of the analogy is that diseases like cancers occur randomly in the population. Arbitrarily drawing boundaries in space and time by counting up the numbers of cancers in a given zip code, street, or school over a period of time is rather like the Texas sharpshooter; such arbitrary selection makes chance variations look like meaningful clusters. Just by chance some zip codes will have more than the average number of cancers. Just by chance, others will have fewer.

The problem is especially acute when the number of cases involved is small, as with rare cancers. In the case of Meadow Street, which is 250 yards long and contains only nine houses, journalist Paul Brodeur revealed that over several decades the residents suffered two malignant brain tumors and a nonmalignant brain tumor. The implication was that these were related in some way to the substation across the street. In fact, epidemiologists in Connecticut have argued persuasively that this number of brain cancers was not out of the ordinary. Even SUNY epidemiologist David Carpenter, who is convinced of a connection between electromagnetic fields and cancer, does not base his conviction on cluster studies, noting that "by statistics alone, it's very possible that there will be a number of cancers in one block and none in the next ten blocks."

To get around the problem of chance variation, epidemiologists typically study large numbers of individuals exposed to a candidate carcinogen or toxin and compare them with an equally large control group not exposed (or exposed to a much lower dose). By using large numbers of cases they can minimize the possibility that any differences between the groups could have appeared merely by chance.

Achieving statistical power is just the first problem,

though. Epidemiologists must also eliminate confounders—other factors that might skew the results, such as the age, sex, and socioeconomic status of the study populations. Some diseases affect old people more frequently than young people, or women more than men, or poor people more than rich people. It is possible, for example, that people who live in houses near power lines are not as affluent or as well-educated as people who live away from them. If this is true, it might well account for any differences in health observed.

Investigators also have to rule out other potential environmental confounders ranging from traffic density to toxins. PCBs were widely used in electrical transformers, for example, and herbicides are sometimes used to clear tracts of land for power lines. Should a correlation be found between power lines and health effects, it would be essential to rule out these potential sources of disease.

Finally, when assessing exposure, investigators ideally ought not to know whether the person or household is a member of the exposed group or a control. Wertheimer and Leeper, for instance, did know which individuals had died of cancer at the time they were classifying houses according to wire codes, and that knowledge could have introduced bias. For this reason alone, many scientists discount their first study.

## THE MULTIPLE COMPARISONS FALLACY

A 1992 study by epidemiologists Maria Feychting and Anders Ahlbom at the Karolinska Institute in Stockholm initially seemed to overcome most of these general obstacles and one major specific one: namely, that researchers investigating exposure to electromagnetic fields have had great difficulty agreeing how best to measure such exposure. In some cases, for instance, they have settled for crude, surrogate measures like job titles that include the word "electrical." Other times they have employed on-site measurements of field strengths. Ideally, of course, researchers would like to know an individual's true exposure to electromagnetic fields at the time disease allegedly started but, because this may have happened far in the past, it is normally deemed impossible.

Epidemiological evidence of health effects from electromagnetic fields has been weak, inconsistent, and nonspecific.

In Scandinavia, however, electric utilities maintain complete historical records of the amount of electricity actually pulsing through particular power lines at any given time. Using a computer program, the Swedish power company Vattenfalls actually used such data about current flowing in its high-voltage transmission lines in past years to calculate the magnetic field at given distances from the wire.

Seizing this opportunity, Feychting and Ahlbom undertook to study everyone with cancer who had lived within 300 meters of Sweden's high-voltage transmission line system over a 25-year period, calculating the actual magnetic fields that children and adults were exposed to at the time of their cancer diagnosis and before. The calculation did not include exposure from local distribution lines, domestic appliances, the wires in the houses, or from sources outside the home (such as trains, underground cables, or office appliances), but it did go far enough to capture a significant part of the subjects' historic exposure to electromagnetic fields. The study also took great pains to avoid confounding variables and sources of bias.

The results, published to worldwide attention in 1992, reported an apparently clear association between magnetic field exposure and childhood leukemia, with a risk ratio of nearly four for the highest exposed group. Surely, here was proof that even physicists and biological naysayers would have to accept. In the aftermath, the Swedish government announced it was investigating whether to move children away from schools near power lines.

But some four years after the Swedish research was published, it serves as a case study of what scientists call the multiple comparisons fallacy. A basic axiom of experimental sciences is that you must specify, in advance, the hypothesis that you are testing. But observational epidemiology sometimes mixes up two distinct kinds of experiments: those designed to generate hypotheses and those designed to test them.

Why does it matter? The answer can be found in the original contractor's report of the Feychting and Ahlbom study. Unlike the final published paper, which gives only a summary of their methods, this remarkable document reveals the comprehensiveness with which they attacked the problem. The study looked at twelve separate cancer rates (four in children and eight in adults), and used three different exposure scales (measured fields using gauss meters, calculated historic fields using the Vattenfalls' records, and measured distances from lines). Within each exposure scale there were further subdefinitions (such as cut-off points for "unexposed," "exposed," "more exposed," and "most exposed").

This initial report generated some 800 separate risk ratios, comparing the incidence of the twelve cancer rates with an astounding number of separate environmental categories—including many hair-splitting distinctions. For example, special categories were made for children who lived in single-family homes versus those who lived in apartments.

Such a method sounds thorough but, because there is no clearly stated hypothesis, we don't know which among these hundreds of comparisons the authors are testing. Unfortunately, by considering all of them, the researchers introduce a great deal of statistical noise. "By the standard way we do statistics, even if nothing is going on, we would expect 5 percent of those 800 to be statistically elevated, and 5 percent to be statistically decreased," explains John Moulder, a radiation biologist at the Medical College of Wisconsin. In other words, random statistical variation would predict some 30 or 40 elevated risk ratios above 1 (implying that electromagnetic fields cause a particular disease) and 30 or 40 decreased ones below 1, (implying that electromagnetic fields protect against that disease). Given such statistical variation, then, it becomes hard to know whether, by one measure of exposure, a finding that leukemia is up in a group of children is real or is merely the result of random noise.

Similarly, if there were no relationship between power lines and cancer, some "significantly" decreased rates of cancer would still be expected. In fact, such examples can be found in the report. Presented in isolation as evidence that electromagnetic fields "protected" against leukemia, these could be just as misleading as presenting the ones with positive risk ratios. In this regard, though, it appears that Feychting and Ahlbom were rather selective in their reporting.

For example, in the contractor's report, the

Continued research on this issue makes little sense when so many urgent medical problems need attention.

researchers compare leukemia rates with calculated magnetic fields at the time of diagnosis, one year before diagnosis, five years before diagnosis, and ten years before diagnosis. They find a statistically significant correlation with calculated fields at the time of diagnosis, but not at one, five or ten years before diagnosis. The authors select only the first for publication, but on what justification? Since cancers generally take several years before they show clinical signs, a correlation between electromagnetic field exposure at the time of a cancer diagnosis should be no more significant than at one year, five years, or even 10 years before diagnosis.

Seen in this context, the published associations look far less compelling. Equally mystifying, while Feychting and Ahlbom reported a "significant correlation" between leukemia and some calculated electromagnetic fields, the authors found no association with magnetic fields they actually measured. In fact, they reported an inverse relationship with measured fields (that is, it appeared that there was less childhood leukemia in homes where they measured large fields). Moreover, they failed to find any positive association with calculated fields for children who lived in apartments, only for those in single-family homes.

Two other Scandinavian studies published in 1993 that made use of calculated historic electromagnetic fields reported inconclusive results. A Danish study by Jorgen Olsen at the Danish Cancer Control Agency found no significant increase for leukemia or brain can-

cer or for overall childhood cancers when 2.5 milligauss was used as the cut-off point to define exposure (as specified in the study design). However, after reanalyzing the data, the researchers determined that the overall incidence of childhood cancer was significantly elevated if 4 milligauss was used as the cut-off point. Meanwhile, though, a Finnish study led by Pia Verkasalo at the University of Helsinki found no significant increase in the incidence of a range of childhood cancers.

It is unclear how many epidemiological studies investigating electromagnetic fields commit the multiple comparisons fallacy or how many of the seemingly positive correlations found can be explained this way. Original contractors' reports are not always available. Yet the issue is fundamental. Outside of epidemiology, most scientists are unanimous: you cannot confuse a study that tests a hypothesis with one that merely generates them.

### Failing the Test

It is important to note that not all the Hill criteria need to be satisfied to establish causality. As Wisconsin's Moulder explains, in some cases "the epidemiology has been so strong that we've concluded something was a carcinogen without any laboratory evidence or any mechanisms. There are other cases when we've decided that something was a carcinogen just based on laboratory data without any actual epidemiological data." But, as he underscores, "you need some real strengths somewhere."

After scores of studies that span more than a decade, though, the contention that electromagnetic fields cause adverse health effects so far fails to meet any of the Hill criteria. The theory lacks biological plausibility. The experimental evidence so far is strongly negative. The epidemiological evidence is weak, inconsistent, and nonspecific. And the epidemiology is plagued by problems such as possible bias, lack of clearly defined measures of exposure, and multiple comparison artifacts.

Even if we suppose that magnetic fields from power lines do cause cancer, the fact that the connection has been so hard to prove means that, by definition, the risk cannot be large. As a worst case, for instance, assuming that Feychting and Ahlbom's conclusions are correct, a Swedish child would face an increased risk of contracting leukemia on the order of one in a million.

The public would certainly be within its rights to want to know about such a risk but would be hard-pressed to know what to do about it. Would moving the Swedish children to another location make them safer? "Absolutely not," says Peter Valberg, a biophysicist and risk analyst with Harvard School of Public Health. "The idea that you would bus the children as far as one mile would not make any sense in terms of the compa-rable risks. We know from real actuarial statistics that being on a bus does carry some real health hazards in terms of injury and death," Valberg says. And in fact Swedish authorities now agree—they decided not to make any policy changes based on the 1992 study.

In the United States, as President Clinton anticipates a long-awaited Environmental Protection Agency (EPA) report on electromagnetic fields, he faces a delicate policy dilemma. If he dismisses public concerns as unfounded, he might appear unsympathetic to people convinced that electromagnetic fields caused their health problems. On the other hand, he cannot support a position that is scientifically untenable. Unfortunately, even after the EPA report is released, Clinton's easiest option is to continue to say that more study is needed and allocate the research funds, either to the EPA or to another program administered by an agency like the National Institutes of Health.

The trouble with that course is that it makes little sense to continue researching this issue when so many urgent medical problems need attention. A policy of "keep on studying" not only focuses citizens' fears on phantom risks rather than on real ones like smoking, driving, or toxic chemical exposure, but it also drains considerable sums of money from mainstream medical research into a scientific backwater. ∎

Reprinted with permission from *Phys. Today* **47**, 23-29 (1994) & letters *Phys. Today* **48**, 13- 15, 71-73 (1995). Copyright 1994 American Institute of Physics.

# CANCER AND POWER LINES

Do the all-pervasive low-frequency electromagnetic fields of modern life threaten our health? Most probably not, judging from comparisons with the natural fields present in the environment and in our bodies.

## William R. Bennett Jr

Epidemiologists[1] in Denver, Los Angeles and Sweden are asking us to believe that magnetic fields of 2 milligauss from power distribution lines are a serious cause of childhood leukemia. What started as a series of sensational articles in *The New Yorker* magazine by Paul Brodeur (later collected into a book[2]), bringing the earliest of these studies to the attention of the general public, has turned into a new growth industry. Several government agencies, not to mention the private electric power industry, have already sponsored multimillion-dollar studies of the problem; a number of small companies selling 60-Hz gaussmeters have sprung into existence and are doing a land-office business; and the public concern over this issue has become a bonanza to groups of people doing epidemiological and biological research on the effects of electromagnetic fields. Hastily contrived legislation in a number of states has legalized the status quo for fields from power lines, and the threat of still more ill-thought-out legislation is on the horizon—mandating, for example, warning labels on toaster ovens and television sets similar to those now found on cigarettes.

The popular articles and epidemiological studies have all been criticized.[3] The studies were retrospective, using data gathered after the fact from secondhand sources. They all suffered from inadequate statistical samples; in some samples the exposed and control groups differed by as little as one case of cancer per year. The studies are mutually inconsistent and self-contradictory, with spot measurements of the fields seldom confirming the his-

torical estimates used in the studies. They are also extremely prone to systematic error. None of the studies involved a reliable quantitative measure of the actual exposure to 60-Hz fields over the daily lives of the individuals. Also, they concentrated on population groups exposed to magnetic fields that are minuscule compared with those occurring naturally on the Earth's surface. To the extent that the fields coupled inside the body are small compared with thermal noise and other unavoidable natural sources, it is foolish to worry about the health effects of fields from power lines. Hence it is useful to examine the physics of the problem.

### Natural sources of exposure

The Earth's magnetic field is generated predominantly by circulating currents of uncertain origin well below the crust. The field varies over the Earth's surface from about 300 mG at the equator to 700 mG at the poles. A representative value over the continental United States is about 450 mG, about 200 times that from typical distribution lines. The magnetic field has a quasiregular diurnal variation of about 0.1–0.3 mG due to photoionization of molecules in the upper atmosphere. Sudden fluctuations often exceeding 100 mG are correlated with unusual solar activity.

The Earth's static electric field is directed downward normal to the earth's surface and is about 120 V/m near ground level, about three times the field from a 12-kV distribution line. Assuming the Earth is a conductor, this value implies a negative charge density on the surface of about $10^{-3}$ coulomb/km$^2$. This charge comes from the combination of collisional ionization of air molecules by protons in the Van Allen radiation belt and the molecular photoionization processes mentioned above. Diurnal fluctuations analogous to those encountered for the magnetic field occur in the electric field. Enormous fluctuations in the ionosphere are correlated with solar activity. Thunderstorms generate extreme localized electric field intensities. A typical lightning bolt—of which there are about 40 million a day worldwide—requires a

**William Bennett** is the Charles Baldwin Sawyer Professor of Engineering and Applied Science and a professor of physics at Yale University. He participated in the Oak Ridge Associated Universities study that produced the report *Health Effects of Low-Frequency Electric and Magnetic Fields* (ORAU, Oak Ridge, Tenn., 1992). This article is derived from his book *Health and Low Frequency Electromagnetic Fields* (Yale U. P., 1994), which is based on the chapter he wrote in the Oak Ridge report.

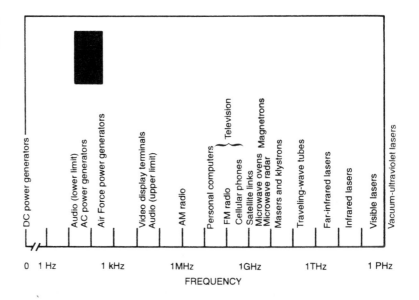

**Frequency ranges** for various electromagnetic power generators. The ELF range is in red. (Adapted from ref. 4.) **Figure 1**

field of about 3 MV/m to ionize air and produces peak currents of 10–20 kiloamps.

## The nature of ELF electromagnetic fields

Maxwell's equations describe the temporal and spatial dependence of electromagnetic fields and give very good agreement with observed classical phenomena over an enormous range in frequency—certainly from dc to optical frequencies. For atomic dimensions and for frequencies comparable to atomic or molecular transitions, a satisfactory theory requires combining Maxwell's equations with quantum theory. However, for describing the effects of extremely-low-frequency fields at dimensions comparable to or larger than 1 μm (characteristic of the dimensions in cell biology) the classical form of Maxwell's equations should be quite reliable. As I. I. Rabi used to tell his students at Columbia when they had trouble with electronic apparatus, "All you have to do is take Maxwell's equations and apply the boundary conditions!"

Although the solution of Maxwell's equations can be formidable when the electromagnetic wavelengths are comparable to the dimensions of the objects involved, there is enormous simplification in the ELF range. By international convention, the ELF band consists of frequencies between 30 and 300 Hz—thereby including the fundamental through third harmonic of most ac power sources. (See figure 1.) The free-space wavelength of a 60-Hz wave is about 3000 km. One can solve most problems by merely finding the corresponding static solutions, for which the electric and magnetic fields separate. One then obtains the full ELF solution by multiplying the static fields by a sinusoidal time variation. The main difficulty in solving problems related to the cancer controversy is determining what the wiring geometries, currents and voltages actually were so that one can calculate the fields. Nevertheless one may easily evaluate the fields for representative conditions. Most cases of interest involve classic examples treated in textbooks on electromagnetic theory.

In spite of the frequent discussion in the popular press about "emissions" from power lines, there is no significant radiation. The Poynting vector $\mathbf{E} \times \mathbf{H}$ is along the direction of the power line. Human exposure to power lines is a near-field, nonradiative problem. Further, the binding energies of biological molecules must be larger than $kT$ at body temperature; from the Bohr relation,

any single-photon dissociation process would require frequencies of more than 6 terahertz. Clearly power-line frequencies are at least 10 billion times too small to produce single-photon dissociation or ionization of such molecules.

## Modern urban sources

I recently calculated and measured values for a variety of typical and "worst case" magnetic and electric fields in the urban environment.[4] (See table 1.) The highest ELF fields of large spatial extent in well-populated environments were encountered near electric railroads, not on urban streets. The calculated fields shown in figure 2 are based on maximum engine horsepower ratings and typical trolley wire voltages and geometries. The peak and average magnetic fields for railroads shown in table 1 are from measurements I made at 2-second intervals in the last car of a Washington-to-New Haven Amtrak train. The largest magnetic fields encountered anywhere in the environment were from home appliances. (See figure 3.) But these fields often involve current loops of small diameter and fall off rapidly away from the device. Most people do not spend much time close to the bigger fields.

As was well known to Benjamin Franklin, the presence above the ground plane of a vertical conductor with a sharp point results in a substantial increase in the local electric field over that originally present. Because people are much more conductive than the surrounding air, there can be a significant increase in the electric field at head level. From theoretical analysis and experimental measurement, we know that the actual fields can go up by a factor of about 20 at head level for a well-grounded person. Thus the maximum fields under a power line might be increased from 60 to 1200 V/m. The highest peak electric fields at head level that I studied were 2 m above the tracks of electric railroads and amounted to about 600 V/m. Hence the worst case would be for a person standing barefoot on the wet tracks of an electric railroad; the fields at head level might then amount to approximately 12 000 V/m. (Of course, dangers much worse than induced electric fields lurk in this situation.)

## Coupling of ELF fields to the body

**Magnetic fields.** Because the permeability of living tissue is close to that of free space, magnetic fields go right through the body. However, direct interaction with

**24** PHYSICS TODAY APRIL 1994

*Biological Effects of Low-Frequency Electromagnetic Fields*

an applied magnetic field could be important only in the presence of permanent magnetic domains that are big enough to provide an interaction energy large compared with $kT$. Even then, the interaction would primarily be important with dc fields. Viscous damping by fluids in tissue plasma severely limits[5] the energy coupled to such a magnetic dipole at cellular dimensions for fields oscillating at 60 Hz.

Permanent domains of magnetite have been found in living organisms from bacteria to marine animals and humans. Torques on these magnetic domains produced by the Earth's static magnetic field may serve as a navigational tool in some animals. A single magnetite domain is about 500 Å wide and has a magnetic moment $\mu$ of about $6 \times 10^{-17}$ A m². Chains of 22 such particles in *Aquaspirillum magnetotacticum* bacteria have been reported, with total magnetic moments $\mu$ of about $1.3 \times 10^{-15}$ A m². Even there, the interaction energy $\mu \cdot B$ with the Earth's magnetic field is only about $kT$ at body temperature.[4] The interaction energy of a single isolated domain, like that found in the human adrenal gland,[6] with a field of only 10 mG would be approximately $0.01 \ kT$. Hence direct interaction with magnetic fields from power lines would be swamped by thermal effects.

**Electric fields.** Charles Polk[7] has noted that the relative values of the conductivity and permittivity of biological tissue with respect to air at power-line frequencies are such that external electric fields are always normal to the surface where they enter the body and the internal field $E_{int}$ is always many orders of magnitude smaller than the external field in air $E_{air}$. This result comes about by application of boundary conditions derived from Maxwell's equations for the normal component of the electric field across the air–tissue interface. Thus assuming $\sigma_{int} \gg \omega\varepsilon_{int}$ and $\omega\varepsilon \gg \sigma_{air}$,

$$|E_{int}/E_{air}| \approx \omega\varepsilon_0/\sigma_{int} \approx 0.7 \times 10^{-8} \qquad (1)$$

where $\omega$ is the angular frequency (evaluated for 60 Hz), $\varepsilon_0$ is the permittivity of free space (approximately that of air), and a value of approximately 0.5 siemens per meter, characteristic of the body's electrolyte, has been used for the internal conductivity $\sigma_{int}$. The solution assumes a steady-state variation of the surface charge distribution between the air and the body at the line frequency. The conductivity and permittivity of biological materials vary negligibly over the ELF frequency range, and the assumptions made in equation 1 are good to better than one part in 1000.

For our worst-case scenario—the external electric field of 12 000 V/m near the head of a barefoot railroad-track walker in the rain—the peak internal field in the body's electrolyte would be only about 80 $\mu$V/m.

## The Lorentz force and Faraday's law

The effective electric fields inside the body due to the magnetic force $q\mathbf{v} \times \mathbf{B}$ on moving charges provide a useful reference.

An astronaut traveling in a west–east orbit 200 miles above the Earth would experience a field of about 0.4 V/m throughout his or her body, while passengers in a jet flying across the country at 500 mph would experience a field of about 0.011 V/m.

Blood flows through the aorta at about 0.6 m/sec during systole. Hence a 10-mG field from a power distribution line would generate electric fields of about 0.6 $\mu$V/m in this flow. In contrast, the corresponding electric field in the aorta due to the Earth's static magnetic field would be about 27 $\mu$V/m, some 45 times larger. To cite an extreme case, a 20 000-G magnetic resonance imaging

magnet acting on aortic blood flow would produce a field of about 1.2 V/m.

Faraday's law states that an electromotive force is induced in a closed conducting loop by a changing magnetic flux. The emf equals the time rate of change of the magnetic flux through the loop and induces a new magnetic field that opposes the change. Taking the magnetic flux to be $\pi r^2 B$, where $B = B_0 \sin 2\pi ft$, we see that the internal field around a circular loop of radius $r$ meters is given by

$$E_{int} = -0.5 \, r \, dB/dt = -\pi rfB_0 \cos 2\pi ft \ \text{V/m} \qquad (2)$$

where $f$ is the frequency in hertz, $t$ is in seconds and $B_0$ is the peak magnetic induction in tesla (1 T = $10^4$ G). For example, a uniform field of 10 mG rms at $f = 60$ Hz would produce an rms electric field of $E_{int} \approx 19 \ \mu$V/m over a circular loop of material 10 cm in radius. For a conductivity $\sigma$ of 0.5 S/m, an rms current density $j = \sigma E$ of approximately 9.5 $\mu$A/m² would be induced in that loop within the body. The effect depends critically on loop size but can be comparable in importance to the direct coupling of external electric fields.

A number of clinical studies have reported beneficial results from the Faraday effect through the use of time-varying magnetic fields to speed up fusion of bone fractures.[8] Therapeutic effects are said to occur for induced electric fields of about 0.1–1 V/m with fundamental repetition frequencies of about 15 Hz administered for 12 hours per day. The waveforms generally used consist of periodic pulse bursts of the type shown in figure 4, with peak values of about 20 G. Because the induced electric fields are proportional to $dB/dt$, they must have strong components distributed throughout the audio spectrum and thus are not ELF fields. For example, the 20-G peak field shown in figure 4 would result in a total rms electric field of 17 V/m over the range from 15 to 20 kHz if applied to a circular area of bone 2 cm in diameter. This field exceeds that induced by power lines by about

## Table 1. RMS Magnetic and Electric Fields

| Source | Magnetic | | Electric | |
|---|---|---|---|---|
| | Typical | Maximum | Typical | Maximum |
| | (milligauss) | | (volt per meter) | |
| High-tension lines | 20–25* | 90[†] | 1000 | 7000 |
| Electric railroad | | | | |
|   13 kV, 60 Hz | 35* | 300[†] | 350 | 700 |
|   11 kV, 25 Hz | 126* | 650[†] | 300 | 600 |
| Transformer | | | | |
|   substation | 15–25* | — | — | — |
| Distribution lines | | | | |
|   (12 kV) | 1–3* | 20[†] | 5–40 | 60 |
| Secondary lines | | | | |
|   (240/120 V) | 5–10 | 100–200[†] | — | — |
| Pole-to-home | 1 | 4 | — | — |
| House wiring | 0.5–1* | 5–10[†] | 1–5 | 10 |

Source: Ref. 4. All fields are at body level. Magnetic fields depend on current load as well as geometry. Fields from parallel wires fall off as $1/r^2$ at large distances $r$ from the line. Magnetic fields from current loops and transformers fall off as $1/r^3$. People are shielded from electric fields inside metal railroad cars, but usually not from magnetic fields.

*Measured average values.

[†]Measured peak values.

six orders of magnitude, and even exceeds the thermal noise discussed below.

## Coupling to the cell membrane

Herman Schwan[9] has noted that the internal electric field (equation 2) is amplified when coupled to the cell membrane. Consider a spherical cell with a radius $r$ of 10 $\mu$m and a membrane thickness $\delta$ of 50 Å ($5 \times 10^{-9}$ m). Because representative values of membrane conductivity range from $10^{-5}$ to $10^{-7}$ S/m, the membrane can be considered an insulator with respect to tissue fluid. Solutions of Laplace's equation in this limit show that the membrane field will be about

$$E_{mem} \approx 1.5 \, E_{int} \, r/\delta \approx 3000 \, E_{int} \qquad (3)$$

where angular variation is ignored. For direct coupling of ELF electric fields, all the voltage drop in going across the cell occurs across the membrane, and the membrane shields the inner portions of the cell from the applied field.

Hence our worst-case limit with $E_{int} \approx 80 \, \mu$V/m (for the barefoot fellow on the railroad tracks) results in a field $E_{mem}$ inside the membrane of approximately 0.24 V/m. For comparison, the electric fields $E_{int}$ of about 19 $\mu$V/m induced in a 20-cm-diameter loop of tissue by the Faraday effect from a 10-mG magnetic field from a distribution line would give rise to $E_{mem}$ values of about 0.057 V/m. The largest magnetic fields encountered in my study—650 mG on the 25-Hz Washington-to-New York branch of Amtrak—would generate values of $E_{int} \approx 515 \, \mu$V/m and $E_{mem} \approx 1.5$ V/m. Comparable values apply to the 60-Hz New York-to-New Haven branch. It doesn't matter too much which of these particular examples one takes; the maximum induced membrane fields will be on the order of 1 V/m for the worst cases encountered.

By contrast, the fields naturally found[10] across the highly insulating cell membranes are $10^7$ V/m. The voltage drop across the Purkinje cells in heart muscle fibers is about 0.09 V, and nerve cell membranes typically have potential drops of 0.05 V across them. For a membrane thickness of 50 Å the naturally occurring fields $E_{mem}$ are approximately $10^7$ V/m—some six or seven orders of magnitude larger than our worst-case limits.

## Thermal fields in tissue

There are natural sources of electrical noise that are unavoidable, the most important of which is the well-known phenomenon of thermal, or Johnson, noise,[11] discovered experimentally by J. B. Johnson at the Bell Laboratories. This noise arises in a resistor from the Brownian motion of electrons and ions. A quantitative theory of thermal noise was first given by Harry Nyquist,[12] who showed that the mean-square voltage across a resistor $R$ in a frequency band $\Delta f$ is given by

$$\langle V^2 \rangle = 4RkT \, \Delta f \qquad (4)$$

This result is quite general and has been checked experimentally for frequencies from near dc through the microwave region.[13]

Robert Adair[14] has applied Nyquist's formula to estimate the unavoidable fields in the cell due to thermal noise. If one considers the resistor to be a cube of tissue of length $d$ placed between the plates of a capacitor, then $R = \rho/d$ and the thermal electric field becomes

$$E_{kT} = \frac{V_{rms}}{d} = \left(\frac{2}{d}\right)\left(\frac{\rho kT \, \Delta f}{d}\right)^{1/2} \approx 0.020 \text{ V/m} \qquad (5)$$

where the resistivity $\rho = 1/\sigma$ is approximately 2 $\Omega$ m for tissue; $d$ is about 20 $\mu$m, corresponding to a cubical volume the size of a cell; $kT$ has been evaluated at body temperature; and a bandwidth $\Delta f$ of 100 Hz has been assumed.

This value for the thermal-noise field is about 1000 times the internal electric field estimated to be caused by a power line and 40 times the electric field directly coupled into the barefoot fellow on the railroad tracks. To induce fields at the cellular level equal to those from thermal noise would require an external electric field of

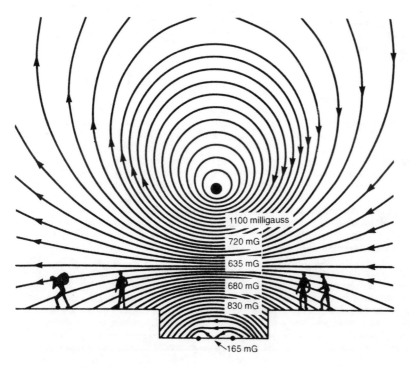

**Electric trains** produce among the highest ELF fields of large spatial extent in well-populated areas. In this drawing a current (red) of 500 A flows into the paper through the trolley wire and is returned in equal amounts by the rails. (Adapted from ref. 4.) **Figure 2**

1100 milligauss
720 mG
635 mG
680 mG
830 mG
165 mG

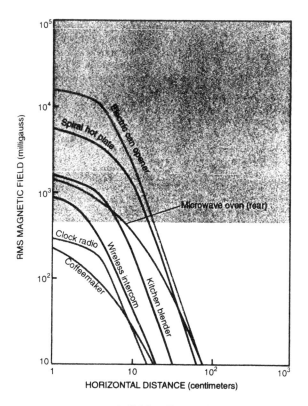
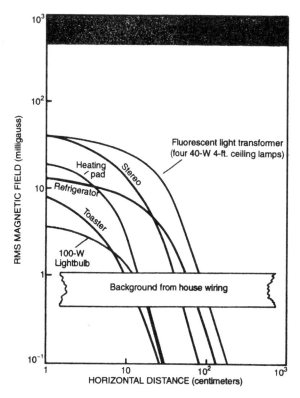

**Magnetic field vs distance** for some home appliances. The shaded background begins at 450 milligauss, the Earth's static field over North America. Left: Appliances producing peak magnetic fields exceeding 100 milligauss. Right: Appliances producing peak magnetic fields less than 100 milligauss. (Adapted from ref. 4.)
**Figure 3**

about 3 MV/m—the corona discharge limit in air. A person immersed in that large an electric field would literally glow in the dark.

Two points should be made regarding the result in equation 5:

▷ The bandwidth $\Delta f$ is not well known. If there is a natural biological filtering process that limits $\Delta f$ to some lower value, such as 15 Hz, then only induced fields within that bandwidth should be considered; note, however, that the filtering process would attenuate applied fields as well as thermal fields.

▷ Although the noise field decreases with the square root of the volume, it is the noise field that actually exists within cell volumes that is important. For example, the noise field from equation 5 should be compared with the field induced by the Faraday effect in a loop $2\pi r$ in circumference and not in something that is $(2\pi r)^{3/2}$ times smaller. However, there can be variations in cell size and shape. Doubling the diameter reduces the noise by 2.8, and so forth.

Although no direct measurements of thermal noise at the cellular level have been reported in the literature, it is clear from fundamental principles that such noise fields must exist.

**Thermal fields in the cell membrane.** Because it has been suggested that induced ELF fields from power lines might cause cellular changes by affecting interactions (such as those involving calcium-ion efflux) in cell membranes, it is important to estimate the thermal fields at the membrane level. Assuming the cell is spherical, the membrane resistance is simply $R_{mem} = \rho\delta/4\pi r^2$, where $\delta$ is the membrane thickness, $\rho = 1/\sigma$ is approximately $10^5$–$10^7$ $\Omega$ m, and $r$ is the cell radius. Taking $r \approx 10\ \mu$m

and $\delta \approx 50$ Å, the membrane resistance varies from about 0.4 to 40 M$\Omega$. Hence the noise field in a 100-Hz bandwidth inside the membrane would be within about a factor of 3 of

$$E_{kT} \approx 280 \ \text{V/m} \qquad (6)$$

where the main uncertainty is in the membrane resistivity. This value is some 300 times the induced fields estimated above for the worst-case external magnetic fields.

**Large aggregates of cells.** James Weaver and R. Dean Astumian[15] have suggested that membrane noise might be vastly reduced in large aggregates of cells electrically connected by gap junctions. Such aggregates occur in major organs such as the heart and liver but are not found with platelets and white cells in the bloodstream—the cells affected in leukemia. If the gap-junction resistance $R_{jcn}$ were zero, the cell membranes in the aggregate would be in parallel electrically, and the net resistance would decrease to $R_{mem}/N$, where $N$ is the number of cells. From the Nyquist formula, the noise would then decrease by $\sqrt{N}$. (The bandwidth would not be reduced by the increased membrane capacitance, because the net $RC$ time constant does not change.) However, this result holds only if $R_{jcn}$ actually is zero—an assumption that hardly justifies extrapolating the results to millions of cells, as Weaver and Astumian do.

Measured values of $R_{jcn}$ between pairs of cells[16] range from about 0.1 M$\Omega$ to at least 8 M$\Omega$ and in some cases to as much as 8 G$\Omega$. I used $R_{jcn}$ values of approximately 0.1–8 M$\Omega$ with normal membrane resistances $R_{mem}$ of 10 M$\Omega$ to 1 G$\Omega$ in a computer model of long-chain aggregates.

*Biological Effects of Low-Frequency Electromagnetic Fields*

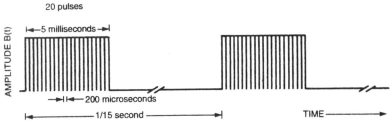

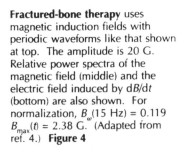

**Fractured-bone therapy** uses magnetic induction fields with periodic waveforms like that shown at top. The amplitude is 20 G. Relative power spectra of the magnetic field (middle) and the electric field induced by $dB/dt$ (bottom) are also shown. For normalization, $B_\omega(15\ \text{Hz}) = 0.119$ $B_{max}(t) = 2.38$ G. (Adapted from ref. 4.) **Figure 4**

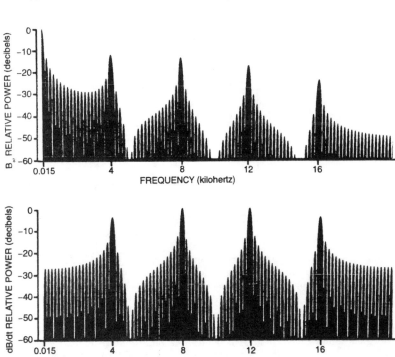

Asymptotic limits for the reduced membrane resistance $(R_{jcn}R_{mem})^{1/2}$ were quickly reached as the chains lengthened, and ranged from 2 to 10 MΩ. Because this is about the range of membrane resistance used to evaluate equation 6, the large-aggregate assumption is not apt to affect our noise argument significantly. If $R_{mem}$ really is much larger than $R_{jcn}$ in relevant cases, it is probable that the values of membrane resistance (and hence thermal noise) were underestimated in obtaining equation 6. Similar conclusions[4] apply to the increased amplification factor (corresponding to 1.5 $r/\delta$ in equation 3) derived by Weaver and Astumian for large aggregates of cells.

## Resonance effects

Some argue that steady-state oscillatory fields could have a larger biological effect than dc or fluctuating fields as a result of some resonance process that occurs by remarkable coincidence at the power-line frequency. This mechanism, of course, could not work simultaneously in the United States at 60 Hz and in Europe at 50 Hz. It is possible in principle to make the bandwidth small enough in the Nyquist formula (equation 4) that thermal noise becomes negligible over that band compared with the induced electric field. However, the thermal electric field depends on the square root of the bandwidth; reducing the bandwidth by a factor of 100 only reduces the noise by a factor of 10. Decreasing the bandwidth means

sharpening the resonance by the same factor. Although very slow variations in the permittivity and conductivity of tissue with frequency have been reported,[17] they are inadequate to produce the required effects. To reduce thermal noise to the level of the electric fields induced in a 20-cm-diameter loop of body tissue by a 60-Hz field of 2 mG, one needs to reduce the bandwidth assumed in the previous examples by a factor of about a million—from 100 Hz to $10^{-4}$ Hz. Nothing approaching that sharp a resonance looks even remotely plausible.

Nevertheless some researchers have reported producing strange "window" effects on the efflux of calcium ions through 1-$\mu$m-diameter channels in cell membranes using ELF magnetic fields in the presence of the Earth's static fields.[18] The results are of marginal statistical significance, the "resonant" frequencies vary from paper to paper, and sometimes the frequencies depend on the presence of dc magnetic fields that are either coaxial or perpendicular to the applied field. Others[19] have reported resonances, at harmonics of the cyclotron frequency, in studies of ion efflux through cell membranes and of cell motility in the presence of applied 100-G magnetic fields. Models proposed to explain the window data have ranged from cyclotron resonance (in which the Faraday effect presumably produces an accelerating electric field) to coherent electric dipole radiation emitted from quantized harmonic-oscillator states of bound ions.

Classical cyclotron resonance can be of no consequence in these weak-magnetic-field experiments with heavy ions moving in viscous fluids. It is a simple matter to show that the cyclotron orbit radii are too large by many orders of magnitude for any such model to make sense at cellular dimensions with ions such as $Ca^{2+}$. Collision and diffusion effects further rule out cyclotron resonance models for such free ions in living tissue.[4]

At the opposite extreme in complexity, V. V. Lednev[20] has proposed a quantum mechanical model based on a three-dimensional isotropic harmonic oscillator in which a $Ca^{2+}$ charge bound to oxygen ligands in calcium-binding proteins has vibrational levels that are widely spaced compared with the cyclotron resonance frequency in an applied magnetic field. An applied constant field splits the first excited state of the oscillator into two levels that are separated by the cyclotron resonance frequency. An alternating magnetic field collinear to the static field is then applied at a frequency near the cyclotron resonance. Lednev argues that the ELF magnetic field drives a coherent mixed state of the two magnetic sublevels to emit electric dipole radiation in the infrared, a process that would be resonant at harmonics of the cyclotron frequency. However—and quite apart from a number of other flaws in the model that I won't enumerate here—the oscillator can't radiate under the conditions assumed. One can calculate the transition probabilities exactly from quantum theory. Assuming the first energy level is approximately $kT$ at body temperature (as would be needed for significant excited-state population), the radiative lifetime for each magnetic substate is about 2 seconds. For the conditions in a cell, these states would be collisionally killed long before any significant electric dipole radiation occurred.[4,21]

Estimates suggest that the thermal fields in these ion-efflux experiments would be much greater than any induced electric fields from the Faraday effect. Because the results from these experiments have not been consistent and involve marginal signal-to-noise levels, it seems likely that the window effects may result from some form of systematic error.[22] Certainly the theories used to explain them do not make much physical sense.

## On balance

It is my opinion that the dangers to human health from low-level ELF fields have been exaggerated beyond reason. I base this conclusion on considerations ranging from the underlying physics to the inconsistent epidemiological data and lack of concrete biological results. It is appalling that close to a billion dollars has already been spent on this problem. I by no means conclude that no further research should be conducted on biological interactions with ELF fields; however, nothing in the available data suggests the need for any sort of crash program. There are far more urgent things to support in the present national concern over the economy, and unwarranted hysteria could end up trivializing concern over legitimate dangers to health such as cigarette smoking and the AIDS epidemic.

## References

1. N. Wertheimer, E. Leeper, Am. J. Epidemiol. **109**, 273 (1979). D. A. Savitz et al., Am. J. Epidemiol. **131**, 763 (1990). S. J. London et al., Am. J. Epidemiol. **134**, 923 (1991). L. Tomenius, Bioelectromagnetics **7**, 191 (1986). M. Fechting, A. Ahlbom, *Magnetic Fields and Cancer in People Residing near Swedish High-Voltage Power Lines*, IMM report 8/92, Karolinska Inst., Stockholm, Sweden (1992). G. Floderus et al., *Occupational Exposure to Electromagnetic Fields in Relation to Leukemia and Brain Tumors: A Case Control Study*, Natl. Inst. Occupational Health, Solna, Sweden (1992).
2. P. Brodeur, *Currents of Death*, Simon and Schuster, New York (1989). See also P. Brodeur, The New Yorker, 7 December 1992, p. 86. But also see E. R. Adair, "Currents of Death Rectified: A Paper Commissioned by the IEEE-USA Committee on Man and Radiation in Response to the Book by Paul Brodeur," IEEE-USA, New York (1991).
3. J. G. Davis et al., Science **260**, 13 (1993). C. Pool, D. Trichopoulos, Cancer Causes Control **2**, 267 (1991). D. Trichopoulos, in *Health Effects of Low-Frequency Electromagnetic Fields*, Oak Ridge Associated Universities, Oak Ridge, Tenn., (1992), p. V1.
4. W. R. Bennett Jr, *Health and Low Frequency Electromagnetic Fields*, Yale U. P., New Haven, Conn. (1994).
5. R. K. Adair, Bioelectromagnetics **14**, 1 (1993).
6. J. L. Kirschvink, J. Exp. Biol. **92**, 333 (1981).
7. *CRC Handbook of Biological Effects of Electromagnetic Fields*, C. Polk, E. Rostow, eds., Chemical Rubber P., Boca Raton, Fla. (1986).
8. C. A. L. Bassett, N. Calo, J. Kort, Clin. Orthop. Related Res. **154**, 136 (1981). R. A. Luben, C. D. Cain, M. C.-Y. Chen, D. M. Rosen, W. R. Adey, Proc. Natl. Acad. Sci. USA **79**, 4180 (1982). R. K. Aaron, D. M. Ciombor, G. Jolly, J. Bone Mineral Res. **4**, 227 (1989).
9. H. P. Schwan, Ann. Biomed. Eng. **16**, 245 (1988).
10. F. N. Netter et al., in *Heart*, F. F. Yonkman, ed., CIBA, Summit, N. J. (1978), pp. 15, 48. R. Plonsey, *Bioelectric Phenomena*, McGraw–Hill, New York (1969).
11. J. B. Johnson, Phys. Rev. **32**, 97 (1928).
12. H. Nyquist, Phys. Rev. **32**, 110 (1928).
13. See, for example, W. R. Bennett, *Electrical Noise*, McGraw–Hill, New York (1960).
14. R. K. Adair, Phys. Rev. A **43**, 1039 (1991).
15. J. C. Weaver, R. D. Astumian, Bioelectromagnetics Suppl. **1**, 119 (1992).
16. W. R. Loewenstein, Ann. N. Y. Acad. Sci. **137**, 441 (1966). M. V. L. Bennett, M. E. Spira, G. O. Pappas, Dev. Biol. **29**, 419 (1972). J. Neyton, A. Trautmann, Nature **317**, 331 (1985).
17. K. R. Foster, H. P. Schwan, CRC Crit. Rev. Biomed. Eng. **17**, 25 (1989).
18. C. F. Blackman et al., Radiation Res. **92**, 510 (1982). C. F. Blackman et al., Bioelectromagnetics **6**, 1 (1985); **9**, 215 (1988); **11**, 159 (1990).
19. A. R. Liboff et al., J. Bioelectricity **8**, 12 (1987). B. R. McCleod et al., J. Bioelectricity **6**, 1 (1987). B. R. McCleod, S. D. Smith, A. R. Liboff, J. Bioelectricity **6**, 153 (1987). S. D. Smith et al., Bioelectromagnetics **8**, 215 (1987). A. R. Liboff, B. R. McCleod, S. D. Smith, U. S. patent 5 077 934, 7 January 1992.
20. V. V. Lednev, Bioelectromagnetics **12**, 71 (1991).
21. R. K. Adair, Bioelectromagnetics **13**, 231 (1992).
22. L. A. Couton, A. T. Barker, Phys. Med. Biol. **38**, 347 (1993). ∎

# DOES PHYSICS REALLY RULE OUT POWER-LINE CANCERS?

In his review article (April 1994, page 23) summarizing the significance of extremely low-frequency electromagnetic fields for human health, William R. Bennett Jr shows that the random thermal electric field in a tissue cell, as estimated by Robert Adair,[1] is "about 1000 times the internal electric field estimated to be caused by a power line" (about 20 $\mu$V/m), and he concludes that power-line fields are thus only a tiny addition to the thermal 60-cycle field naturally present in the cell. Adair's estimate is based on the well-known relationship for the thermal noise generated in a circuit by a resistive element, as applied to a cell.

The linear circuit-element model is not suitable for the determination of thermal fields in a cell, for several reasons. Cells are linked to neighboring cells of a tissue in a three-dimensional structure that does not resemble an electrical circuit, which is a one-dimensional, multiply-connected structure. For the transmission of low-frequency fields, tissue is more nearly a homogeneous, isotropic medium. Furthermore a cell is too small an element to maintain equilibrium thermodynamic electromagnetic fields at the cell temperature. Equally important, the thermal electric and magnetic fields in a system at thermodynamic equilibrium are thermodynamic properties that cannot depend on the medium's transport properties, such as its electrical resistivity, which is a component of Adair's model.

It is easy to prove that the thermally generated electric fields in human tissue are indeed much smaller than those caused by typical power-line sources. Suppose we consider human body tissue as a homogeneous, isotropic, electrically conducting medium of conductivity $\sigma$ that is in radiative thermodynamic equilibrium with an external environment at a temperature $T$. In the environment, the electric and magnetic field intensities are essentially those of a vacuum blackbody radiation field and have spectral energy densities given by[2]

$$\left(\varepsilon_0 \frac{\langle E^2\rangle}{2}\right)_\nu = \left(\frac{\langle B^2\rangle}{2\mu_0}\right)_\nu = \frac{4\pi \nu^2 kT}{c^3}$$

in the limit of low frequencies $\nu \ll kT/h$, which is the case for 60-cycle power-line radiation. For a temperature $T$ of 300 K, a frequency $\nu$ of 60 Hz and a bandwidth $\Delta\nu$ of 1 Hz, the calculated environmental rms electric and magnetic fields are $1.25 \times 10^{-15}$ V/m and $4.18 \times 10^{-20}$ gauss. If we consider the exchange of energy across the plane surface separating the environment from a tissue sample and use the conditions for refraction of electromagnetic waves,[3] we find that the electric and magnetic field intensities are the same inside the tissue as they are in the environment, as given above, provided the electric permittivity $\varepsilon$ and magnetic permeability $\mu$ are $\varepsilon_0 + i\sigma$ and $\mu_0$, respectively. This relationship holds even though the transmission coefficient of the interface is very small,[3] on the order of $\sqrt{\varepsilon_0 \nu/\sigma}$. Thus the electric field in tissue is 12 orders of magnitude smaller than Adair's estimate and certainly negligible compared with the electric field induced by power lines, even if a wider bandwidth is assumed.

A tissue sample warmer than the environment will not maintain a level of electric and magnetic fields corresponding to its temperature $T$ unless the sample is optically dense. For this to be so, the sample dimension $L$ must be a fraction of the skin depth (which is approximately $1/\sqrt{\mu_0 \sigma \nu}$) that is larger than the transmission coefficient:

$$L > \frac{1}{\sigma}\left(\frac{\varepsilon_0}{\mu_0}\right)^{1/2}.$$

For tissue, which has a conductivity $\sigma$ of about 1 siemen per meter, $L$ must be larger than about 1 cm. Thus animals would experience equilibrium fields at body temperature. Even if it were proper to consider a single cell as a circuit element, it is too small in length by a factor of a thousand to generate internally an equilibrium electric field, so Adair's calculation is not pertinent. (On the other hand, for a metal conductor, $L$ is about $1 \times 10^{-8}$ m, so ordinary circuit elements maintain thermal equilibrium electric fields within the circuit.)

If the field in a homogeneous medium is as small as calculated above, why are larger fields measured in resistive circuit elements? The reason is that low-frequency waves can propagate around the circuit with little loss, because the surface of the conducting elements is highly reflecting. The medium is one-dimensional rather than three-dimensional, and the energy spectrum does not go to zero at $\nu = 0$, as the three-dimensional blackbody spectrum does, but remains constant and independent of frequency, giving rise to higher fields at low frequencies than for the three-dimensional case.

It is not surprising that the thermally generated fields within tissue are essentially the same as those in the surrounding environment at the same temperature, namely those of a blackbody radiation field. The microscopic processes that give rise to these fields are reversible, and the field levels are independent of macroscopic irreversibilities such as electrical resistivity. Fields generated by power lines or electronic equipment are well in excess of the thermodynamic equilibrium values at ambient temperatures and are bound to exceed the thermal levels in tissue.

The thermodynamically generated fields are random in phase and direction, in contrast with the external field induced by power lines. In commenting on self-organization in living cells, Benno Hess and Alexander Mikhailov[4] point out that energy from external sources that is far from thermodynamic equilibrium, as is the field of power lines, can organize thermal fluctuations within cells. Whether this effect exists for power-line fields remains to be seen.

## References

1. R. K. Adair, Phys. Rev. A **43**, 1039 (1991).
2. L. D. Landau, E. M. Lifshitz, *Electrodynamics of Continuous Media*, Pergamon, Oxford (1960).
3. W. K. H. Panofsky, M. Phillips, *Classical Electricity and Magnetism*, Addison–Wesley, Reading, Mass. (1962).
4. B. Hess, A. Mikhailov, Science **264**, 223 (1994).

JAMES A. FAY
*Massachusetts Institute of Technology*
*Cambridge, Massachusetts*

In his very interesting and informative article "Cancer and Power Lines," William Bennett discusses the electric field engendered in biological tissue by the 60-Hz external electric field caused by power lines. He invokes the ELF approximation to find the ratio of the amplitudes of these internal and external electric fields. Following Charles Polk, he states that a simple application of Maxwell's equations and the appropriate boundary conditions indicates that the internal electric field $E_{\text{int}}$ is normal to the surface and many orders of magnitude less than the external field $E_{\text{air}}$:

$$|E_{\text{int}}/E_{\text{air}}| \sim \omega\varepsilon/\sigma$$

where $\omega$ is the angular frequency and $\varepsilon$ and $\sigma$ are the permittivity and conductivity of tissue, respectively. Bennett assumes $\varepsilon$ to be the permittivity of free space $\varepsilon_0$ and $\sigma$ to be 0.5 siemens per meter and finds the amplitude ratio to be approximately $7 \times 10^{-8}$. Subsequently in the article he uses this value to argue that electric fields induced in biological materials are negligible.

All this is somewhat disquieting, for there is no need to invoke the ELF approximation. The reflection and refraction of plane electromagnetic waves incident from a dielectric onto a plane conductor are well known and covered in many electromagnetic textbooks. For the case in which the electric field is in the plane of incidence some pertinent results can be summarized as follows:

▷ The transmitted wave propagates with a very small angle of refraction (less than $4 \times 10^{-3}$ degrees for the values chosen by Bennett).

▷ The ratio of the amplitudes of the transmitted and incident electric fields is given by

$$|E_{\text{int}}/E_{\text{air}}| \sim 2(\omega\varepsilon/\sigma)^{1/2}$$

which reduces to approximately $1.6 \times 10^{-4}$ for the values chosen. This ratio is about four orders of magnitude greater than that stated by Bennett and should replace $7 \times 10^{-8}$ when one is discussing the magnitude of the internal field.

Since the transmitted wave propagates nearly normally to the interface, the normal component of the internal electric field is indeed very much smaller than the total internal field,

$$|E_{\text{int,normal}}/E_{\text{air}}| \sim 2\omega\varepsilon/\sigma$$

in approximate agreement with Bennett.

Surely, however, it's the total internal electric field induced in the biological material that should concern us, not just its insignificant normal component.

Of course I have assumed a particularly simple geometry for these calculations, and in practice the wavelength of the radiation is much greater than the dimensions of the biological material, so no doubt the insistence on more appropriate boundary conditions would vary these results. But would the application of more appropriate boundary conditions necessarily validate the calculations presented by Bennett?

DAVID N. PINDER
*Massey University*
*Palmerston North, New Zealand*

In his excellent review William Bennett makes a clear case against the leading candidates for a mechanism underlying a postulated connection between cancer and 60-Hz electromagnetic fields. Although his estimates for the strengths of ac magnetic fields inside cells are lower than those of some other workers,[1] the main point is that the energy imparted to any identifiable intracellular dipole is six to seven orders of magnitude less than thermal energies. This appears to be a compelling argument, yet a more tempered verdict may be in order, especially as some empirical evidence, while not definitive, does suggest such a link.[2]

So far no one seems to have considered a collective mechanism. There are over $2 \times 10^{10}$ nitrogen atoms in human DNA, providing a direct coupling of magnetic fields to the genetic code. Oscillatory magnetic fields might induce, through the Einstein–de Haas effect,[3] twisting and writhing of DNA strands during cell division. My estimate is that, allowing for thermal factors that greatly diminish the response, only $3 \times 10^7$ base pairs, rather than the full $3 \times 10^9$ of the human genome, are required to obtain energy changes exceeding the strengths of topological bonds. Biological activity is extremely sensitive to geometric factors, so an actual bond need not be broken; it would be sufficient to disturb the conformation of a molecule at a sensitive stage in cell reproduction to induce an effect.

The coupling of an ac magnetic field to a paramagnetic medium in the presence of a dc magnetic field (such the Earth's field) can result in substantial changes in the induced magnetization, even when the strength of the driving field is small.[4] The magnitude and *orientation* of the dc field are more important than the amplitude of the driving field, precisely as has been observed in biological experiments.[5] Indeed, if the applied field is too strong, saturation will occur and the effect will go away. Reasonable estimates for the spin relaxation times of organic molecules in an aqueous environment[6] are commensurate with a strong induced magnetization at low applied-field strengths and frequencies.

From a mechanical standpoint, the equations of motion governing the re-

---

*Biological Effects of Low-Frequency Electromagnetic Fields*

sponse of a long chain such as a relatively free DNA strand are identical to those for a spinning top.[7] They are of third order, leading to a textbook instability.[8] These considerations suggest that one must give the Einstein–de Haas effect careful consideration before dismissing the biological effects, especially on the young, of frequent exposure to ac magnetic fields.

## References

1. C. Polk, E. Postow, *CRC Handbook of Biological Effects of Electromagnetic Fields*, CRC P., Boca Raton, Fla. (1986).
2. R. Goodman, C. A. L. Bassett, A. S. Henderson, Science **220**, 1283 (1983).
3. H. Haken, H. C. Wolf, *Atomic and Quantum Physics*, 2nd ed., Springer-Verlag, New York (1987).
4. C. Kittel, *Introduction to Solid State Physics*, 3rd ed., Wiley, New York (1967).
5. A. R. Liboff, T. Williams, D. M. Strong, R. Wistar, Science **223**, 818 (1984).
6. I. Ando, G. A. Webb, *Theory of NMR Parameters*, Academic, New York (1983).
7. C. J. Benham, Proc. Natl. Acad. Sci. USA **74**, 2397 (1977).
8. R. A. Becker, *Introduction to Theoretical Mechanics*, McGraw–Hill, New York (1960).

ROGER BECKER
*University of Dayton*
*Dayton, Ohio*

One aspect of the possible initiation of cancer by power lines was omitted from William Bennett's otherwise excellent review. I refer to the generation of atmospheric ions and complex organic molecules by the corona discharges common around insulators and joints in high-tension lines, especially in wet and humid conditions. I would expect that very strange chemicals could be generated by the corona, especially in regions where atmospheric pollution is high. If these chemicals were directly introduced into the bloodstream via the lungs, even in minute quantities, they could cause cancer over a period of time. Can Bennett (or anyone else) offer any words of wisdom about this aspect of this important topic?

IVOR BRODIE
*SRI International*
*Menlo Park, California*

Accepting the article by William R. Bennett Jr as guidance on the question of health effects of electromagnetic fields seems to me analogous to accepting the advice of the village blacksmith on how to fix your Swiss watch. There is no doubt that Bennett's calculations are impressive. They are probably sound and correct as well. However, the question remains, Are they relevant to the question being addressed?

Bennett treats this question as though it were just another physics problem dealing with electromagnetic fields and the ordinary properties of matter. Presumably, then, it is much simpler than high-temperature superconductivity, since we don't really know yet how to calculate the observed properties of these superconductors. If biology is just applied physics of a straightforward nature, why isn't medical practice transparent, why aren't chronic diseases (such as chronic fatigue syndrome or Alzheimer's disease) well defined and treatable, and why isn't the mystery of consciousness resolved? Is it possible that biological systems are a little more subtle than is credited to them in Bennett's article? What, for example, does the fact that a lightning bolt may have a peak current of 10–20 kiloamps tell us about why electrical workers are known to have an increased cancer risk over "normals"?

There is some confusion in the public mind over the distinction between oscillating electromagnetic fields in the so-called diffraction zone and the fields representing radiated energy. Is this issue of vital importance in this controversy? After all, many professionals also have some difficulty sorting out that part of the total field responsible for the radiated energy. Moreover, of what relevance is the fact that the free-space wavelength of a 60-Hz wave is 3000 km? This field, nonetheless, does reverse its direction 120 times per second. Perhaps this fact and the day in–day out persistence of power-line fields are more significant factors in assessing possible health effects on the human body than is the wavelength of 60-Hz radiation.

Who today, physicist or otherwise, can objectively define states of ill health, let alone measure degrees of ill health objectively? Why then does Bennett treat the possible implications of epidemiological studies so dismissively? So they are less controlled and less objective than the laboratory-based studies so familiar to the physicist. Does this mean they have no value and even where public health may be involved we should ignore them? Ethical considerations prevent us from deliberately subjecting humans to field tests in the laboratory. However, many animal experiments indicate that there are deleterious biological effects from ELF magnetic fields. Animals can't talk and in any case objective testing is very difficult. But this does not mean that a problem does not exist.

*continued on page 71*

*continued from page 15*

Bennett's calculations are no doubt useful in trying to analyze the problem, but they cannot be used to sweep the whole problem under the rug. Other superficialities are present in Bennett's article. For example, to imply that Paul Brodeur's articles in *The New Yorker* started this whole series of concerns is to be imprisoned by a narrow perspective. Admittedly the articles helped bring these concerns to popular attention, at least in the US, but they preceded Brodeur. And why were Brodeur's articles "sensational"? Because they exaggerated the truth or because they revealed possible truths that were unsuspected?

There are many ways to ill spend the public money. In my view, trying to get at the bottom of this particular health issue is not one of the major offenders. It is in the public interest to have the perspective and the expertise represented in Bennett's article as a contribution to dealing with this whole question. My concern is primarily that Bennett's oversimplification as well as his expertise be placed in perspective. The human organism is a very complicated nonlinear system, consisting in the conventional reductionist model of many highly nonlinear subsystems. Anyone familiar with the so-called butterfly effect will express strong reservations about deducing any simple conclusions about such a system from linear calculations and linear comparisons. Although I am a theoretical physicist with some Galilean reverence for the powers of deductive argument, I believe this is one circumstance where we are well advised to seek out the empirical evidence before drawing definitive conclusions.

LYNN E. H. TRAINOR
*University of Toronto*
*Toronto, Ontario, Canada*

William Bennett's interesting article did much to clarify and dispel many of the misconceptions concerning extremely low-frequency electromagnetic fields. Unfortunately one of Bennett's examples serves to reinforce a common misconception in ordinary electricity and magnetism. By way of introduction to his discussion of the $\mathbf{v} \times \mathbf{B}$-type electric field caused in, for example, blood flowing in an aorta by the presence of a magnetic field, Bennett mentions that because of the Earth's magnetic field "passengers in a jet flying across the country at 500 mph would experience a field of about 0.011 V/m." Presumably his point is that this $\mathbf{v} \times \mathbf{B}$ electric field is small as a result of the numerical values of

$v$ and $B$. In fact the field here is rigorously zero regardless of the values of $v$ and $B$.

Consider just the conducting airplane itself moving through the magnetic field. It is well known that a charge redistribution will occur on the outer surface of the conductor so as to produce a uniform electric field $\mathbf{E} = -\mathbf{v} \times \mathbf{B}_{Earth}$ inside the conductor (including any cavity within the conductor). We can now insert the comoving passenger "for free"; all charges within the passenger experience zero net Lorentz force. According to the passenger the (nonrelativistic) fields will be $(\mathbf{E}, \mathbf{B}) = (0, \mathbf{B}_{Earth})$. According to a person "in the lab frame," that is, stationary with respect to the Earth, the fields inside the plane will be $(\mathbf{E}, \mathbf{B}) = (-\mathbf{v} \times \mathbf{B}_{Earth}, \mathbf{B}_{Earth})$. The whole phenomenon is just the usual Faraday-cage shielding as seen by the passenger.

KENNETH R. BROWNSTEIN
*University of Maine*
*Orono, Maine*

William R. Bennett Jr's interesting examination of the possibly negligible relation between cancer and power lines attributes the charge on the Earth to "the combination of collisional ionization of air molecules by protons in the Van Allen radiation belt and the molecular photoionization" in the upper atmosphere. Without detracting from Bennett's analysis, it should be pointed out that his explanation for maintenance of the Earth's charge, variations of which were popular in the early years of this century, has long since been replaced by C. T. R. Wilson's suggestion[1] involving thunderclouds.

In 1887 F. Linss[2] noted that the conduction current carried by atmospheric ions would neutralize the bound charge on the Earth in a very short time. The relaxation time was later found to be on the order of 1000 seconds. After several explanations for the continued presence of charge on the Earth were demonstrated to be untenable, Wilson suggested in the 1920s that thunderclouds provide the principal supply currents. He pointed out that electrified clouds:
▷ extract negative ions from the more conductive upper atmosphere by attraction to the positively charged cloud tops
▷ lower negative charges to the Earth via lightning
▷ induce an upward flow of positive ions from the Earth by point discharge under the influence of the strong negative charges accumulated in the lower regions of thunderclouds.

In the years since, Wilson's hypothesis has been tested by many investigators, and there is now general agreement that it provides a satisfactory explanation as to *where* the current maintaining the Earth's charge originates. There is no similar agreement, however, about the mechanisms and processes by which thunderclouds generate this current; controversies continue among the proponents of various explanations[3] for thunderstorm electrification.

### References

1. C. T. R. Wilson, J. Franklin Inst. **208**, 10 (1929).
2. F. Linss, Meteorol. Z. **4**, 345 (1887).
3. C. P. R. Saunders, J. Appl. Meteorol. **32**, 642 (1993). B. Vonnegut, Bull. Am. Meteorol. Soc. **75**, 53 (1994).

CHARLES B. MOORE
*New Mexico Institute of Mining and Technology*
*Socorro, New Mexico*
BERNARD VONNEGUT
*State University of New York, Albany*

BENNETT REPLIES: Although several of the above letters are interesting and clarifying (such as the one by Charles B. Moore and Bernard Vonnegut), none of them alter the main point of my article, namely, that the magnitude of field exposure near ground level from typical power lines (and especially from urban distribution lines and transformer substations) is very small compared with the unavoidable exposure one gets from natural physical and biological sources. Hence exposure to the former fields alone cannot be regarded as a serious threat to health.

James A. Fay assumes that biological material at body temperature only reaches thermodynamic equilibrium through radiative processes. That simply is not even approximately true, and Fay's calculations are irrelevant. In this largely liquid environment, local thermal equilibrium is established primarily by collision processes. Even for $h\nu = kT$ at body temperature, the typical oscillator will have radiative lifetimes in excess of several seconds, whereas the lifetimes against collision destruction of the oscillator states will be on the order of a picosecond.[1] As can be seen from the principle of detailed balancing, these collision processes establish both Boltzmann and Maxwellian distributions in the local temperature. Thus the random thermal (Brownian) motion of charged particles in resistive material that produces Johnson noise will be well described by the Nyquist formula in terms of the local temperature (Robert Adair's assump-

---

*Biological Effects of Low-Frequency Electromagnetic Fields*

tion[2]). The linear circuit model is clearly an approximation, but it is a very reasonable one for treating isolated cells in the body electrolyte or even clusters of cells connected by gap junctions. The large membrane resistance isolates the inside of the cell electrically from the outside electrolyte. Because the fluids inside and outside the cell are highly conductive compared with the membrane, the membrane is encased by equipotential surfaces and is equivalent to a lumped resistor for the calculation of noise. Indeed, some authors have found noise measurement in a known bandwidth to be a useful method for determining cell membrane resistance.[3]

David N. Pinder is concerned that the transmitted electric fields from power lines at a biological interface in the Polk model do not agree well with those based on plane-wave refraction. He seems to feel that the high-frequency plane-wave approximation is more fundamental. Quite the opposite is true in the present case. The wavelength (5000 km) associated with power-line fields is infinite for all practical purposes, and the problem is nearly a static one. To an excellent approximation the electric and magnetic fields from the line decouple and are completely independent of each other. For example, the magnetic field is actually zero if no current is flowing in the line, whereas the electric field from the line remains nearly independent of load on the line. In the plane-wave approximation the magnetic field is assumed to be proportional to the electric field. There are no plane waves in the present case, and the problem is entirely a near-field, quasistatic one. Charles Polk's result follows directly from the basic continuity relations in this limit, and the approximation should be extremely good.[1] Here, the external electric field is closely normal to the surface of the body. Pinder's plane-wave model would have to correspond to an incident wave propagating parallel to the surface. The answer to Pinder's final question is simply "Yes." (A more appropriate calculation *does* give my result.) Nevertheless it is worth noting that my conclusions were not critically dependent on an attenuation factor as small as $10^{-8}$. Even if the factor were 10 000 times larger, the induced fields would still be negligible compared with thermal noise at the cell level for most cases studied.

Roger Becker's comments on a possible collective mechanism for a diamagnetic interaction between the large number of nitrogen atoms in human DNA and external magnetic fields from power lines are highly speculative. Any motion induced by

60-Hz fields at the cell level will be strongly damped by viscosity effects. Few things are likely to have as large a collective magnetic interaction as a long chain of magnetite domains. For example, Joseph Kirschvink[4] estimated from his model of the problem that it would take more than 1400 milligauss from a 60-Hz field in the presence of cellular protoplasm to open an ion channel with a magnetite particle having a moment as large as $2 \times 10^{-15}$ A m$^2$ (about 34 domains). Such fields are enormous compared with those from power lines. (Incidentally, I did not mean to imply in my article that biological interactions with static Earth-level fields are not well established in some cases; there was a misprint in my remarks on *Aquaspirillum magnetotacticum* bacteria in which the interaction energy with the Earth's field was printed as $kT$ rather than $10\,kT$. However, there is no reason to believe interactions with such static fields are carcinogenic; evolution alone argues to the contrary.) As I noted briefly in my article, the early experimental biological results by Abraham Liboff and others that Becker cites as possible evidence for coupling effects of ELF ac magnetic fields in the presence of large Earth-level dc magnetic fields have not been consistent and have involved marginal signal-to-noise ratios. The required field relationships, "resonant" frequencies and "window effects" have varied from one paper to another by the original authors. More important, several recent attempts by independent investigators to reproduce these experimental results have failed.[5]

As Ivor Brodie suggests, there might conceivably be confounding effects resulting from carcinogenic ionization products produced by corona discharge from power lines. I did discuss that possibility in my book;[1] however, the only relevant data that I could find did not show any significant concentration under power lines of products such as ozone above normal background levels. Corona discharge would only be important from high-tension lines, and those are typically at least 30 meters in the air. In most instances the discharge products would be short-lived and blown away by the wind before reaching ground level. If there were an adequate concentration of pollution to produce worrisome "strange chemicals" as discharge products, it would probably be difficult to distinguish their effects from those of the pollutants themselves. It also should be noted that recent high-tension lines use groups of triangularly spaced wires to mini-

mize corona discharge.

Lynn E. H. Trainor raises a barrage of "questions" that appear mostly to be statements of a personal point of view. I too think the human body is a remarkable and complex mechanism—certainly much more impressive than a Swiss watch and not likely to be explained completely in a simple, straightforward fashion by application of the basic laws of physics. Having agreed to that, one can either try to see what basic things may be said about the electromagnetic field–cancer problem in an objective manner or go on to some other topic. I did consider the epidemiological evidence in some detail in the introduction to my book[1] but was persuaded that such a discussion would be outside the scope of an article for PHYSICS TODAY. The statistical accuracy of the epidemiological studies is marginal and they are all very prone to systematic error (including the ones on electrical workers that Trainor mentions but does not cite). I did not mean to imply that Paul Brodeur started all current interest in the biological effects of electromagnetic fields, but he does deserve a lot of credit for stirring up panic on the cancer issue in the general public. The numerous exaggerations and misrepresentations in Brodeur's book[6] based on his *New Yorker* articles have been discussed in detail elsewhere.[7] The very title of his book states that there has been a "cover-up." His last *New Yorker* article on the subject[8] ends with the question "How many more cancers will it take?" (To do what, shut down the entire electric power industry?) Those are just a few examples of what I meant by "sensationalism." As I stated in my PHYSICS TODAY article, I most certainly did *not* conclude that no further research should be conducted on biological interactions with ELF fields. The question is, How much public money should really be spent on this problem? I, evidently, had vastly underestimated the recent expenditures at a mere billion dollars. While he was serving as science adviser to President Bush, D. Allan Bromley estimated that the present EMF–cancer scare had cost American society more than \$23 billion since 1989!

Kenneth R. Brownstein is of course quite right in noting that the electric field inside a completely closed conductor is rigorously zero and that only an electric field of $-\mathbf{v} \times \mathbf{B}_{Earth}$ is seen in a reference frame traveling at velocity $\mathbf{v}$ through a uniform magnetic field ($\mathbf{B}_{Earth}$) equal to that of the Earth. Nevertheless there are many situations in which people do travel

*Biological Effects of Low-Frequency Electromagnetic Fields*

fast in conveyances that are not completely closed conductors—for example, riding on motorcycles, in open convertibles or soft-top cars, in airplanes with fiberglass bodies and in metal-covered jet planes with appreciable window area (as in the cockpit of a jet fighter plane). Similarly, astronauts go on space walks outside their spaceships, and so on. The point was (and it was a minor one) that there are plenty of common activities in which one is exposed to electric fields of this type that are much larger than those coupled into the body at ground level below typical power lines.

## References

1. W. R. Bennett Jr, *Health and Low-Frequency Electromagnetic Fields*, Yale U. P., New Haven, Conn. (1994).
2. R. K. Adair, Phys. Rev. A **43**, 1039 (1991).
3. See, for example, C. F. Stevens, Biophys. J. **12**, 1028 (1972); A. A. Verveen, L. J. DeFelice, Prog. Biophys. Mol. Biol. **28**, 189 (1974).
4. J. L. Kirschvink, Phys. Rev. A **46**, 2178 (1992); see discussion of figure 1. Also see the reply by R. K. Adair, Phys. Rev. A **46**, 2185 (1992), and R. K. Adair, Bioelectromagnetics **14**, 1 (1993).
5. A. V. Prasad, M. W. Miller, E. L. Carstensen, Ch. Cox, M. Azadniv, A. A. Brayman, Radiat. Environ. Biophys. **30**, 305 (1991). L. A. Couton, A. T. Barker, Phys. Med. Biol. **38**, 347 (1993). A. V. Prasad, M. W. Miller, Ch. Cox, E. L. Carstensen, H. Hoops, A. A. Brayman, Health Phys. **66**, 305 (1994).
6. P. Brodeur, *Currents of Death: Power Lines, Computer Terminals and the Attempt to Cover Up Their Threat to Public Health*, Simon and Shuster, New York (1989).
7. E. R. Adair, "*Currents of Death* Rectified: A Paper Commissioned by the IEEE-USA Committee on Man and Radiation in Response to the Book by Paul Brodeur," IEEE-USA, New York (1991). J. R. Jauchem, J. Clin. Epidemiol. **45**, 1137 (1992).
8. P. Brodeur, The New Yorker, 7 December 1992, p. 86.

WILLIAM R. BENNETT JR
*Yale University*
*New Haven, Connecticut*

*Biological Effects of Low-Frequency Electromagnetic Fields*                    *39*

Reprinted by permission of Blackwell Science, Inc. from *Proc. Soc. Exp. Bio. Med.* **209**, 309- 324 (1995).

# MINIREVIEW

# Biological Effects of Power-Frequency Fields As They Relate to Carcinogenesis

## (43905A)

JOHN E. MOULDER*,[1] AND KENNETH R. FOSTER†

*Department of Radiation Oncology,* Medical College of Wisconsin, Milwaukee, Wisconsin 53226 and Department of
Bioengineering,† University of Pennsylvania, Philadelphia, Pennsylvania 19104*

*Abstract.* There is a widespread public perception that exposure to electricity is linked
to cancer. The public concern stems largely from epidemiological studies which appear to show a relationship between cancer incidence and exposure to power-
frequency electromagnetic fields. This review will discuss the biophysics of power-
frequency electromagnetic fields as it relates to biological effects, summarize the
current state of the cancer epidemiology, and then concentrate on the laboratory
studies that are relevant to addressing the possibility that power-frequency fields are
carcinogenic.

Review of the epidemiological evidence shows that the association between exposure to power-frequency fields and cancer is weak and inconsistent, and generally
fails to show a dose-response relationship. The laboratory studies of power-frequency
fields show little evidence of the type of effects on cells or animals that point towards
power-frequency fields causing or contributing to cancer. Finally, from what is known
about the biophysics of power-frequency fields, there is no reason to even suspect
that they would cause or contribute to cancer. Application of "Hill's criteria" to epidemiological and laboratory studies shows that the evidence for a causal association
between exposure to power-frequency fields and the incidence of cancer is weak.
[P.S.E.B.M. 1995, Vol 209]

There is a widespread public perception that exposure to electricity is linked to cancer. Most of
the concern about electric power and cancer
stems from epidemiological studies which appear to
show a relationship between exposure to power-
frequency magnetic fields and the incidence of cancer.
The first of these studies, published by Wertheimer
and Leeper (1) in 1979, reported a relationship between residence near certain types of powerlines and
the incidence of childhood leukemia and brain cancer.
This was followed in 1982 by reports from Milham (2)
and Wright *et al.* (3) that workers in "electrical occupations" had a higher than expected incidence of leukemia. Over 100 epidemiological studies have followed, some of which report that excess cancer, particularly leukemia and brain cancer, is associated with
exposure to power-frequency fields. These reports of
excess cancer have been met with considerable skepticism in the scientific community, in part because few
were based on actual measurements of fields, and in
part because of the absence of plausible mechanisms
through which these fields could cause or contribute to
cancer.

This review will discuss the biophysics of power-

[1] To whom requests for reprints should be addressed at Radiation Oncology,
Medical College of Wisconsin, 8700 West Wisconsin Avenue, Milwaukee, WI
53226.

0037-9727/95/2094-0309$10.50/0
Copyright © 1995 by the Society for Experimental Biology and Medicine

frequency fields as it relates to biological effects, summarize the current state of the cancer epidemiology, and then concentrate on the laboratory studies that are relevant to addressing the possibility that power-frequency fields are carcinogenic.

## Biophysics of Power-Frequency Fields

x-rays, ultraviolet (UV) light, visible light, microwaves (MW), radiofrequency (RF) energy, and electromagnetic fields from electric power systems are all parts of the electromagnetic (EM) spectrum, and are characterized by their frequency or wavelength. The frequency is the rate at which the EM field changes direction, and is usually given in Hertz (Hz) where 1 Hz is one cycle per second. In an EM wave, the frequency (f) and the wavelength ($\lambda$) are related by the equation:

$$\lambda = (\text{speed of light})/f$$

so that as the frequency rises the wavelength gets shorter. Electric power has a frequency of 50 Hz in most of the world (60 Hz in the United States) and a wavelength of about 5000 km. By contrast, AM radio has a frequency around $10^6$ Hz and a wavelength of around 300 m; MW ovens have a frequency of 2.54 $\times$ $10^9$ Hz and a wavelength of about 12 cm; and x-rays have frequencies of over $10^{15}$ Hz and wavelengths of 100 nm or less.

**Terminology.** We will use the term "power-frequency" to refer to both the 50- and the 60-Hz alternating current (AC) frequencies used in electric power systems, and the term "power-frequency field" to refer to the sinusoidal electric and magnetic fields produced by 50- and 60-Hz lines and devices. The phrase "EMF" will be avoided since it is an imprecise term which could apply to many very different types of fields, and because the term has a long-standing usage in physics to refer to an entirely different quantity, electromotive force. We will also avoid the terms "electromagnetic radiation" and "nonionizing radiation" since power-frequency sources produce no appreciable radiation. Power-frequency fields are also properly referred to as extremely low frequency (or ELF) fields, a broader term often used to cover the range from >0 Hz to 3000 Hz (4).

**Fields Versus Radiation.** In general, EM sources produce both radiant energy (radiation) and nonradiant fields. Radiation travels away from its source, and continues to exist even if the source is turned off. In contrast, some electric and magnetic fields exist near an EM source that are not projected into space, and that cease to exist when the energy source is turned off. Powerlines are far too short compared with the wavelength of 50/60-Hz radiation (5000 km) to be effective radiation sources. While powerlines theoretically radiate some energy, they do so

with such low efficiency that this effect can for all practical purposes be ignored.

**Magnetic Versus Electric Fields.** The fact that exposure to power-frequency fields occurs at distances that are much shorter than the wavelength of 50/60-Hz radiation has important implications, because under such conditions (called "near-field"), the electric and magnetic fields can be considered independent entities. This is in contrast to EM radiation, in which the electric and magnetic fields are inextricably linked.

Electric fields exist whenever electric charges are present, regardless of whether current is flowing; their units in the SI system are volts/meter (V/m). Magnetic fields are produced by moving charges (e.g., current flowing through a conductor); their units in the SI system are amperes per meter (A/m). For historic reasons, it is more common to specify magnetic fields using a different quantity, the flux density, whose units in the SI system are Tesla (T). Another unit of flux density, often used in the United States, is the Gauss (G), where 10,000 G equals 1 T (1 G = 0.1 mT = 100 $\mu$T).

The magnetic fields associated with powerlines, transformers, and appliances easily penetrate buildings or tissue and are difficult to shield. By contrast, power-frequency electric fields are easily shielded by conductive objects and have little ability to penetrate buildings or tissue. Because power-frequency electric fields do not penetrate the body, it is generally assumed that any biologic effect from routine exposure to power-frequency fields must be due to the magnetic component of the field, or to the electric fields and currents that these magnetic fields induce in the body.

The strength of an electric field is proportional to the voltage of the source and its distance to the observer. Thus, the electric fields beneath high-voltage transmission lines far exceed those below the lower-voltage distribution lines. The magnetic field strength, by contrast, is proportional to the current in the lines, so that a low-voltage distribution line with a high current load may produce a magnetic field that is as high as some high-voltage transmission lines. In fact, electric distribution systems account for a far higher proportion of the population's exposure to magnetic fields than the larger and more obvious high-voltage transmission lines.

**Typical Field Intensities.** Within the right-of-way of a high-voltage (115–765 kV) transmission line, fields can approach 10 $\mu$T and 10,000 V/m. At the edge of a transmission right-of-way, the fields will be 0.1–1.0 $\mu$T and 100–1000 V/m. Ten meters from a 12-kV distribution line, fields will be 0.2–1.0 $\mu$T and 2–20 V/m. Actual electric fields depend on design and voltage, and since the voltage of a line is closely regulated, the resulting electric fields are essentially constant. By contrast, the magnetic fields depend not only on voltage and design, but also on current load, and thus can be highly variable from day to day, and even within a day.

Fields within residences vary from over 200 μT and 200 V/m a few centimeters from appliances that contain electric motors, to less than 0.02 μT and 2 V/m in the center of some rooms (5).

Exposures in excess of 100 μT and 5000 V/m have been reported for workers in some occupations (e.g., arc welders and electrical cable splicers). However, in typical occupations whose job titles imply exposure to power-frequency fields, mean exposures are 0.5–4 μT and 100–2000 V/m (5). Indeed, the magnetic field exposure of workers in many of these "electrical" occupations is little different from that of other individuals.

## Interactions of Electromagnetic Sources with Biological Material

The nature of the interaction of EM fields and radiation with biological material depends on the frequency of the EM source; and for reasons discussed below, the known mechanisms through which ionizing radiation, optical radiation, RF, and MW affect biological material have no relevance for power-frequency fields. Although we usually discuss EM sources as though they produce waves of energy, sometimes EM energy acts like particles, particularly at the higher frequencies. The particle nature of EM energy is important because it is the energy per particle (photon) that determines whether EM energy can directly affect chemical structure.

**Direct Effects.** At the frequency of vacuum-UV and above ($2 \times 10^{15}$ Hz and above), photons have sufficient energy to break chemical bonds (ionization), and this part of the EM spectrum is termed ionizing. The well-known human health hazards of ionizing radiation are the result of the breaking of chemical bonds in DNA. Severe damage to DNA can kill cells, resulting in tissue damage or death. Lesser damage to DNA can result in permanent changes in the cells, which may lead to mutation or cancer.

At frequencies below that of vacuum-UV light, photons do not have sufficient energy to break chemical bonds, and this part of the EM spectrum is termed nonionizing.[2] At power frequencies, for example, the photon energy is a factor of $10^{-6}$ smaller than that needed to break even the weakest chemical bond. Although nonionizing sources cannot break chemical bonds, there are possible mechanisms of direct inter-

action. Electric fields can exert direct mechanical forces on charges or cellular structures within a tissue, orient dipolar molecules, and depolarize cell membranes. Magnetic fields can also directly exert forces, but since biological materials are largely nonmagnetic, these forces are very weak. These direct effects are generally far weaker than those produced by random thermal agitation (thermal noise) and, to cause significant changes in a biological system, generally require fields that far exceed those that exist in ordinary environments (6, 7). The well-known direct hazards of electric power, shock and burns, generally require that the subject directly contact a charged surface and are outside the scope of this review.

**Indirect Effects.** An additional mechanism by which nonionizing EM sources, such as RF, MW, and power-frequency fields can cause biological effects is by inducing electric currents that cause heating. This heating can kill cells, and if enough cells are killed, long-term and possibly permanent tissue damage can occur. The efficiency with which a nonionizing EM source can induce electric currents, and thus produce heating, depends on the frequency of the source. At frequencies below those used for broadcast AM radio (below $5 \times 10^5$ Hz), EM sources couple poorly with the bodies of humans and animals, and thus are very inefficient at inducing electric currents and causing heating. Power-frequency magnetic fields in excess of 500 μT are needed to induce electric currents of a magnitude similar to those that occur naturally in the human body (4, 8). Well-accepted safety standards exist to protect persons from power-frequency fields that could induce such currents (4, 9).

**Signal Amplification.** The above considerations show that the interactions of power-frequency fields with the human body are very weak at typical environmental levels. This does not rule out the possibility of some biological effect, but special conditions would clearly be required (10). The literature abounds with speculations about how power-frequency fields might overcome signal-to-noise problems via various resonance and/or signal amplification mechanisms (11–14); however, these speculations often fail to adequately consider the issue of thermal noise, and/or are open to challenge on other technical grounds (7, 8, 15–17).

**Other ELF Fields.** The electric currents produced by a magnetic field are proportional to the rate of change (i.e., the time-derivative) of the magnetic field. Pulsed fields (square-wave, sawtooth, etc.) have a higher rate of change than do sinusoidal fields of the same frequency and field strength, and thus induce much higher currents. Similarly, electric currents induced in the body by alternating magnetic fields are proportional to their frequency, so that frequencies above power-frequency induce higher currents for a given field strength than do power-frequency fields.

---

[2] Many of the biological effects of UV, visible, and infrared frequencies are also direct effects that depend on the photon energy, but they involve electronic excitation rather than ionization and do not occur at frequencies below that of infrared light (below $3 \times 10^{11}$ Hz).

Since induced electric currents are likely to be involved in any biological effect produced by power-frequency magnetic fields (4, 8), studies with pulsed and higher-frequency fields are of limited relevance to an assessment of the possible health risks associated with power-frequency fields. However, since transients and higher frequency harmonics exist in electrical environments, the biological effects of other types of ELF fields cannot be ignored. Thus, while our review of the literature on the biological effects that may be associated with the generation, transmission, distribution, and use of electricity will concentrate on studies of power-frequency sinusoidal magnetic fields, it will also consider other types of ELF fields.

## Epidemiology of Power-Frequency Fields and Cancer

There have been two basic types of power-frequency epidemiology studies: studies of children (1, 18–23) (Table I) and adults (24–29) (Table II) living near distribution and/or transmission lines, and studies of adults working in occupations with presumed exposure to power-frequency fields (2, 3, 30–36) (Table III). Interpretation of these studies is greatly complicated by exposure assessment problems. If power-frequency fields were carcinogenic and were at all similar to other known carcinogens, it would be the cumulative exposure for many years prior to disease diagnosis that should correlate with cancer incidence. Unfortunately, these exposure data do not exist and cannot be reliably reconstructed.

**Residential Exposure Studies.** Interpretation of the residential exposure studies (Table I and II) is further complicated by the lack of consensus as to the appropriate exposure metric. The original studies that suggested a relationship between power lines and childhood leukemia used a combination of the type of wiring and the distance to the residence as a surrogate measure of exposure, a system called "wirecodes". Other studies have used distance from transmission lines or substations as surrogate measures of exposure, and some of the recent studies have used contemporary measured fields or calculated historic fields as measures of exposure. One of the most puzzling features of the residential exposure studies is that the correlation of "exposure" with cancer incidence is higher when wirecodes or calculated fields are used as an exposure metric than when fields are directly measured in the homes (19–21). In general, the various surrogate measures of exposure do not correlate well with each other, or with contemporary measured fields; none of these measures of exposure is obviously superior, and none is common to all the major studies.

There have also been a few epidemiologic studies that have examined the relationship between the use of electrical appliances and cancer (19, 20, 37–39). These studies have shown little consistent association between the use of electrical appliances and cancer incidence, although the most recent of these studies (39) has actually shown a decreased incidence of leukemia among adult users of personal appliances, a decrease which reaches statistical significance for certain subgroups.

**Table I.** Childhood Cancer and Residential Exposure to Power-Frequency Fields

| | |
|---|---|
| Major studies: | Wertheimer & Leeper 1979 (1); Tomenius 1986 (18); Savitz *et al.* 1988 (19); London *et al.* 1991 (20); Feychting & Ahlbom 1993 (21); Olsen *et al.* 1993 (22); Verkasalo *et al.* 1993 (23) |
| Cancer sites: | Leukemia (15 studies), CNS cancer (7 studies), lymphoma (6 studies), overall cancer (4 studies) |
| Exposure assessment: | Contemporary measurements (4 studies), retrospective calculations (3 studies), proximity to lines (5 studies), wirecodes[a] (5 studies) |
| Results: | • No statistically significant associations have been found between measured fields and leukemia, brain cancer, or total cancer incidence (19–21). |
| | • One study (21) reported a statistically significant association between retrospective calculated fields and leukemia, but others (22, 23) did not. |
| | • Several studies (1, 19, 20) have reported statistically significant associations between wirecodes and brain cancer and/or leukemia incidence. |
| | • No studies have shown statistically significant associations between brain cancer and measured fields (19, 21), retrospective calculated fields (21–23), or proximity to lines (18, 21). |
| | • A statistically significant association with overall cancer incidence was reported in one study for calculated fields (22) and in one for proximity (18), but this was not observed in other studies (21, 23). |
| | • For the studies as a whole, the relative increase in cancer incidence (RR) was 1.5–1.9, but RR values as low a 1.0 (no effect) or as high as 3 cannot be excluded. |
| Dose-response: | • Two studies have reported statistically significant dose-response trends for leukemia and wirecodes (20) or calculated fields (21), but otherwise no statistically significant dose trends have been found. |

[a] See text.

**Table II.** Adult Cancer and Residential Exposure to Power-Frequency Fields

| | |
|---|---|
| Major studies: | Wertheimer & Leeper 1982 (24); McDowall 1986 (25); Coleman et al. 1989 (26); Youngston et al. 1991 (27); Schreiber et al. 1993 (28); Feychting & Ahlbom 1994 (29) |
| Major sites: | Leukemia (5 studies), CNS cancer (2 studies), total cancer (3 studies) |
| Exposure assessment: | Contemporary measurements (1 study), retrospective calculations (1 study), proximity to lines (4 studies), wirecodes[a] (1 study) |
| Results: | • A statistically significant association of brain cancer and total cancer with wirecodes was reported in one study (24), but no significant association was seen in other studies (25, 28, 29).<br>• No statistically significant association of leukemia with exposure was found for any measure of exposure in any study (24–29).<br>• For the studies as a whole, the relative increase in cancer incidence is about 1.1, but RR values below 1.0 (protection) or as high as 1.6 cannot be excluded. |
| Dose-response: | • No studies have reported statistically significant dose-response trends. |

[a] See text

**Table III.** Adult Cancer and Occupational Exposure to Power-Frequency Fields

| | |
|---|---|
| Major recent studies: | Floderus et al. 1993 (30); Sahl et al. 1993 (31), Guenel et al. 1993 (32), Theriault et al. 1994 (33); London et al. 1994 (34); Tynes et al. 1994 (35); Savitz & Loomis 1995 (36) |
| Major sites studied: | Leukemia (25+ studies), brain (18+ studies), breast (5+ studies), melanoma (5+ studies), lymphoma (5+ studies), all cancer (6+ studies) |
| Exposure assessment: | Early studies were based on job titles; some later studies have exposure assessment for job categories, but not for individuals. |
| Results: | • Some studies report an excess incidence of leukemia, brain cancer, breast cancer and/or lymphoma in some "electrical" occupations.<br>• For leukemia, brain cancer, breast cancer and/or lymphoma, the studies as a whole show a relative increase in cancer of 1.1 to 1.2, but RR values as low as 1.0 (no effect), and as high as 1.5 cannot be excluded.<br>• No overall cancer increase has been reported in "electrical" occupations, but RR values below 1.0 (protection) or as high as 1.1 cannot be excluded. |
| Dose-response: | • Only a few studies (e.g., London et al. [34]) have reported statistically significant dose-response relationships. |

**Occupational Exposure Studies.** Interpretation of the occupational exposure studies (Table III) is complicated by a lack of actual dosimetry. The original studies that suggested a link between occupational exposure to power-frequency fields and cancer were based on job titles as listed on death certificates. Some of the latest studies have improved upon this by using job descriptions, supplemented by data from workers doing those jobs, to develop exposure categories. However, no studies to date have been based on direct measurements of the exposure of the actual subjects of the study. In fact, given the low incidence of the cancers implicated by the studies, it is difficult to see how any sufficiently large study could be mounted with adequate direct measurements of the subjects' exposure. Even if such personal dosimetry were available, there is no consensus as to the appropriate exposure metric, since arguments have been made for time-weighted average fields, peak fields, rate of change of fields, or even transients.

**Multiple Testing Issues.** Interpretation of many of the studies is further complicated by multiple testing issues. When studies include multiple exposure metrics and/or multiple types of cancer, the investigator can compare many different subgroups. Each comparison (by the commonly accepted statistical criteria) has a 5% probability of yielding a "statistically significant" difference between the groups, even if there were no real differences. A related problem arises when the investigator groups subjects into categories based on arbitrarily chosen exposure cutpoints. Were the cutpoints chosen in advance, this would not be a problem, but often multiple cutpoints are analyzed after the fact. Between multiple exposure metrics, multiple cutpoints, multiple cancer sites, and subgroup analysis, a study may contain 50 or more calculations of relative risk,[3] each individually analyzed for significance at 5%. To make matters worse, the investigator may preferentially publish the "positive" findings, raising the issue of publication bias.

In general this issue of multiple testing has not been adequately considered in analysis of the litera-

---

[3] The excess cancer found in epidemiological studies is usually quantified in a number called the relative risk (RR). This is the risk of an "exposed" person getting cancer divided by the risk of an "unexposed" person getting cancer. Since no one is unexposed to power-frequency fields, the comparison is actually "high exposure" versus "low exposure". A RR of 1.0 means no effect, a RR of less than 1.0 means a decreased risk in exposed groups, and a RR of greater than 1.0 means an increased risk in exposed groups.

ture on power-frequency fields and cancer, although an interesting exception can be seen in the multiple cutpoint analysis done by Olsen et al. (22). Publication bias is also clearly a problem, and a review by the United Kingdom National Radiation Protection Board (40) sites several specific examples.

## Evaluating the Epidemiological Evidence

A specific set of criteria, first clearly enunciated by Hill (41), are widely used to assess epidemiological and laboratory studies of agents that may pose human health risks (Table IV). These "Hill's criteria" must be applied with caution. First, one must examine the entire published literature, not just pick the reports that support or contradict the existence of a health hazard. Second, one must directly review the important source documents, rather than base judgments on academic or regulatory reviews. Third, satisfying the individual criteria is not a yes-no matter, support for a criterion can be strong, moderate, weak, or nonexistent. Lastly, the criteria must be viewed as a whole; no individual criterion is either necessary or sufficient for concluding that there is a causal relationship between exposure to an agent and a disease.

How well do the epidemiological studies of power-frequency fields and cancer stand up to Hill's criteria (Table IV)? First, the association of power-frequency fields with cancer is not strong. A strong association is one with a RR of 5 or more. Tobacco smoking, for example, shows a RR for lung cancer 10–30 times that of nonsmokers. Most of the power-frequency studies that show statistically significant elevations in cancer incidence have RRs of less than three, and the studies as a whole have RRs in the 1.0 to 1.8 range (Table I–III). Second, while there are studies showing statis-

tically significant association of cancer incidence with exposure to power-frequency fields, few studies show the same positive result, and even the positive studies are often inconsistent with each other. Many of the studies are also internally inconsistent, showing statistically significant risks for some measures of exposure, but not for others (Table I and II). Third, the specificity of the reported association of cancer with power-frequency fields is also very weak, with at least six different types of cancer being reported in excess in two or more studies. A quick overview of the residential and occupational epidemiological studies appears to indicate that exposure to power-frequency fields is associated principally with brain cancer and leukemia. However, this appearance is misleading, since in many studies leukemias and/or brain cancer are the only types of cancer evaluated. Fourth, even the studies which have reported a statistically significant excess of some type of cancer for some measure of exposure, have generally not found a statistically significant dose-response relationship (Table I–III).

## Relationship of Laboratory Studies to Epidemiology in Risk Evaluation

Overall, application of Hill's criteria (Table IV) shows that the current epidemiological evidence for a connection between power-frequency fields and cancer is weak, because the existing studies are neither strong nor particularly consistent, and because there is so little evidence for a dose-response relationship. Clearly, there are at least several roles for laboratory evidence in this evaluation. First, if there were strong in vitro or in vivo evidence that power-frequencies were carcinogenic, it would make the epidemiology more convincing. Second, if there were mechanisms

**Table IV.** Is There a Causal Relationship Between Power-Frequency Fields and Cancer?

| The classical "Hill's criteria" (41) | Hill's criteria applied to power-frequency fields and cancer | Strength of evidence[a] |
|---|---|---|
| Strength? | • How strong are the relative risks for an association between power-frequency fields and cancer? | Weak-possible |
| Consistency? | • Are the studies of associations between power-frequency fields and cancer internally and externally consistent? | Weak-possible |
| Specificity? | • Since many carcinogens cause multiple types of cancer, this criterion may be of limited relevance. | Weak |
| Temporal relationship? | • Since exposure to these fields is pervasive, this criterion is unevaluable. | — |
| Dose-response curve? | • Does the incidence of cancer increase with increased exposure to power-frequency fields? | None-weak |
| Biologically plausible and coherent? | • Are there mechanisms that could connect these fields with cancer, and that are consistent with what is known about cancer biology and about electromagnetics? | None |
| Experimental evidence? | • Is there laboratory evidence that these fields are carcinogenic? | None-weak |
| Overall | • How strong is the evidence for a causal relationship between power-frequency fields and cancer? | Weak |

[a] On a 5-point scale of how well the data as a whole support as causal relationship between exposure to power-frequency fields and an increased risk of cancer: none, weak, possible, probable, strong.

that could explain an interaction of power-frequency fields of the intensity encountered in residential and occupational settings with biological systems, then many of the questions concerning the appropriateness of various exposure metrics could be resolved. On the other hand, if appropriate laboratory studies were done and these studies consistently failed to show any evidence for carcinogenicity, then we would tend to dismiss this weak and inconsistent epidemiology. In other words, while weak epidemiology cannot establish causality on its own, weak epidemiology combined with strong laboratory evidence and plausible mechanisms can satisfy the criteria for causality.

**Bioeffects of Intense Fields.** Power-frequency fields intense enough to induce electric currents in excess of those that occur naturally (above 500 μT) have shown reproducible effects, including effects on humans (4, 9, 42, 43). However, these "bioeffects" have no obvious connection to carcinogenesis and have not been observed at the field intensities encountered in occupational and residential settings.

**Genotoxicity.** If power-frequency fields were carcinogenic, they could be either genotoxic or epigenetic (in older terminology, either initiators or promoters). Genotoxic agents directly damage the genetic material of cells (the DNA), often affect many types of cells, and may cause more than one kind of cancer. Genotoxins may not have thresholds for their effect; in other words, as the dose of the genotoxin is lowered the risk gets smaller, but it may never go away.

**Epigenetic Activity.** An epigenetic agent, on the other hand, is something that increases the probability that a genotoxin will damage the genetic material of cells, or that a genotoxic exposure will result in cancer. Promoters are a particular kind of epigenetic agent that increase the cancer risk in animals already exposed to a genotoxic carcinogen. Epigenetic agents (including promoters) usually affect only certain types of cells and may cause only certain types of cancer. Epigenetic agents generally have thresholds for their effect, so that as the dose of an epigenetic agent is lowered a level is reached at which there is no (rather than very little) risk.

## Power-Frequency Fields and Genotoxicity

There are many approaches to measuring genotoxicity. Whole-organism exposure studies can be used to see whether exposure causes cancer or mutations. Cellular studies can be done to detect DNA or chromosomal damage. The genotoxicity studies done to date are summarized in Table V. This summary includes nonmammalian as well as mammalian data, and includes both pulsed fields and ELF fields at other than power-frequency. Such broad coverage is warranted, since any evidence for genotoxicity from any system exposed to any related type of field would be relevant to the question of carcinogenicity.

**Whole Organism Genotoxicity.** The biggest gap in the range of endpoints assessed is that very few mammalian exposure studies have been published (see Loscher & Mevissen [44] for summaries of some of the unpublished work). Bellossi *et al.* (45) exposed leuke-

**Table V.** Assessment of the Genotoxicity of Power-Frequency Fields[a]

| Endpoint | Results |
| --- | --- |
| Carcinogenesis | • Sinusoidal fields not a carcinogen in mice (46).<br>• Pulsed 12- and 460-Hz fields not leukemogenic in mice (45). |
| Mutagenesis | • Sinusoidal fields not mutagenic in mice (47), Drosophila (126), yeast (62), mammalian cells (63), or bacteria (61, 63).<br>• Pulsed fields not mutagenic in bacteria (60). |
| Chromosome aberrations (occupational-exposure) | • No excess sister chromatid exchanges (SCEs) (67–70).<br>• Excess chromosome aberrations in smokers only (69, 70).<br>• Excess chromosome aberrations in non-smokers in one study (67), but not in other studies (68–70). |
| Chromosome aberrations (*in vitro*) | • Sinusoidal fields do not cause chromosome aberrations in human lymphocytes[b] (53, 54).<br>• Sinusoidal fields do not cause SCEs in human[b] (54–56) or rat lymphocytes (57).<br>• Pulsed fields caused aberrations in human lymphocytes in one study (65), but not in a replicate (59) or in CHO cells (66). |
| DNA strand breaks | • Sinusoidal fields do not cause DNA strand breaks in human cells[b] (49), CHO cells[b] (48), or plasmids (50).<br>• Pulsed fields do not cause DNA strand breaks in human cells[b] (52). |
| Cell transformation | • No increase in transformation of mammalian cells (64). |
| Micronucleus formation | • Neither sinusoidal[b] (56, 58) nor pulsed (59) fields increase micronuclei formation in mammalian cells. |

[a] Studies are of 50/60 Hz magnetic fields unless otherwise specified.
[b] Electric fields and combined electric and magnetic fields were also tested.

mia-prone mice for five generations and found no effect on leukemia rates; however, since the study used 12 and 460 Hz pulsed fields at 6000 μT, the relevance of this to environmental power-frequency fields is unclear. Rannug *et al.* (46) found that 50 and 500 μT fields at 50-Hz did not significantly increase the incidence of skin tumors or leukemia in mice. In a multigeneration mouse exposure study which used 300 μT (plus 15 kV/m) or 1000 μT (plus 50 kV/m) 60-Hz fields, Benz *et al.* (47) found no increase in mutation rates, fertility, or sister chromatid exchanges.

**Cellular Genotoxicity.** Cellular genotoxicity studies have been much more extensive (Table V); the most obvious gap is the lack of studies using cell transformation endpoints. Published laboratory studies have reported that power-frequency magnetic fields do not cause DNA strand breaks (48–52), chromosome aberrations (53, 54), sister chromatid exchanges (SCEs) (54–57), micronuclei formation (56, 58, 59), or mutations (60–63), and do not transform cells (64). Many of these laboratory studies also examined power-frequency electric fields and combinations of power-frequency electric and magnetic fields, and as with the studies of magnetic fields alone, the studies of electric fields and combined fields showed no evidence of genotoxicity.

**Positive Reports of Genotoxicity.** There are two published reports of genotoxicity. Khalil and Qassem (65) reported that a 1050 μT pulsed field caused chromosome aberrations, but Scarfi *et al.* (59) were unable to replicate this observation, and Takahashi *et al.* (66) found no effect in similar studies with CHO cells. Nordenson *et al.* (67) reported that switchyard workers exposed to spark discharges[4] had increased chromosomal defects, but Bauchinger *et al.* (68) found no such increase in a similar study. Two other studies (69, 70) found some evidence of increased chromosomal aberrations in workers exposed to spark discharges, but only if they were also smokers.

**Summary of Genotoxicity.** The evidence is quite convincing that power-frequency fields are not genotoxic. Only the lack of cell transformation and long-term animal exposure studies keeps the data from being totally convincing. This conclusion is supported by two recent comprehensive reviews on this subject. McCann *et al.* (71) wrote, "The preponderance of evidence suggests that neither ELF nor static electric and magnetic fields have a clearly demonstrated potential to cause genotoxic effects," and Murphy *et al.* (72) wrote, "Considering the total body of available information, there is little evidence that exposure to

[power-frequency fields] directly causes genetic changes in biological systems."

**Power-Frequency Fields and Epigenetic Activity**

Even before the evidence accumulated that power-frequency fields were not genotoxic, some investigators suggested that these fields were promoters. As a result, extensive investigations have been conducted of the possible epigenetic activity of power-frequency fields. These studies are summarized in Table VI.

**Classical Promotion Assays.** Promoters are a specific class of epigenetic agents. In a classical promotion test, animals are exposed to a known genotoxin at a dose that will cause cancer in some, but not all, animals. Another set of animals are exposed to the genotoxin, plus another agent. If the agent plus the genotoxin results in more cancers than are seen for the genotoxin alone, then that agent is a promoter. Copromotion is a related assay in which the agent is tested with both a known genotoxin and a known promoter.

Published studies have reported that power-frequency magnetic fields do not promote chemically induced skin (46, 73–75) or liver cancers (76, 77). For chemically induced breast cancer, published studies have reported promotion at 20 μT (78) and 100 μT (79), but other studies did not find promotion at 0.3–1.0 μT (80), 100 μT (81), or 30,000 μT (82). The report by Beniashvili *et al.* (78) of promotion of chemically induced breast cancer at 20 μT is difficult to evaluate, as the study has been published only in preliminary form, and critical experimental details are missing.

**Cellular Epigenetic Activity.** Some types of studies are relevant to the carcinogenic potential of agents, but are neither classic genotoxicity nor promotion tests. The most common of these are cellular studies that test whether an agent enhances the activity of a known genotoxin; these studies could be regarded as the cellular equivalent of a promotion study. Published studies have reported that power-frequency magnetic fields do not enhance the mutagenic effects of known genotoxins (61, 63) and do not inhibit the repair of DNA damage induced by ionizing (83) or UV (62) radiation.

**Positive Reports of Epigenetic Activity.** In addition to the two reports of promotion of chemically induced breast cancer (78, 79), three studies have indicated that power-frequency fields might have some epigenetic activity. Rosenthal *et al.* (54) reported that a 5,000 μT power-frequency field might increase the frequency of SCEs induced in lymphocytes by antineoplastic drugs; and Hintenlang *et al.* (84) reported that 600–1,500 μT power-frequency fields increased the frequency of tetraploidy in lymphocytes when combined with high doses of ionizing radiation. Neither study has been replicated. Cain *et al.* (64) re-

---

[4] Spark discharges are unique to the electrical environment of high-voltage sources, where electric fields can reach intensities of up to 20 kV/m. The peak value of the body current at the point of a spark discharge can reach several amps (67).

**Table VI.** Assessment of the Epigenetic Potential of Power-Frequency Fields[a]

| Endpoint | Results |
|---|---|
| Promotion (chemically induced skin tumors) | • No promotion or co-promotion at 2000 μT (73, 74).<br>• No promotion at 50 or 500 μT delivered continuously (46, 75) or intermittently (75). |
| Promotion (chemically induced mammary tumors) | • Promotion at 20 μT (78) and 100 μT (79).<br>• No promotion at 0.3–1.0 μT (80), 100 μT (81), or 30,000 μT (82). |
| Promotion (chemically induced liver tumors) | • No promotion at 0.5–500 μT (76).<br>• No co-promotion at 0.5 or 500 μT (77). |
| Inhibition of DNA repair | • No effect on UV-induced DNA damage in yeast at 1000 μT (62).<br>• No effect on radiation-induced DNA damage in human lymphocytes at 1000 μT (83). |
| Enhancement of transformation | • Enhanced co-transformation of mammalian cells at 100 μT (64) in some, but not all experiments.[b] |
| Enhancement of genotoxicity | • Enhancement of ionizing radiation damage in human lymphocytes at 600 μT (84).<br>• Enhancement of chemically-induced sister chromatid exchanges in human lymphocytes at 5000 μT for some, but not all agents (54).<br>• No enhancement of chemical mutagenesis in bacteria at 0.12–120 μT (61).<br>• No enhancement of viral-induced mutagenesis in human cells at 1 or 10 μT (63). |

[a] All studies are of 50/60 Hz sinusoidal magnetic fields.
[b] See text and Footnote 5.

ported that a 100 μT power-frequency field could enhance cell transformation; the effect was only seen in the presence of a chemical promoter, and the authors subsequently reported[5] that they could not replicate the study.

**Summary of Epigenetic Activity.** In general, power-frequency fields do not appear to have epigenetic activity. However, there are areas that need further exploration. The reports of promotion of chemically induced breast cancer (78, 79) and enhancement of genotoxicity (54, 84) need to be replicated, and if they are replicated the dose-response relationship for the effect needs to be established.

## Bioeffects of Power-Frequency Fields That Might Be Related to Cancer

Biological effects other than genotoxicity, promotion, or enhancement of genotoxicity might be related to cancer. In particular, agents that have dramatic effects on cell growth (mitogenic effects), on the function of the immune system, or on hormone balances, might contribute to cancer without meeting the classic definitions for genotoxicity, promotion, or epigenetic activity. Studies of these issues are summarized in Table VII.

**Cell and Tumor Growth.** There have been scattered reports that power-frequency fields can enhance cell proliferation (54) or tumor growth (74, 79, 81), but the few positive reports have involved fields of 100 μT and above, and the vast majority of the studies* have shown no effect. Two other studies have been cited to support the idea that power-frequency fields might be mitogens. Liboff *et al.* (92) are often quoted as reporting effects on cell growth for fields as low as 16 μT, but the study only reports increased uptake of a DNA precursor, an observation which may or may not indicate an effect on proliferation. Phillips *et al.* (93) reported enhanced growth of tumor cells at 100 μT, but the statistical significance of the effect has been questioned, and the study could not be replicated (94).

**Immunosuppression.** In the early 1970s, some investigators speculated that the immune system might have a role in preventing the development of cancer, a theory known as the "immune surveillance hypothesis" (95, 96). Subsequent studies have shown that this hypothesis is not generally valid (95, 96). Suppression of the immune system is associated with increased rates of certain types of cancer, particularly lymphomas, but not with leukemia or brain cancer (95, 96). While some studies have reported that power-frequency fields can have effects on cells of the immune system (97), no studies have shown the type or magnitude of immune suppression that is associated with an increased incidence of lymphomas or other cancers in humans or animals.

---

[5] Cain CD, Thomas DL, Adey WR. 60-Hz magnetic field strength dependency and TPA-induced focus formation in co-culture of C3H/10T1/2 cells. Abstract P-1, Annual Review of Research on Biological Effects of Electric and Magnetic Fields from the Generation, Delivery and Use of Electricity, Albuquerque, November 1994.

---

* References 46, 49, 53, 55–57, 73, 75–77, 80, 82, 85–91.

**Table VII.** Assessment of Biological Effects That Might Be Related to Carcinogenesis[a]

| Endpoint | Results |
|---|---|
| Effects on tumor growth | • Enhanced growth of chemically induced skin tumors at 2000 $\mu$T in one study (74), but not in another (73), and not at 50 or 500 $\mu$T (46, 75).<br>• Enhanced growth of chemically-induced mammary tumors at 100 $\mu$T (79, 81), but not at 0.3–1.0 $\mu$T (80) or 30,000 $\mu$T (82).<br>• No growth effect on mammary tumors at 100–2000 $\mu$T[b] (88), on liver tumors at 0.5–500 $\mu$T (76, 77), or on leukemia at 1.4–500 $\mu$T (87). |
| Effects on cell growth | • Increased proliferation in human lymphocytes at 5000 $\mu$T (54).<br>• No effect on growth of mammalian cells at 220–30,000 $\mu$T (56, 57, 86, 89).<br>• No effect on growth of human lymphocytes at 100–220 $\mu$T[b] (53, 55, 56).<br>• No effect on growth of human tumor cells at 0.2–2500 $\mu$T[b] (49, 85, 90, 91). |
| Growth-related effects | • Increased thymidine uptake in human fibroblasts at 16+ $\mu$T (92).<br>• Increased colony-forming ability of tumor cells at 100 $\mu$T[c] (93). |
| Immune suppression | • Scattered reports of minor effects on components of the immune system at 2000 $\mu$T and above, but no evidence of immune-suppression (97). |
| Altered hormone balance | • Decreased night-time melatonin in rats at 1–50 $\mu$T (100), 0.2–1.0 $\mu$T (103), and at 0.3–1.0 $\mu$T (80), but not at 0.10 $\mu$T (100) or 1 $\mu$T (102).<br>• Inconsistent effect on melatonin in Siberian hamsters at 100 $\mu$T (104).<br>• Reports of decreased night-time melatonin levels due to exposure to sinusoidal electric fields and static magnetic fields (98, 127).<br>• No effect on melatonin levels in sheep at 4 $\mu$T (101).<br>• No evidence that melatonin has significant anti-cancer activity in humans (106, 107). |

[a] All studies are of 50/60 Hz sinusoidal magnetic fields unless otherwise noted.
[b] Electric fields and combined electric and magnetic fields also tested.
[c] Attempt at replication failed (94).

**The "Melatonin Hypothesis".** Some investigators have suggested that power-frequency fields might suppress the production of melatonin, and that melatonin might have "cancer-preventive" activity (98, 99). This is highly speculative. There have been reports that electric fields and static magnetic fields can affect melatonin production (98), but studies using power-frequency magnetic fields have not shown consistent effects (80, 100–104). The second component of the hypothesis, that a decrease in melatonin levels will lead to an increase in cancer, is also unproven. In the late 1970s and early 1980s there was interest in using melatonin as an anti-cancer agent (105), but clinical trials of melatonin continue to show that it is largely ineffective (106, 107).

**Reproducibility and Replication.** If a reproducible biological effect is defined as one that has been reported in the peer-reviewed literature by more than one laboratory, without contradictory reports appearing elsewhere; then there may be no reproducible effects of ELF magnetic fields below about 200 $\mu$T. While there are reports of effects for fields as low as about 1 $\mu$T, none of these reports have been replicated.

The lack of confirmation of the laboratory studies is due to many factors. First, many reports on the biological effects of power-frequency fields have never been published in the peer-reviewed literature and

cannot be scientifically evaluated. Second, no attempts have ever been made to replicate many of the published reports of biological effects; and one positive report, standing in isolation, is hard to evaluate. Third, when attempts have been made to replicate some of the published studies, these replications have often failed to show the effect (89, 108, 109). Lastly, the investigators in this field use a wide variety of biological systems, endpoints, and exposure conditions, which makes studies extremely hard to compare or evaluate. A recent review (110) concluded:

> Despite earlier reports of the effects in a diverse range of models there has not been a single positive replication of any study during 1993, instead the range of unreplicated studies has continued to grow. The few replications that have been attempted have all failed to confirm the original findings.

## Mechanisms for Biological Interactions

Three general biophysical mechanisms have been proposed that could account for biological effects of strong ELF magnetic fields. Biological effects could be due to induced electric currents (4, 8, 9), to direct effects on magnetic biological material (12), or to effects on rates of certain chemical reactions (111). However, when quantitatively analyzed all these mechanisms are found to require fields in tissue that far exceed the fields that are induced by typical environmental exposures.

**Induced Currents.** Power-frequency magnetic fields can induce electric currents, and induced electric currents definitely can cause biological effects (4, 8, 9). However, the currents induced in the body by fields of less than 50 $\mu$T are weaker than the currents that occur naturally (8). Moreover, the currents induced by a 5 $\mu$T power-frequency field are less than those induced in the body by walking through the Earth's static magnetic field (8). Thus, as emphatically pointed out by Adair (7, 8), if power-frequency magnetic fields of the intensity encountered in residential and most occupational settings do have biological effects, they are not mediated by induced electric currents.

The above argument presumes that 50 or 60 Hz sinusoidal power-frequency fields are the only time-varying electromagnetic fields found in conjunction with the transmission, distribution, and use of electric power. If this presumption is not true, and large transients and/or significant higher-order harmonics are present, then it is possible that electric currents stronger than those that occur naturally in the body could be induced at field levels that are present in residential and occupational settings.

**Magnetic Biological Material.** Small magnetic particles (magnetite, $Fe_3O_4$) have been found in bacteria that orient in the Earth's static magnetic field (12). While investigators (12) have speculated that such magnetic particles may also exist in fish, honeybees, and birds, their presence in mammalian cells is still unproven, and their biological function in mammalian tissue is unknown. Kirschvink *et al.* (12) have suggested that power-frequency magnetic fields could cause biological effects by acting directly on such particles. However, calculations show that this would require fields of 2–5 $\mu$T or above at 50/60 Hz (7, 12, 112).

**Free Radical Reactions.** *Static magnetic fields* can influence the reaction rates of chemical reactions that involve free radical pairs (111, 113). Since the free radicals involved in these reactions have lifetimes in the microsecond range, whereas power-frequency fields have a cycle time in the millisecond range, a power-frequency field will act like a static field during the time scale over which these reactions occur. However, since any effects of the power-frequency field would be additive with the Earth's static field (30–70 $\mu$T), no detectable biological effects would be expected below about 50 $\mu$T (111).

**Resonance Theories.** Some of the biophysical constraints on possible mechanisms for biological effects of weak power-frequency magnetic fields could be overcome if there were resonance mechanisms that could make cells (or organisms) uniquely sensitive to power-frequency fields. Several such resonance mechanisms have been proposed, but none have survived scientific scrutiny (8, 15–17), and much of the experimental evidence that prompted the speculations in the first place cannot be independently reproduced (89, 108, 109). There are also severe incompatibilities between known biophysical characteristics of cells and the conditions required for such resonances (8, 15–17).

**Summary.** None of the above mechanisms appear to be able to explain the existence of biological interactions at field levels that are present in residential and occupational settings. Thus, if power-frequency fields below 5 $\mu$T do actually have biological effects, the mechanisms must be found, in Adair's (8) words, "outside the scope of conventional physics."

## How Strong Is the Evidence?

**Hill's Criteria.** As discussed earlier, a review of the epidemiological evidence shows that the association between exposure to power-frequency fields and cancer is weak, inconsistent, and nonspecific. The laboratory studies of power-frequency fields show little evidence of the type of effects on cells or animals that point towards power-frequency fields causing or contributing to cancer. Finally, from what is known about the biophysics of power-frequency fields, and about the effects of power-frequency fields on biological systems, there is no reason even to suspect that they would cause or contribute to cancer.

A formal evaluation of the evidence using Hill's criteria (Table IV) indicates that the evidence for an association between power-frequency fields and cancer is weak. Other reviewers who have formally used Hill's criteria to evaluate the data have given overall evaluations ranging from "at best weak" evidence (114, 115) to "possible" evidence (116, 117).

**Independent Review.** A number of independent bodies have reviewed the research on power-frequency fields over the past several years. Of particular note are reviews by the Public Utility Commission of Texas (118), the Connecticut Academy of Science and Engineering (119), Oak Ridge Associated Universities (commissioned by the U.S. Committee on Interagency Radiation Research and Policy Coordination) (120), the United Kingdom National Radiological Protection Board (4, 121), the French National Institute of Health and Medical Research (INSERM) (122), and the French Academy of Medicine (123). None of these reviews have concluded that power-frequency magnetic or electric fields of the intensity encountered in residential, or in most occupational, settings are confirmed human health risks.

**Standards and Guidelines.** A number of governmental and professional organizations have developed exposure standards for power-frequency fields. Most generally applicable are those developed by the British National Radiation Protection Board (NRPB) (4), and the International Commission on Non-Ionizing Radiation Protection (ICNIRP)[6] (9). These standards are based on keeping the electric currents induced by power-frequency fields to a level less than those that occur naturally in the body. The NRPB guidelines (4) for residential and occupational exposure to 60-Hz fields are 10 kV/m for the electric field and 1330 μT for the magnetic field (at 50-Hz the standards are 12 kV/m and 1600 μT). For the general public, the ICNIRP magnetic field exposure standard (9) is 100 μT for continuous exposure and 1000 μT for short-term exposure. For occupational exposure, the ICNIRP standard is 500 μT for continuous exposure and 5000 μT for short-term exposure.

**Consensus.** There is, then, a broad consensus in the scientific community that no causal association has been established between residential and occupational exposure to power-frequency fields, and the risk of cancer. There is also a broad consensus that exposure to these fields has not been, and probably cannot be, proven to be absolutely safe. The controversy in the scientific community is over whether power-frequency fields might be shown to be hazardous by future studies, and the related issue of what additional studies should be done, and what priority should be given to those studies.

## What Additional Studies Are Needed?

No number and type of additional studies will be sufficient to satisfy those who demand total assurance that there are absolutely no health effects. Given the ambiguities of risk research and the nature of the scientific method, there will always be loose ends and unexplained findings. Nevertheless, there appear to be certain areas where additional studies might be useful.

**Epidemiology.** Large studies, with individual dose assessment, control of known confounders, and the capability of examining dose-response relationships would have a major impact on risk assessment. Individual dose assessment, however, would appear to require prospective studies, and it is not clear that any such studies are planned or even feasible. It is difficult to see how more retrospective occupational and residential exposure studies will resolve anything, particularly if they are based on surrogate measures of exposure. However, there are areas where small epidemiological studies might have a great impact. If, for example, a confounder were identified in the childhood leukemia-wirecoding studies (see for example,

Jones *et al.* [124]), or a carcinogen was identified in some "electrical occupations," almost all basis for concern about power-frequency fields and cancer would vanish.

**Animal.** An obvious gap in the genotoxicity studies is the relative lack of long-term animal exposure studies. Such studies are underway in the United States and elsewhere. A positive finding of carcinogenicity in these studies, particularly if it was for leukemia or CNS cancer, would require a major reevaluation of the public health implications of occupational and residential exposure to power-frequency fields. However, a negative outcome would have little impact. First, almost no one expects that power-frequency fields will be found to be genotoxic. Second, proponents of the idea that these fields do cause cancer could simply claim that the exposures were done under the wrong conditions.

In addition to long-term exposure studies, the two positive reports of promotion of chemically induced breast cancer (78, 79) need to be replicated, and if they are replicated the dose-response relationship for the effect needs to be established. Promotion studies of leukemia and CNS cancer would also be valuable, but there are no established promotion models for either type of cancer.

**Cellular.** An obvious gap in the cellular genotoxicity studies is the relative lack of cellular transformation assays. Without getting into the argument about whether transformation measures genotoxicity or epigenetic activity, clearly either positive or negative finding of enhancement of transformation would influence thinking. There are also two isolated reports of enhancement of genotoxicity (54, 84) that need to be replicated, and if they are replicated the dose-response relationship for the effect needs to be established.

## The Public Controversy About "EMF and Cancer"

Regardless of the scientific review of the data, the public controversy remains. This is seen in the continuing litigation over cancers that have been alleged to be caused by occupational and residential exposures, and by the public opposition that meets almost all attempts to site new powerlines and substations or to upgrade existing facilities. The public concern is sustained by the occasional reports of positive findings, by the inability of scientists to guarantee that no risk exists, and by statements from scientists and government officials that more research is needed. This public concern is further encouraged by several lay-oriented books that allege that there has been a conspiracy to conceal the health risks of power-frequency fields from the general public (125). Concern has also been nourished by uneven reporting on this issue by the mass media. For example, the 1993 report from

---

[6] The 1990 "interim standard" was confirmed by the ICNIPR in a press release dated May 12, 1993.

Sweden (21) of a positive association between calculated historic fields and childhood leukemia received wide media coverage in the United States, but the parallel negative reports from Denmark (22) and Finland (23) received little or no mention, and the recent Swedish study (29) showing no association between adult residential exposure and cancer received essentially no coverage.

Public concern about electricity and cancer will continue either until future research shows that the fields are hazardous (an outcome we personally consider unlikely), or until the public learns that science cannot provide absolute guarantees that anything is absolutely safe (an outcome, unfortunately, that we consider equally unlikely).

This review draws heavily on an electronic FAQ (Frequency Asked Questions) document called ''Powerlines & Cancer FAQs'' which J. Moulder maintains in the USENET newsgroup called ''sci.med.physics''. We would like to acknowledge the many readers of sci.med.physics who have contributed suggestions, comments, and corrections to the FAQ sheet. The current version of ''Powerlines & Cancer FAQs'' can be found on USENET or obtained by FTP, e-mail, Gopher, or World Wide Web from any of the many sites that archive USENET FAQ sheets.

1. Wertheimer N, Leeper E. Electrical wiring configurations and childhood cancer. Am J Epidemiol 109:273–284, 1979.
2. Milham S. Mortality from leukemia in workers exposed to electrical and magnetic fields. N Engl J Med 307:249, 1982.
3. Wright WE, Peters JM, Mack TM. Leukaemia in workers exposed to electrical and magnetic fields. Lancet 2(8308):1160–1161, 1982.
4. National Radiation Protection Board. Restrictions on human exposure to static and time varying electromagnetic fields and radiation. Doc NRPB 4(5):1–69, 1993.
5. Kaune WT. Assessing human exposure to power-frequency electric and magnetic fields. Environ Res 101(Suppl 4):121–133, 1993.
6. Schwan HP, Foster KR. RF-field interactions with biological systems: Electrical properties and biophysical mechanisms. Proc IEEE 68:104–113, 1980.
7. Adair RK. Constraints of thermal noise on the effects of weak 60-Hz magnetic fields acting on biological magnetite. Proc Nat Acad Sci USA 91:2925–2929, 1994.
8. Adair RK. Constraints on biological effects of weak extremely-low-frequency electromagnetic fields. Phys Rev A 43:1039–1048, 1991.
9. Jammet HP, Bernhardt JH, Bosnjakovic BFM, Czerski P, Grandolfo M, Harder D, Knave B, Marshall J, Repacholi MH, Sliney DH, Stolwijk DH. Interim guidelines on limits of exposure to 50/60 Hz electric and magnetic fields. Health Phys 58:113–122, 1990.
10. Foster KR. Health effects of low-level electromagnetic fields: phantom or not-so-phantom risk? Health Phys 62:429–435, 1992.
11. Weaver JC, Astumian RD. The response of living cells to very weak electric fields: The thermal noise limit. Science 247:459–462, 1990.
12. Kirschvink JL, Kobayashi-Kirschvink A, Diaz-Ricci JC, Kirschvink SJ. Magnetite in human tissues: A mechanism for the biological effects of weak ELF magnetic fields. Bioelectromag Suppl 1:101–113, 1992.
13. Litovitz TA, Krause D, Montrose CJ, Mullins JM. Temporally incoherent magnetic fields mitigate the response of biological systems to temporally coherent magnetic fields. Bioelectromag 15:399–409, 1994.
14. Blanchard JP, Blackman CF. Clarification and application of an ion parametric resonance model for magnetic field interactions with biological systems. Bioelectromag 15:217–238, 1994.
15. Sandweiss J. On the cyclotron resonance model of ion transport. Bioelectromag 11:203–205, 1990.
16. Adair RK. Criticism of Lednev's mechanism for the influence of weak magnetic fields on biological systems. Bioelectromag 13:231–235, 1992.
17. Galt S, Sandblom J, Hamnerius Y. Theoretical study of the resonant behavior of an ion confined to a potential well in a combination of AC and DC magnetic fields. Bioelectromag 14:299–314, 1993.
18. Tomenius L. 50-Hz electromagnetic environment and the incidence of childhood tumors in Stockholm County. Bioelectromag 7:191–207, 1986.
19. Savitz DA, Wachtel H, Barnes FA, John EM, Tvrdik JG. Case-control study of childhood cancer and exposure to 60-Hz magnetic fields. Am J Epidemiol 128:21–38, 1988.
20. London SJ, Thomas DC, Bowman JD, Sobel EE, Cheng TC, Peters JM. Exposure to residential electric and magnetic fields and risk of childhood leukemia. Am J Epidemiol 134:923–937, 1991.
21. Feychting M, Ahlbom A. Magnetic fields and cancer in children residing near Swedish high-voltage power lines. Am J Epidemiol 138:467–481, 1993.
22. Olsen JH, Nielsen A, Schulgen G. Residence near high voltage facilities and risk of cancer in children. Br Med J 307:891–895, 1993.
23. Verkasalo PK, Pukkala E, Hongisto MY, Valjus JE, Järvinen PJ, Heikkilä KV, Koskenvuo M. Risk of cancer in Finnish children living close to power lines. Br Med J 307:895–899, 1993.
24. Wertheimer N, Leeper E. Adult cancer related to electrical wires near the home. Int J Epidemiol 11:345–355, 1982.
25. McDowall ME. Mortality of persons resident in the vicinity of electrical transmission facilities. Br J Cancer 53:271–279, 1986.
26. Coleman MP, Bell CMJ, Taylor HL, Primag-Zakel M. Leukemia and residence near electricity transmission equipment: A case-control study. Br J Cancer 60:793–798, 1989.
27. Youngson JHAM, Clayden AD, Myers A, Cartwright RA. A case/control study of adult haematological malignancies in relation to overhead powerlines. Br J Cancer 63:977–985, 1991.
28. Schreiber GH, Swaen GMH, Meijers JMM, Slangen JJM, Sturmans F. Cancer mortality and residence near electricity transmission equipment: A retrospective cohort study. Int J Epidemiol 22:9–15, 1993.
29. Feychting M, Ahlbom A. Magnetic fields, leukemia, and central nervous system tumors in Swedish adults residing near high-voltage power lines. Epidemiology 5:501–509, 1994.
30. Floderus B, Persson T, Stenlund C, Wennberg A, Öst Å, Knave B. Occupational exposure to electromagnetic fields in relation to leukemia and brain tumors: A case-control study in Sweden. Cancer Causes Control 4:465–476, 1993.
31. Sahl JD, Kelsh MA, Greenland S. Cohort and nested case-control studies of hematopoietic cancers and brain cancer among electric utility workers. Epidemiology 4:104–114, 1993.
32. Guénel P, Raskmark P, Andersen JB, Lynge E. Incidence of cancer in persons with occupational exposure to electromagnetic fields in Denmark. Br J Indust Med 50:758–764, 1993.
33. Thériault G, Goldberg M, Miller AB, Armstrong B, Guénel P, Deadpan J, Imbernon E, To T, Chevalier A, Cyr D, Wall C. Cancer risks associated with occupational exposure to magnetic fields among utility workers in Ontario and Quebec, Canada, and France: 1970–1989. Am J Epidemiol 139:550–572, 1994.
34. London SJ, Bowman JD, Sobel E, Thomas DC, Garabrant DH, Pearce N, Bernstein L, Peters JM. Exposure to magnetic fields among electrical workers in relationship to leukemia risk in Los Angeles County. Am J Indust Med 26:47–60, 1994.
35. Tynes T, Reitan JB, Anderson A. Incidence of cancer among workers in Norwegian hydroelectric power companies. Scand J Work Environ Health 20:339–344, 1994.

36. Savitz DA, Loomis DP. Magnetic field exposure in relation to leukemia and brain cancer mortality among electric utility workers. Am J Epidemiol **141**:123–134, 1995.

37. Preston-Martin S, Peters JM, Yu MC, Garabrant DH, Bowman JD. Myelogenous leukemia and electric blanket use. Bioelectromag **9**:207–213, 1988.

38. Savitz DA, John EM, Kleckner RC. Magnetic field exposure from electric appliances and childhood cancer. Am J Epidemiol **131**:763–773, 1990.

39. Lovely RH, Buschbom RL, Slavich AL, Anderson LE, Hansen NH, Wilson BW. Adult leukemia risk and personal appliance use: A preliminary study. Am J Epidemiol **140**:510–517, 1994.

40. Doll R, Beral V, Cox R, Day NE, Gardner MJ, Grant EH, McKinlay AF, Muirhead CR, Stather JW. Electromagnetic Fields and the Risk of Cancer. Chilton: National Radiation Protection Board, 1992.

41. Hill AB. The environment and disease: Association or causation? Proc Royal Soc Med **58**:295–300, 1965.

42. Barlow HB, Kohn HI, Walsh EG. Visual sensations aroused by magnetic fields. Am J Physiol **148**:372–375, 1947.

43. Tenforde TS. Biological interactions and potential health effects of extremely-low-frequency magnetic fields from power lines and other common sources. Annu Rev Publ Health **13**:173–196, 1992.

44. Löscher W, Mevissen M. Animal studies on the role of 50/60-Hz magnetic fields in carcinogenesis. Life Sci **54**:1531–1543, 1994.

45. Bellossi A. Effect of pulsed magnetic fields on leukemia-prone AKR mice. No effect on mortality through five generations. Leuk Res **15**:899–902, 1991.

46. Rannug A, Ekström T, Mild KH, Holmberg B, Gimenez-Conti I, Slaga TJ. A study on skin tumor formation in mice with 50 Hz magnetic field exposure. Carcinogenesis **14**:573–578, 1993.

47. Benz RD, Carsten AL, Baum JW, Kuehner AV. Mutagenicity and toxicity of 60 Hz magnetic and electric fields (Appendix 10). In: Ahlbom A, Albert EN, Fraser-Smith AC, Gradzonsky AJ, Marron MT, Martin AO, Persinger MA, Shelanski ML, Wolpow ER, Eds. Biological Effects of Power Line Fields. New York: New York State Power Lines Project, 1987.

48. Reese JA, Jostes RF, Frazier ME. Exposure of mammalian cells to 60-Hz magnetic or electric fields: Analysis for DNA single-strand breaks. Bioelectromag **9**:237–247, 1988.

49. Fiorani M, Cantoni O, Sestili P, Conti R, Nicolini P, Vetrano F, Dacha M. Electric and/or magnetic field effects on DNA structure and function in cultured human cells. Mutat Res **282**:25–29, 1992.

50. D'Agruma L, Colosimo A, Angeloni U, Novelli G, Dallapiccola B. Plasmid DNA and low-frequency electromagnetic fields. Biomed Pharmacother **47**:101–105, 1993.

51. Weisbrot DR, Khorkova O, Lin H, Henderson AS, Goodman R. The effect of low frequency electric and magnetic fields on gene expression in Saccharomyces cerevisiae. Bioelectrochem Bioenerg **31**:167–177, 1993.

52. Fairbairn DW, O'Neill KL. The effect of electromagnetic field exposure on the formation of DNA single strand breaks in human cells. Cell Mol Biol **4**:561–567, 1994.

53. Cohen MM, Kunska A, Astemborski JA, McCulloch D, Paskewitz DA. Effect of low-level, 60-Hz electromagnetic fields on human lymphoid cells: I. Mitotic rate and chromosome breakage in human peripheral lymphocytes. Bioelectromag **7**:415–423, 1986.

54. Rosenthal M, Obe G. Effects of 50-Hertz electromagnetic fields on proliferation and on chromosomal aberrations in human peripheral lymphocytes untreated and pretreated with chemical mutagens. Mutat Res **210**:329–335, 1989.

55. Cohen MM, Kunska A, Astemborski JA, McCulloch D. The effect of low-level 60-Hz electromagnetic fields on human lymphoid cells. II: Sister-chromatid exchanges in peripheral lymphocytes and lymphoblastoid cell lines. Mutat Res **172**:177–184, 1986.

56. Livingston GK, Witt KL, Gandhi OP, Chatterjee I, Roti Roti J. Reproductive integrity of mammalian cells exposed to power frequency electromagnetic fields. Environ Mol Mutagen **17**:49–58, 1991.

57. Zwingelberg R, Obe G, Rosenthal M, Mevissen M, Buntenkötter S, Löscher W. Exposure of rats to a 50-Hz, 30-mT magnetic field influences neither the frequencies of sister-chromatid exchanges nor proliferation characteristics of cultured peripheral lymphocytes. Mutat Res **302**:39–44, 1993.

58. Saalman E, Onfelt A, Gillstedt-Hedman B. Lack of c-mitotic effects in V79 Chinese hamster cells exposed to 50 Hz magnetic fields. Bioelectrochem Bioenerg **26**:335–338, 1991.

59. Scarfi MR, Lioi MB, Zeni O, Franceschetti G, Franceschi C, Bersani F. Lack of chromosomal aberration and micronucleus induction in human lymphocytes exposed to pulsed magnetic fields. Mutat Res **306**:129–133, 1994.

60. Moore RL. Biological effects of magnetic fields: studies with microorganisms. Can J Microbiol **25**:1145–1151, 1979.

61. Juutilainen J, Liimatainen A. Mutation frequency in Salmonella exposed to weak 100-Hz magnetic fields. Hereditas **104**:145–147, 1986.

62. Ager DD, Radul JA. Effect of 60-Hz magnetic fields on ultraviolet light-induced mutation and mitotic recombination in Saccharomyces cerevisiae. Mutat Res **283**:279–286, 1992.

63. Nafziger J, Desjobert H, Benamar B, Guillosson JJ, Adolphe M. DNA mutations and 50 Hz electromagnetic fields. Bioelectrochem Bioenerg **30**:133–141, 1993.

64. Cain CD, Thomas DL, Adey WR. 60 Hz magnetic field acts as co-promoter in focus formation of C3H/10T1/2 cells. Carcinogenesis **14**:955–960, 1993.

65. Khalil AM, Qassem W. Cytogenetic effects of pulsing electromagnetic field on human lymphocytes in vitro: Chromosome aberrations, sister-chromatid exchanges and cell kinetics. Mutat Res **247**:141–146, 1991.

66. Takahashi K, Kaneko I, Date M, Fukada E. Influence of pulsing electromagnetic field on the frequency of sister-chromatid exchanges in cultured mammalian cells. Experientia **43**:331–332, 1987.

67. Nordenson I, Mild KH, Östman U, Ljungberg H. Chromosomal effects in lymphocytes of 400 kV-substation workers. Radiat Environ Biophys **27**:39–47, 1988.

68. Bauchinger M, Hauf R, Schmid E, Dresp J. Analysis of structural chromosome changes and SCE after occupational long-term exposure to electric and magnetic fields from 380 kV-systems. Radiat Environ Biophys **19**:235–238, 1981.

69. Skyberg K, Hansteen IL, Vistnes AI. Chromosome aberrations in lymphocytes of high-voltage laboratory cable splicers exposed to electromagnetic fields. Scand J Work Environ Health **19**:29–34, 1993.

70. Valjus J, Norppa H, Järventaus H, Sorsa M, Nykyri E, Salomaa S, Järvinen P, Kajander J. Analysis of chromosomal aberrations, sister chromatid exchanges and micronuclei among power linesmen with long-term exposure to 50-Hz electromagnetic fields. Radiat Environ Biophys **32**:325–336, 1993.

71. McCann J, Dietrich F, Rafferty C, Martin AO. A critical review of the genotoxic potential of electric and magnetic fields. Mutat Res **297**:61–95, 1993.

72. Murphy JC, Kaden DA, Warren J, Sivak A. Power frequency electric and magnetic fields: A review of genetic toxicology. Mutat Res **296**:221–240, 1993.

73. McLean JRN, Stuchly MA, Mitchel REJ, Wilkinson D, Yang H, Goddard M, Lecuyer DW, Schunk M, Callary E, Morrison D. Cancer promotion in a mouse-skin model by a 60-Hz magnetic field: II. Tumor development and immune response. Bioelectromag **12**:273–287, 1991.

74. Stuchly MA. Tumor co-promotion studies by exposure to alternating magnetic fields. Radiat Res **133**:118–119, 1993.

75. Rannug A, Holmberg B, Ekström T, Mild KH, Gimenez-Conti I, Slaga TJ. Intermittent 50 Hz magnetic field and skin tumor promotion in SENCAR mice. Carcinogenesis **15**:153–157, 1994.

76. Rannug A, Holmberg B, Mild KH. A rat liver foci promotion study with 50-Hz magnetic fields. Environ Res **62**:223–229, 1993.

77. Rannug A, Holmberg B, Ekström T, Mild KH. Rat liver foci

study on coexposure with 50 Hz magnetic fields and known carcinogens. Bioelectromag 14:17–27, 1993.

78. Beniashvili DS, Bilanishvili VG, Menabde MZ. Low-frequency electromagnetic radiation enhances the induction of rat mammary tumors by nitrosomethyl urea. Cancer Lett 61:75–79, 1991.

79. Löscher W, Mevissen M, Lehmacher W, Stamm A. Tumor promotion in a breast cancer model by exposure to a weak alternating magnetic field. Cancer Lett 71:75–81, 1993.

80. Löscher W, Wahnschaffe U, Mevissen M, Lerchl A, Stamm A. Effects of weak alternating magnetic fields on nocturnal melatonin production and mammary carcinogenesis in rats. Oncology (Basel) 51:288–295, 1994.

81. Baum A, Mevissen M, Kamino K, Mohr U, Löscher W. A histopathological study of alterations in DMBA-induced mammary carcinogenesis in rats with 50 Hz, 100 μT magnetic field exposure. Carcinogenesis 16:119–125, 1995.

82. Mevissen M, Stamm A, Buntenkötter S, Zwingelberg R, Wahnschaffe U, Löscher W. Effects of magnetic fields on mammary tumor development induced by 7,12-dimethyl-benz(a)anthracene in rats. Bioelectromag 14:131–143, 1993.

83. Frazier ME, Reese JA, Morris JE, Jostes RF, Miller DL. Exposure of mammalian cells to 60-Hz magnetic or electric fields: Analysis of DNA repair of induced, single-strand breaks. Bioelectromag 11:229–234, 1990.

84. Hintenlang DE. Synergistic effects of ionizing radiation and 60 Hz magnetic fields. Bioelectromag 14:545–551, 1993.

85. Paradisi S, Donelli G, Santini MT, Straface E, Malorni W. A 50-Hz magnetic field induces structural and biophysical changes in membranes. Bioelectromag 14:247–255, 1993.

86. Adolphe M, Friese V, Protet R, Cabanes J. Étude de l'effet d'un champ magnétique de faible intensitié sur la prolifération de plusieurs molèles de cellules en culture [Effect of a low-intensity magnetic fields on the proliferation of several lines of cultured cells]. C R Soc Biol (Paris) 181:282–286, 1987.

87. Thomson RAE, Michaelson SM, Nguyen QA. Influence of 60-Hertz magnetic fields on leukemia. Bioelectromag 9:149–158, 1988.

88. Baumann S, Cooper R, Berman E, House D, Joines W. Lack of effects from 2000-Hz magnetic fields on mammary adenocarcinoma and reproductive hormones in rats. Bioelectromag 10:329–333, 1989.

89. Parkinson WC, Hanks CT. Experiments on the interaction of electromagnetic fields with mammalian systems. Biol Bull 176(S):170–178, 1989.

90. Liburdy RP, Sloma TR, Sokolic R, Yaswen P. ELF magnetic fields, breast cancer, and melatonin: 60 Hz fields block melatonin's oncostatic action on ER + breast cancer cell proliferation. J Pineal Res 14:89–97, 1993.

91. Revoltella RP, Trombi L, Petrini M, Grassi B, Manara G, Dalle Mese E. Low-frequency electromagnetic fields do not affect cell growth, erythroid differentiation, and virus production in variant lines of untreated and dimethyl sulfoxide-treated friend erythroleukemia cells. Electro Magnetobiol 12:135–146, 1993.

92. Liboff AR, Williams T, Strong DM, Wistar R. Time-varying magnetic fields: Effects on DNA synthesis. Science 223:818–820, 1984.

93. Phillips TL, Winters WD, Rutledge L. *In vitro* exposure to electromagnetic fields: changes in tumor cell properties. Int J Radiat Biol 49:463–469, 1986.

94. Ahlbom A, Albert EN, Fraser-Smith AC, Grodzonsky AJ, Marron MT, Martin AO, Persinger MA, Shelanski ML, Wolpow ER. Biological Effects of Power Line Fields. New York: New York State Power Lines Project, 1987.

95. Krueger GRF. Abnormal variation of the immune system as related to cancer. Cancer Growth Prog 4:131–161, 1989.

96. Penn I. Why do immunosuppressed patients develop cancer? Crit Rev Oncogen 1:27–52, 1989.

97. Walleczek J. Electromagnetic field effects on cells of the immune system: The role of calcium signaling. FASEB J 6:3177–3185, 1992.

98. Reiter RJ, Richardson BA. Magnetic field effects on pineal indoleamine metabolism and possible biological consequences. FASEB J 6:2283–2287, 1992.

99. Stevens RG, Davis S, Thomas DB, Anderson LE, Wilson BW. Electric power, pineal function, and the risk of breast cancer. FASEB J 6:853–860, 1992.

100. Kato M, Honma K, Shigemitsu T, Shiga Y. Effects of exposure to a circularly polarized 50-Hz magnetic field on plasma and pineal melatonin levels in rats. Bioelectromag 14:97–106, 1993.

101. Lee JM, Stormshak F, Thompson JM, Thinesen P, Painter LJ, Olenchek EG, Hess DL, Forbes R, Foster DL. Melatonin secretion and puberty in female lambs exposed to environmental electric and magnetic fields. Biol Reprod 49:857–864, 1993.

102. Kato M, Honma K, Shigemitsu T, Shiga Y. Horizontal or vertical 50-Hz, 1 microT magnetic fields have no effect on pineal gland or plasma melatonin concentration of albino rats. Neurosci Lett 168:205–208, 1994.

103. Kato M, Honma K, Shigemitsu T, Shiga Y. Circularly polarized 50-Hz magnetic field exposure reduces pineal gland and blood melatonin concentrations of Long-Evans rats. Neurosci Lett 166:59–62, 1994.

104. Yellon SM. Acute 60-Hz magnetic field exposure effects on the melatonin rhythm in the pineal gland and circulation of the adult Djungarian hamster. J Pineal Res 16:136–144, 1994.

105. Cohen M, Lippman M, Chabner BA. Role of the pineal gland in the aetiology and treatment of breast cancer. Lancet 2(8094):814–816, 1978.

106. Lissoni P, Barni S, Cattaneo G, Tancini G, Esposti G, Esposti D, Fraschini F. Clinical results with the pineal hormone melatonin in advanced cancer resistant to standard antitumor therapies. Oncology (Basel) 48:448–450, 1991.

107. Barni S, Lissoni P, Paolorossi F, Crispino S, Archili C. A study of the pineal hormone melatonin as a second line therapy in metastatic colorectal cancer resistant to fluorouracil plus folates. Tumori 76:58–60, 1993.

108. Prasad AV, Miller MW, Carstensen EL, Azadniv M, Brayman AA. Failure to reproduce increased calcium uptake in human lymphocytes at purported cyclotron resonance exposure conditions. Radiat Environ Biophys 30:305–320, 1991.

109. Prasad AV, Miller MW, Cox C, Carstensen EL, Hoops H, Brayman AA. A test of the influence of cyclotron resonance exposures on diatom motility. Health Phys 66:305–312, 1994.

110. The Possible Biological Effect of Low-Frequency Electromagnetic Fields—Supplement to the Public Affairs Board Report No. 10. London: Institute of Electrical Engineers, 1994.

111. Scaiano JC, Cozens FL, McLean J. Model for the rationalization of magnetic field effects in vivo. Application of the radical-pair mechanism to biological systems. Photochem Photobiol 59:585–589, 1994.

112. Polk C. Effects of extremely-low-frequency magnetic fields on biological magnetite. Bioelectromag 15:261–270, 1994.

113. Schulten K. Magnetic field effects in chemistry and biology. Adv Solid State Phys 22:61–83, 1982.

114. Thériault G. Cancer risks due to exposure to electromagnetic fields. Recent Res Cancer Res 120:166–180, 1990.

115. Poole C, Trichopoulos D. Extremely low-frequency electric and magnetic fields and cancer. Cancer Causes Control 2:267–276, 1991.

116. Bates MN. Extremely low frequency electromagnetic fields and cancer: the epidemiologic evidence. Environ Health Perspect 95:147–156, 1991.

117. Aldrich TE, Laborde D, Griffith J, Easterly C. A meta-analysis of the epidemiological evidence regarding human health risk associated with exposure to electromagnetic fields. Electro Magnetobio 11:127–143, 1992.

118. Buffler PA, Burgess PE, Smith GL, Beauchamp RA, Higgins HA, Linder SH, McLain ME, Zweiacker PL. Health Effects of Exposure to Powerline-Frequency Electric and Magnetic Fields. Austin: Public Utility Commission of Texas, 1992.

119. Electromagnetic Field Health Effects. Hartford, CT: Connecticut Academy of Science and Engineering, pp1–43, 1992.

120. Davis JG, Bennett WR, Brady JV, Brent RL, Gordis L, Gordon WE, Greenhouse SW, Reiter RJ, Stein GS, Susskind C, Trichopoulos D. Health Effects of Low-Frequency Electric and Magnetic Fields. Oak Ridge: Oak Ridge Associated Universities, 1992.

**POWER-FREQUENCY FIELDS AND CANCER    323**

121. Electromagnetic Fields and the Risk of Cancer. Chilton: National Radiation Protection Board, 1993.
122. Guénel P, Lellouch J. Synthesis of the Literature on Health Effects from Very Low Frequency Electric and Magnetic Fields. Paris: National Institute of Health and Medical Research (INSERM), 1993.
123. Roucayrol JC. Sur les champs électromagnétiques de trèsbasse fréquence et la santé [Extremely low frequency electromagnetic fields and health]. Bull Acad Nat Méd 177:1031–1040, 1993.
124. Jones TL, Shih CH, Thurston DH, Ware BJ, Cole P. Selection bias from differential residential mobility as an explanation for associations of wire codes with childhood cancer. J Clin Epidemiol 46:545–548, 1993.
125. Morgan MG. Exposé treatment confounds understanding of a serious public-health issue. Sci Am 262(6):118–123, 1990.
126. Otaka Y, Kitamura S, Furuta M, Shinohara A. Sex-linked recessive lethal test of Drosophila melanogaster after exposure to 50-Hz magnetic fields. Bioelectromag 13:67–74, 1992.
127. Reiter RJ. Static and extremely low frequency electromagnetic field exposure—Reported effects on the circadian production of melatonin. J Cell Biochem 51:394–403, 1993.

Reprinted with permission from *Phys. Rev. A* **43**, 1039-1049 (1991). Copyright 1991 by the American Physical Society.

PHYSICAL REVIEW A         VOLUME 43, NUMBER 2         15 JANUARY 1991

# Constraints on biological effects of weak extremely-low-frequency electromagnetic fields

Robert K. Adair

*Department of Physics, Yale University, New Haven, Connecticut 06511*

(Received 8 June 1990)

Concerns have been raised over the possibility that extremely-low-frequency (ELF) electromagnetic fields are carcinogenic and leukegenic. An examination of the physical interaction of such fields with the body shows that such interactions are too weak to have a significant effect on human biology at the cell level. Because of the high electrical conductivity of tissues, the coupling of external electric fields in air to tissue in the body is such that the effects of the internal fields on cells is smaller than thermal noise. Static magnetic fields smaller than the earth's field of 50 $\mu$T and varying fields weaker than the 4-$\mu$T 60-Hz fields that are equivalent in effect to that from walking in the earth's field, cannot be expected to generate significant biological effects. Moreover, the interactions of such weak fields at the cell level are also small compared to thermal noise. These conclusions would be modified by 60-Hz cell resonances. But such resonances are shown to be incompatible with cell characteristics and the requirement from equipartition that the mean resonance energy must be $kT$. Hence, any biological effects of weak ELF fields on the cellular level must be found outside of the scope of conventional physics.

## I. INTRODUCTION

Very weak extremely-low-frequency (ELF) electromagnetic fields from common electric appliances and lighting, from local home and workplace distribution wiring, and from the major national electric grids, are an ubiquitous part of modern civilization. Since the magnitudes of these "leakage" fields are very small, and seemingly small compared to natural fields in the body, it has been commonly assumed that the fields could not affect any biological activity significantly, and hence, could not constitute a health hazard.

However, concerns have been raised[1] over the possibility that the biological effects of the fields have not been properly understood and that the fields may in fact generate changes on the cell level that might have carcinogenic and leukegenic consequences. Such effects have been largely associated with the breaking of molecular bonds of macromolecules such as those responsible for the genetic information. Since the extremely low frequency (60 Hz in North America and largely 50 Hz elsewhere) of the ELF fields means that the characteristic quantum energies are approximately equal to $10^{-14}$ eV, it has generally been accepted that such fields cannot disrupt these molecules and hence cannot induce carcinogenic or leukegenic effects.

However, it may be that less catastrophic effects of ELF fields on cells in the body may induce actions which we do not yet understand that alter the biology of the structures significantly. If such interactions of the ELF fields at the cell level are to result in any significant biological effects, those interactions must be significantly greater than the ordinary thermal interactions of the molecules with their environment. But we show that any effects on the cell level of fields in the body generated by weak external ELF fields will be masked by thermal noise

effects and, hence, such fields cannot be expected to have *any* significant effect on the biological activities of the cells.

In any material the charge density fluctuates thermally according to thermodynamic imperatives generating fluctuating electric fields. Although there are other sources of biological noise, such as noise generated by muscle excitation and activity, electrokinetic noise from the squeezing of electrolytes through tissues, and the $1/f$ noise from cell membrane activity, that contribute fields as great as 0.1 V/m at frequencies less than 100 Hz, we emphasize the generally smaller thermal noise inasmuch as the magnitude of that noise stems from fundamental thermodynamic bases and must constitute an irrefutable constraint on biology.

For similar reasons, we emphasize effects on the cell level. Over larger regions, the impact of weak ELF external fields is limited more by biological and physiological considerations than by the competition with Johnson-Nyquist noise and is hence outside of the chosen scope of this paper. Since the bulk of the experimental results that have been interpreted as an indication of effects of such fields concern mechanisms on the cell level such as changes in ion transport through cell membrane walls and increases in genetic transcription errors, the analyses of mechanisms that might operate at the level of the cell are of primary importance. Any possible carcinogenic effects of weak ELF radiation would also most likely operate at the cellular level.

In the quantitative features of this discussion of the effects of low frequency, low intensity, electromagnetic fields on biological materials, we will consider especially 60-Hz oscillations, and define *weak* fields as electric field strengths that do not exceed 300 V/m in air and magnetic field strengths no greater than 50 $\mu$T (or 0.5 G), the strength of the earth's field—the mean electric field at the earth's surface is about 100 V/m. The fields will, in general, be near-fields, and not radiative. Indeed, for the most part, we will not be talking about *radiation*—nonionizing or otherwise.

## II. EXTERNAL FIELDS AND NOISE FIELDS

### A. Coupling of tissue and air for electric fields

For environmental concerns, the immediate measure of possible hazard is that field in the air about the tissues. Since the tissues are conducting, a constant external electric field will induce almost no field at all in the tissues though an alternating external electric field will induce small fields. At low frequencies, $\nu$, the fields $E_i$ in the tissues will be very much smaller than the fields $E_0$ in the air external to the tissues:[2]

$$E_i \approx 3\epsilon_0 \omega \rho_t E_0 , \tag{1}$$

where $\omega = 2\pi\nu$ is the angular frequency and $\rho_t \approx 2 \ \Omega \, m$ is the resistivity of the electrolyte saturating the tissue.[3] At 60 Hz, $E_i \approx 2 \times 10^{-8} E_0$. Hence, for fields in the air of 300 V/m, we can expect field strengths in the conducting tissues of about $6 \times 10^{-6}$ V/m. The cell membrane will have a specific resistance of the order of $\rho_{mem} \approx 10^5 \rightarrow 10^7$ $\Omega \, m$ and can then be considered as an insulator relative to the tissue electrolyte. In the valid approximation that the resistivity of the membrane material, $\rho_{mem} \gg \rho_t$, the resistivity of the tissue, the field in the membrane, $E_{mem}$ of thickness $d$ of a cell of radius $r$ will be about

$$E_{mem} \approx 1.5 E_i \frac{r}{d} . \tag{2}$$

Hence, taking a typical cell radius of 10 $\mu$m and a membrane thickness of 50 Å, for a field in the tissue electrolyte $E_i = 6 \times 10^{-6}$ V/m, induced by an external field of 300 V/m, we can expect a field $E_{mem} \approx 3000 E_i \approx 2 \times 10^{-2}$ V/m in the insulating membrane.

The internal elements of the cell, such as the nucleus and the genetic material, are shielded by the resistive cell membrane and the fields they are subjected to are quite negligible.[2]

The fields in different areas of air, tissue, and cell are shown in Fig. 1 normalized to a field in the air of 300 V/m. Too often, discussion of the effects of weak fields is complicated by misunderstandings concerning the region in which the field is defined. Since we are addressing environmental concerns, the fields labeled "external" in this report are *always* fields in the air about the tissues.

### B. Thermal electrical noise

A most important fundamental constraint on effects of very electric weak fields is the requirement that they not be masked by the noise fields generated by thermal fluctuations in charge densities. The magnitude of these Johnson-Nyquist noise fields generated in an element of matter can be expressed precisely in terms of the mean-square voltage $\overline{V_{kT}^2}$ over a frequency interval $\Delta\nu$ induced across the element:

$$\overline{V_{kT}^2} = 4RkT\Delta\nu , \tag{3}$$

where $R$ is the resistance of the sample between the points where the voltage is measured.

Although this noise voltage must follow from thermal fluctuations in the charge density in the sample material, the result—characteristic of thermodynamic results—is independent of detail; in particular of the detailed character of the charge carriers which may be conduction electrons, ions, or bound charges sensibly displaced by thermal buffeting.

Often the noise fields will be of more interest than the noise voltages which are, however, better defined. Taking the sample as a cube with a side $d$ for convenience, $R = \rho/d$, where $\rho$ is the characteristic resistivity of the material, $E_{kT}^2 \propto 1/d^3$. As a consequence of averaging over fluctuations, the electric-field noise limit varies inversely as the square root of the volume considered. Although $E_{kT}^2$ was evaluated for a cube, the value depends only on the volume of the sample. The noise does not vary with volume as one might expect for random electric-field fluctuations since the field fluctuations—taken to originate in charge-density fluctuations—are correlated through the conservation of charge and Gauss's theorem.

Since the thermal noise is larger for small volumes—where the statistical fluctuations of electron densities are proportionally larger—than for larger volumes, to make the most useful assessment of the effects of thermal noise it is desirable to choose the smallest volume commensurate with the biological action. This increase in effective noise field strength as the sample size is reduced extends to the molecular level. The characteristic molecular field strengths required to substantially change the momenta of molecules in a typical thermal collision, for example,

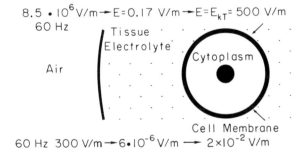

8.5 • 10⁶V/m → E=0.17 V/m → E=E_kT= 500 V/m
60 Hz

Air

60 Hz 300 V/m → 6•10⁻⁶ V/m → 2×10⁻² V/m

FIG. 1. Electric fields in tissues, cell membranes, and cell cytoplasm, induced by ELF external fields in the air outside of the tissue. The fields labeled above describe an externally induced field in the cell membrane that is equal to the Johnson noise, from dc to 100 Hz, measured from the cytoplasm inside the cell to the electrolyte outside of the cell across the cell membrane. The very large air field so postulated is larger than the dielectric breakdown strength for air of about 10⁶ V/m and is then unobtainable in practice. The lower numbers describe the fields induced in the tissue and membrane by an external field of 300 V/m.

are of the order of $kT/er \approx 10^8$ V/m, where $r \approx 1$ Å is the interaction length relevant in the collision. Hence, very large electric-field fluctuations can be expected as a consequence of "collisions" with surrounding molecules.

### C. Noise fields in tissues

We estimate the thermal noise generated in a quantity of tissue by examining the results of a hypothetical measurement of the voltage across the plates of a parallel plate capacitor where a cube of tissue of length $d$ on a side is held between the plates. The voltage across such a capacitor will be a *useful* measure of the local electric field at low frequencies. To estimate the thermal electric-field noise, we consider the system an equivalent parallel circuit of the membrane resistance $R$ and the capacitance $C$ between the plates. The time-average noise voltage $V_{kT}$ can then be expressed as

$$\overline{V_{kT}^2} = 4RkT\Delta\nu = 4\frac{\rho}{d}kT\Delta\nu, \quad E_{kT} = \frac{\overline{V}_{kT}}{d} . \quad (4)$$

Using the above relations and taking $\rho = 2\Omega$ m for tissue and a frequency span $\Delta\nu = 100$ Hz, i.e., from dc to 100 Hz, we find that the noise field generated in the electrolyte in a cubical volume the size of a cell, 20 $\mu$m on a side, is about 0.02 V/m, which is about 3000 times larger than the field induced by a 300-V/m external field.

Though the field is large, the thermal noise *potential difference* over 20 $\mu$m is but 3 $\mu$V. In general, thermal noise voltages between different regions of tissue will be very much less than 1 $\mu$V.

Experiments have shown that some fish, especially sharks, do respond to very weak electric fields. These are fields in the water surrounding the fish and are, therefore, strongly coupled to the watery tissue of the fish. In salt water, the fields are more strongly coupled by a factor of approximately $5 \times 10^7$ than fields in air to tissue. With special receptors known as the ampullae of Lorenzini, which act as low-pass filters and extend over lengths near a meter, the response of sharks to quite small fields—as fields as small as 0.5 $\mu$V/m have been detected—does not violate thermal noise limits.[4]

### D. Noise fields in cell membranes

A popular "explanation" of purported biological effects of external low-level ELF electromagnetic fields is that these effects are derived from the effects of the electric fields on the complex properties of the cell membranes. The fields are presumed to modify such membrane activities as the opening and closing of ion-conducting channels and the catalytic activity of membrane-associated enzymes. Of course if externally imposed fields are to have any important effect, those fields at the cell activity sites must not be swamped by the thermal Johnson noise fields.

Certain processes such as the passage of ions through the cell membrane walls may be likely defined by thermodynamic criteria and hence depend upon the potential difference—which is typically of the order of 50 mV—between the cytoplasm inside the cell and the electrolyte

outside the cell. For such mechanisms the noise voltage across the membrane from the relatively highly conducting interior cytoplasm to the conducting electrolyte might be more significant than any local noise level. (The natural potential difference across the membrane will be of the order of 50 mV to be compared with the noise voltage across the membrane of $\approx 10^{-6}$ V and the thermal kinetic energy of an ion of $\frac{3}{2}kT \approx 37$ meV.) The time-average noise level from cytoplasm to electrolyte, across the whole membrane of thickness $d \approx 50$ Å, of a spherical cell of radius $r = 10^{-5}$ m will be

$$\overline{V_{kT}^2} = 4RkT/\Delta\nu \quad \text{where} \quad R_{\text{mem}} = \frac{\rho d}{4\pi r^2} , \quad (5)$$

where the resistivity of the membrane material is taken as $\rho_{\text{mem}} = 10^6$ $\Omega$ m. With these values $R_{\text{mem}} = 4 \times 10^6$ $\Omega$. Taking an ELF frequency band of 100 Hz, $V_{kT} \approx 2.6 \times 10^{-6}$ V and $E_{kT} = V_{kT}/d \approx 500$ V/m. (Since the resistivity of the membrane material is uncertain within a factor of 10, the field strengths calculated here are uncertain by a factor of 3.) This thermal noise voltage is probably much smaller than the $1/f$ noise, possibly associated with the flow of ions through cell membrane orifices, and smaller by a factor of $\approx 5 \times 10^{-5}$ than the normal potential difference of 0.05 V across the cell wall.[5] But the noise voltage across the membrane—and the noise field in the membrane—is about 25 000 times[6] the voltage and field induced by the canonical external field of 300 V/m.

It has been argued that the externally induced fields in the cell membrane may affect such biological activities as the catalytic actions by membrane-associated enzymes. If such induced fields are to affect the processes, those fields must be greater than the fields due to thermal fluctuations.

Since these kinds of biological activities would appear to be local, determined not by average fields over the whole cell membrane, but by conditions in a small sector of the membrane with a volume no larger than $d^3$, where $d \approx 50$ Å is the membrane thickness, it would seem that it would be the *local* thermal electric-field fluctuations in such small regions that should be compared to the induced fields. Since the volume in question is quite small, and the effective noise fields over small volumes are greater than for larger volumes, we might expect that the local electric-field noise would be much greater than that which is averaged over the whole membrane. The electrical properties of such a small sector are not necessarily simple but we can *estimate* that thermal noise generated in a small quantity of membrane material proceeding, as before, by examining the results of a hypothetical measurement of the voltage across the plates of a parallel-plate capacitor where an isolated cube of membrane material 50 Å on a side is held between the plates. The time average of the fluctuating noise voltage $V_{kT}$ is again

$$\overline{V_{kT}^2} = 4RkT\Delta\nu \quad \text{where now} \quad R = \frac{\rho_{\text{mem}}}{d} \approx 2 \times 10^{14} \ \Omega . \quad (6)$$

If we use the mean resistivity of the membrane material of $\rho = 10^6$ $\Omega$ m, for the small sector, which is simplistic, and taking again only frequencies less than 100 Hz, the mean noise voltage across this small isolated sample will be $\approx 0.02$ and the thermal noise electric field over this frequency is then $E_{kT} \approx \overline{V_{kT}}/d \approx 3.7 \times 10^6$ V/m, which is about $2 \times 10^8$ times that from a 300 V/m external field.

### E. Electric-field effects

Although the small values of the ratios of induced to noise electric fields must largely exclude any possibility that those induced fields can induce biological activity in cells, one can reach much the same conclusions by considering interactions in more detail. To be definite, we consider fields of $E_i = 6 \times 10^{-6}$ V/m in tissue, and $E_m = 2 \times 10^{-2}$ V/m in membranes 50-Å thick with cells of radius $r = 10^{-5}$ m, induced by external fields of 300 V/m and we compare the energies transferred to the elements to $kT$.

For membrane or tissue, the energy transferred by the field to an ion—or any singly charged element—in tissue or membrane will not be much larger than $E_i er \approx 10^{-9} kT$, where $e$ is the electronic charge; this is to say neither the kinetic energy nor the direction of motion of a charged element can be sensibly affected by such small fields.

An imposed external field will tend to align electric dipoles so that, even in the face of thermal agitation, there will be a statistical excess of dipoles aligned with the field. The proportion of $P$ that are aligned can be estimated as $P \approx W/kT$, where $W$ is the alignment energy. We can make a useful estimate of a *maximum* magnitude of such an interaction energy by considering the interaction of the field $E_i$ in the tissue with a whole cell neglecting, for the purpose of the maximal estimate, the macroscopic shielding provided by the cell membrane. The electric dipole moment per unit volume of cytoplasm will be $\mathbf{P} = \epsilon_0(K-1)\,\mathbf{E}$ where $K$ is the dielectric constant and $K - 1 \approx 80$ as for water and the volume $\mathcal{V}$ is that of a cell 10 $\mu$m in diameter. Then the interaction energy $W$ will be about

$$W \approx (\mathbf{E} \cdot \mathbf{P})\mathcal{V} \approx 80 E_i^2 \epsilon_0 \mathcal{V} \approx 2.5 \times 10^{-14} kT \;. \tag{7}$$

We can also consider the alignment of macromolecules that display permanent electric dipoles. Taking a characteristic magnitude of such a dipole moment as $er$, where $r = 200$ Å, the alignment energy of the molecule in the membrane will be $W \approx E_{\mathrm{mem}} er \approx 3 \times 10^{-8} kT$.

### F. Magnetic fields

#### 1. Static magnetic fields

A kind of restricted anthropic principle places immediate limits on the biological effects of static magnetic fields. We live—and have lived through evolutionary history—in the earth's magnetic field of about 50 $\mu$T. Hence, the biological effects of static magnetic fields that are less than the earth's field must not seriously affect our health. Nevertheless, we examine the effects of static fields in more detail.

Since magnetic fields exert no force on stationary charges and act on moving charges only in a direction normal to their motion, static magnetic fields do not add—or subtract—energy from single charges. The magnetic forces do change the direction of motion of charges but that effect is extremely small compared to effects of thermal fluctuations. However, charged particles in orbit generate magnetic dipole moments that interact directly with magnetic fields. Molecules, atoms, and nuclei possess magnetic dipole moments $\mu$ of the order of magnitude of

$$\mu = g \frac{e}{2m} \hbar \;, \tag{8}$$

where the value of $g$ depends upon the specific structure but is usually near 1, for atoms and molecules $m = m_e$ is the mass of the electron, and for nuclei $m$ is the nuclear mass. The alignment energies for a field $B$ are then $B\mu$ and for $B_e = 50$ $\mu$T, the earth's field, these energies are of the magnitude of $10^{-7} kT$ for atoms and molecules and typically less than $10^{-10} kT$ for nuclei. Hence, the net alignment— and the net magnetization of biological material induced by such weak fields is quite small (though significant effects have been observed for very large fields $B \gg 1$ T). Such alignments will result in a net (paramagnetic) magnetic moment in a volume of material which in turn will interact with the field defining an energy. For a volume of the whole cell, this energy will only be of the magnitude of $kT$—about 14 orders of magnitude less than the thermal energy of the cell. Arguments similar to those applied to paramagnetic materials apply to the smaller diamagnetic moments.

For most (paramagnetic and diamagnetic) materials, the molecules or atoms do not act collectively. But for ferromagnetic materials, all of the atomic dipoles in a domain line up and the magnetic susceptibilities are greater by factors approximately equal to $10^7$ than for paramagnetic materials. Consequently, the earth's 50-$\mu$T field does affect those (rare) cells that contain ferromagnetic matter.

About 15 years ago, Blakemore[7] found anaerobic bacteria (single celled, of course) that, "fearing" fresh air, fled preferentially downwards guided along the lines of the earth's field by a compass of ferromagnetic material, in particular a chain about 2-$\mu$m long of grains of magnetite $Fe_3O_4$. A simple calculation[7] shows that the alignment energy in the earth's field $B_e$ is $\mu B_e \approx 10 kT$, where $\mu$ is the magnetic moment of the bacterial lodestone. This is enough to ensure efficient alignment of the cell in the earth's field so that the creature swims in the right direction. Hence, with the aid of ferromagnetic materials, a cell can—barely—sense a 50-$\mu$T field. But $Fe_3O_4$ is found in few other cells. And without the crafting of such compasses, we cannot expect the effects of magnetic fields on cells to compete with thermal fluctuations.

We note that under rather special circumstances, moderate magnetic fields, of the order of $10^{-2}$–$10^{-3}$ T, may affect chemistry. A covalent binding of a molecule may break such that each piece retains one member of the singlet-state electron pair that cemented the binding. Then as a consequence of different hyperfine magnetic interactions between the valence electron and nuclei in the two fragments, the two electrons may precess at different rates and the phase between their amplitudes which defines the initial singlet state will transform to a triplet state reducing the possibility that the two fragments will rejoin.[9]

However, if the local external magnetic field acting on the ions is stronger than the effect of the nuclear fields, the precessions that lead to the singlet-triple interchange will be suppressed and the ions will be more likely to rejoin. Since this suppression requires magnetic fields that are typically two orders of magnitude greater than the 50-$\mu$T limit we have adopted, we need not consider the possibility of such effects.

### 2. Changing magnetic fields

Since life evolved in the presence of static magnetic fields of the order 1 G or 100 $\mu$T, the absence of biological effects of static fields should not be surprising. But changing magnetic fields generate electric fields. These magnetically induced electric fields are more pervasive than the electric fields induced by external electric fields, since neither the electric shielding of the cell by the conducting electrolyte nor the shielding of the cell nucleus and the cell genetic material by the conducting cell membrane, operates. The induced electric fields in biological material are nearly independent of the conductivity of that material and its surroundings.

But can weak 60-Hz oscillating magnetic fields produce electric fields of consequence, that is, electric fields greater than those generated by thermal noise? Using the integral form of Faraday's law,

$$\oint_S \mathbf{E} \cdot d\mathbf{s} = \frac{d\left[\int_A \mathbf{B} \cdot d\mathbf{a}\right]}{dt} \propto \frac{dB}{dt} , \qquad (9)$$

where $A$ is an area through which the field $\mathbf{B}$ passes and $S$ is a path bounding the area. If we take a typical effective human body area as that of a circle with a radius of $r = 10$ cm, we estimate the mean amplitude of the electric field induced by a 60-Hz oscillating magnetic field of amplitude $B = 50$ $\mu$T acting over the body, as

$$\overline{E}_B = \frac{B\omega r}{2} \approx 10^{-3} \text{ V/m} . \qquad (10)$$

Then how will this induced field compare with low-frequency thermal noise fields acting on cells? For a conservative comparison, we consider the noise field of $E_{kT} \approx 0.02$ V/m calculated in Sec. II B for the electrolyte occupying a volume the size of a cell. This is the noise, over a bandwidth $\delta\nu = 100$ Hz, generated by a volume the size of a cell taken conveniently as a cube $d \approx 20$ $\mu$m on a side. Hence, the noise fields in cell-sized regions of the electrolyte are greater than the electric fields induced by the changing magnetic field by a factor greater than about 20.

But any biological events of interest must take place in elements of the cell, not in the electrolyte. Since the mean noise field is proportional to the square root of the resistance of the material, and inversely proportional to

the square root of the volume of interest, the electric-field noise in those smaller cell elements, characterized by larger specific resistances, will be much greater though the field induced by the changing magnetic field will not be very different. For example, the mean ELF noise field across the membrane, between the electrolyte and the cytoplasm, was found to be of the order of 500 V/m; about 200 times the magnetically induced field of 0.001 V/m multiplied by the factor of $1.5r/d$ from Eq. (2). The effective electric noise fields in the small internal elements of the cell, such as the nucleus and the genetic material, can be expected to be no smaller than that of a volume of cytoplasm the size of that element. Typically, that noise will be of the magnitude of the noise generated in a cube of cytoplasm 1 $\mu$m on a side, which will be about 1 V/m, about 1000 times greater than the magnetically induced field. Hence, low-frequency, low-intensity magnetic fields cannot be expected to induce biological activity through interactions with individual cells.

Even as electric fields, albeit small, are generated in human tissues by weak ELF magnetic fields, electric fields of similar strengths are produced in the course of our motion through the earth's field. A field $E$ will be generated throughout the body by moving through the earth's field $B_e$ at a velocity $v$; $E = B_c v$. The electric field of approximately $7 \times 10^{-5}$ V/m induced by walking will be about equal to the maximum field generated by a 4-$\mu$T (40 mG) 60-Hz magnetic field. Indeed, this electric field induced by walking will be greater at the sites of DNA, RNA, and the cell nucleus than that produced by any external ELF electric field. Riding in a car on the highway increases the equivalent level to about 70 $\mu$T (700 mG) while a passenger in a jet plane will see electric fields similar to the maximum from a $7 \times 10^{-4}$-T (7-G) 60-Hz magnetic field (here we neglect shielding effects in car and plane which will reduce the magnetic fields somewhat).

We can feed these simple results into our version of the anthropic principle to conclude that weak changing magnetic fields—like the changes from 60-Hz sine waves—are most unlikely to induce biologically deleterious effects. The magnetic field that a cell passes through from the walking of its host through the earth's field in the United States induced the same electric fields in the cell as a 4-$\mu$T 60-Hz oscillating magnetic field. But 4 $\mu$T is far larger than the fields from power lines, local and home wiring, and home appliances.

One might argue that there may be some special significance in the oscillatory character of the 60-Hz field; perhaps there are sympathetic resonant responses. But we show in Sec. III that ELF resonances at the cell level are not possible.

### 3. Rapid changes in the magnetic field

Though the effects of pulsed fields are nominally outside of the discussions of weak ELF (sine wave) fields considered here, the sawtooth magnetic waves associated with the fly-back transformers in television sets and video display terminals have raised concerns similar to those associated with ELF fields. As an example, we consider a sawtooth wave where the magnetic field increases from zero to 50 $\mu$T linearly over a period of approximately 50 $\mu$s and then returns to zero in a time less than 1 $\mu$s; and then repeats at a repetition rate of approximately 20 kHz. The constraints on the effects of such fields are similar to those established for ELF fields.

We consider the effects of pulses on biological elements from the electric-field pulse generated by the changing magnetic field. The magnitude of that field $E(t)$ can be estimated using the same approximations as for sine-wave fields:

$$E(t) = \frac{r}{2} \frac{dB(t)}{dt} , \qquad (11)$$

and we write

$$\int E(t)dt = E_m \delta t = \frac{r}{2} \int \frac{dB}{dt} dt = \frac{r}{2} \delta B = B_0 \frac{r}{2} , \qquad (12)$$

where $E_m$ is the mean induced electric field and $\delta t$ is the time over which the magnetic field changes by an amount $\delta B$. Hence, the impulse added to an element holding a charge $q$ by the electric-field pulse will be

$$dp = E_m q \delta t = q \frac{r}{2} B_0 , \qquad (13)$$

where $B_0$ is the change in the magnetic field. The impulse depends only on the change in magnetic field and is independent of the rate of change.

The mean component of momentum in the direction of the pulsed field from thermal agitation of the element on which the field acts will be

$$p_{kT} \approx \sqrt{mkT} , \qquad (14)$$

where $m$ is the effective mass of the element. If the pulse is to affect biological processes significantly, it must produce momentum changes in cell elements greater than that received at high frequency from thermal buffeting; that condition is $dp > p_{kT}$.

The momentum $dp$ may accrue to the translational momentum of a free cell element, such as a calcium ion, or may add to vibrational or rotational motion of a more complex element such as a macromolecule.

For a charge $q = e$ and a value of $r = 0.1$ m, the momentum transfer for a change in the field $B_0 = 50$ $\mu$T is $dp \approx 4 \times 10^{-25}$ N s. But this is much smaller than the thermal momentum $p_{kT} \approx 1.7 \times 10^{-23}$ N s for a calcium ion and very much smaller than the thermal momentum $dp \approx 10^{-21}$ N s for a macromolecule with a mass of 40 000 amu, where the pulse couples through the dipole moment to incite vibration or rotation.

For a protein molecule held in the cell membrane, the effective field may be increased by a factor of the order of 1000 [Eq. (2)] through polarization of the membrane for pulses longer than 1 $\mu$s. (This polarization also acts to shield the interior of the cell from the electric field.) With this increment, $dp \approx p_{kt}$. But the molecule undergoes this characteristic impulse $p_{kT}$ of the order of $10^4$ times in a microsecond generating a mean impulse about 100 times $dp$. For shorter pulses the mean thermal impulse, proportional to the square root of the pulse duration, is reduced but the membrane passes the pulse through its capacitance and is not so strongly polarized.

Consequently weak magnetic pulses can have no biological effect no matter the rise time.

## III. RESONANCES

### A. Bandwidths

In the description of thermal noise which is commonly used, the square of the mean noise voltage is proportional to the frequency bandwidth over which the noise is measured—or relevant. Hence, if the acceptance of the biological system is such that only a narrow band of frequencies initiates the biological effects, the relative noise interference is reduced. Certain biological actions act as bandpass filters. In particular, those biological activities that have long intrinsic time constants can act as simple, plausible, low-pass filters. If an activity requires a time of 0.01 s, it is plausible that perturbations that change sign often in that time would have little overall effect. There are biological relaxation effects that admit transfer functions that peak at low frequencies—very much as a bandpass filter—but these peaks are quite broad.

However, since we have effectively assumed a low bandpass acceptance in using a frequency band of only 100 Hz in our discussions, if we are to find striking gains in signal-to-noise ratios in ELF actions, we must look further to resonant mechanisms that act as narrow bandpass filters. However, the existence of such low-frequency, narrow-band, or high-$Q$ resonances at the cellular level can be shown to be inconsistent with the properties of cells in biological media. We examine the properties of resonances.

The effective width of the passband depends not only on the characteristics of the biological system, but of the signal. A signal, e.g., an ELF wave, that lasts a time $t$ must have an intrinsic frequency spread $\delta v \approx 1/t$. Hence if the bandwidth $\delta v$, approximately equal to $v/Q$ for resonances, is very narrow, $\delta v \ll v$, the effective bandwidth will be determined by the characteristics of the signal rather than of the system. In that case, the effective frequency acceptance will be inversely proportional to $1/t$ and the effective signal-to-noise ratio will be proportional to $\sqrt{t}$. Or if the signal is integrated (or *averaged*) over a long time $t_{max}$, the signal-to-noise ratio will be much improved, but only if the effective system width is small compared to $1/t_{max}$. Weaver and Astumian[10] suggest averaging times $t_{max}$ of the order of 1000 s (or about 20 min). Such a long averaging time could only be relevant if the intrinsic bandwidth of the system were as small as 1/1000 Hz; if the signal were tuned that accurately; and if the time constant of the biological system were longer than 20 min. At 60 Hz—assuming a resonant biological process with a $Q \geq 60\,000$, exquisitely tuned to $60 \pm 0.001$ Hz—the signal-to-noise voltage from a 20-min exposure would be improved by a factor of $\sqrt{1000} \approx 30$ over a 1-s exposure and a factor of about 250 over that from a single pulse.

Even with the factor of 250, which assumes an integration time of about 20 min and a resonance width of 0.001 Hz (centered, *accidentally*, at exactly 60 Hz) the field in the membrane of about 0.018 V/m, induced by an 60-Hz external signal field of 300 V/m, would be 100 times smaller than the noise field over a frequency span of about $\delta \nu \approx 0.001$ Hz of about $500/250 = 2$ V/m.

### B. Coupling and damping

Moreover, if a resonance is to store energy, the damping of the resonance must be sufficiently small that it will make at least one cycle without interruption. If the resonance is to be in the ELF range, that cycle will take a very long time in terms of characteristic molecular collision or interaction times. Consequently, the resonance state must have a very small probability of being interrupted if it is to be significant.

We can estimate the characteristic interaction time or energy exchange time for the smallest elements in a solid as roughly $a/v \approx 10^{-11}$ s, where $a$ is a mean spacing of molecules and $v$ is a velocity of a bombarding molecule of mass $m$ where $\frac{1}{2}mv^2 \approx kT$. Then if the resonance is not to be deexcited by an interaction acting as a collision of the second kind in $\frac{1}{60}$ of a second, the probability of that deexcitation in an interaction must be of the order of $10^{-9}$. So small a deexcitation probability is difficult to reconcile with the large excitation probability required if the resonance is to be excited by a weak, long-wavelength electric field. If the cell element is as large as the cell membrane or the cell itself, and if the $Q$ is large enough to allow the coherent contributions of many ELF cycles, the constraints are more severe.

At the long ELF wavelengths, the electric field $E$ must couple to a resonance through a dipole interaction. The estimates we made in Sec. II E of the strength of the coupling of an electric field to the cell or elements of the cell, showed that for a characteristic set of interactions, the coupling was of the order of $10^{-9}kT$. Hence, the interaction energy would appear to be insufficient to generate oscillations that might produce biological effects even if the $Q$ of the resonance is sufficiently high so that the energies of many cycles can be added coherently. (At $10^{-9}kT$ per cycle, the system would have to accumulate energy for six months from a 60-Hz oscillation to reach an energy of $1\,kT$.)

We can also consider the damping of resonances—or any other motion of cell elements—in terms of the viscous resistance to that motion. To estimate the magnitude of damping, we consider a model of the motion of a spherical body of radius $a$ through cytoplasm or electrolyte where the viscosity $\eta \approx 7 \times 10^{-4}$ kg cm$^{-1}$ s$^{-1}$ is taken as that of water. For convenience we consider that the body is coupled to the field through a charge $q$. Then the drift velocity $v_E$ under a field $E$ will be

$$v_E = \frac{Eq}{6\pi \eta a} \ . \tag{15}$$

It is useful to compare the distance $L_E = v_E \delta t$ the body will move in a time $\delta t$ with the mean distance $L_{kT}$ the body will move in that time from thermal agitation or Brownian motion:

$$L_{kT} = \left[ \frac{2kT}{6\pi \eta a} \delta t \right]^{1/2} . \tag{16}$$

Using these relations, a time $\delta t = 1/\omega_{60} = 1/(2\pi \times 60)$ relevant for 60-Hz oscillations, and a (large) canonical field strength $E = 1$ V/m, we find for $a = 3 \times 10^{-10}$ m and $q = 2e$ (e.g., a calcium ion), $L_E = 1.1 \times 10^{-10}$ m while $L_{kT} = 2.4 \times 10^{-6}$ m. For a large element (e.g., a very large macromolecule with a large dipole moment) where $a = 1$ $\mu$m and $q = e$, $L_E \approx 5.5 \times 10^{-11}$ m while $L_{kT} = 4 \times 10^{-8}$ m. In either case, the amplitude $L$ is strongly limited by viscosity and the motion induced by the field $E$ is swamped by the Brownian motion.

Although the numerical values were derived from the model of a spherical body moving through water, the magnitudes are relevant for vibrational or rotational motion.

Hence, the narrow-banding, signal integration afforded by possible cellular resonances would not seem to work well enough to account for biological activity of weak ELF fields at the cell level. But there are further problems: we find that the size of cells is incommensurate with simple ELF resonances.

### C. Resonance amplitudes

A resonant system stores energy (allowing the integration of perturbing signals) which is transferred from one form to another at the resonant frequency. For mechanical systems, the energy oscillates between potential and kinetic storage; in the case of $LC$ electrical resonances, the energy oscillates between storage in electric and magnetic fields. Moreover, from the equipartition theorem, the resonance at thermal equilibrium must store an energy equal to $kT$.

The characteristic angular frequency $\omega = 2\pi \nu$, and stored energy $W$ of a resonant system are

$$\omega = \left[ \frac{K}{M} \right]^{1/2} , \quad W = \frac{1}{2}M\omega^2 A^2 , \tag{17}$$

where $A$ is the amplitude of excursion of a characteristic mass $M$ and $K$ is a spring constant. From the equipartition theorem $W = kT$. For ELF frequencies, such as 60 Hz, $\omega \approx 377$ s$^{-1}$ is small and $MA^2$ must be large, too large to fit within the mass and amplitude constraints of a cell. *There can be no ELF cellular resonances.*

We illuminate this categorical statement with explicit examples:

(i) As an extreme, we consider the physiologically unlikely oscillation of a whole cell with a mass of $\approx 5 \times 10^{-13}$ kg, and a radius of about 5 $\mu$m. If the energy of oscillation of the whole cell is equal to $kT$, the amplitude $A$ of oscillation will be 0.34 $\mu$m or about 7% of the radius of the cell.

(ii) However, the oscillation of smaller parts of the cell may be less unlikely. Without concern for the mechanical details of such an oscillation, we consider a 60-Hz resonance of the cell membrane, with a mass of about $2 \times 10^{-15}$ kg, or any other equally massive sector of the cell. With the smaller mass, the amplitude must be approximately equal to 5 $\mu$m and equal to the radius of the cell.

(iii) And there has been interest in ion resonances, especially of $^{40}$Ca with a mass of $6.6 \times 10^{-26}$ kg. The ampli-

TABLE I. Masses and corresponding amplitudes for systems oscillating with an energy of $kT$ at resonant frequencies of 60 and 16 Hz.

| Element | Mass (kg) | Amplitude 60 Hz | 16 Hz |
|---|---|---|---|
| Whole cell | $5 \times 10^{-13}$ | 0.34 $\mu$m | 1.35 $\mu$m |
| Cell membrane | $2 \times 10^{-15}$ | 5 $\mu$m | 20 $\mu$m |
| Calcium ion | $6.6 \times 10^{-26}$ | 1 m | 4 m |

tude at 60 Hz corresponding to such a mass is about 1 m. Such results are presented in Table I for 60- and 16-Hz oscillations.

### D. Specific resonances

Since there are some data that are claimed to constitute evidence of the biological activity of weak ELF fields that suggest that the fields act only over narrow "windows" of frequency, for completeness, we discuss detailed characteristics of a set of specific resonances

#### 1. Mechanical resonances

It is interesting to look at a specific oscillation in detail to gain some appreciation for the strength of the prohibition against mechanical oscillations. To maximize $M$, we choose a hypothetical oscillation of a whole cell where a spherical cell of quiescent radius $r = 5$ $\mu$m vibrates in a quadrupole mode changing from a prolate to an oblate spheroid in the course of a cycle. We take the density of the cell cytoplasm as 1 g/cm$^3$ and set the energy of the vibration at $kT \approx 4.3 \times 10^{-21}$ J. With these constraints, we calculated the amplitude of the 60-Hz oscillation, measured in the direction of the axis, as about 1 $\mu$m. This is a substantial oscillation—the radius in the direction of the axis changes by about 20%.

In the course of the oscillation, the kinetic energy of motion of the cell material must be stored in an energy associated with the distortion. Assuming that the cytoplasm is effectively an incompressible liquid, this potential-energy storage must be found in the energy required to stretch the membrane inasmuch as the surface area of the cell increases by about 1.5% as the cell changes from a spherical to an ellipsoidal shape. Setting this energy to $kT$, we find that the surface energy of the membrane is required to be about $10^{-9}$ J/m$^2$, a value about $10^8$ smaller than the surface energy of water. Conversely, the natural oscillation frequency of a water droplet of the size of the cell would be about 640 000 Hz.

In summary, if the kinetic energy of the cell vibrating at 60 Hz is to be as large as $kT$, the whole cell must take part in an oscillation. And then the effective forces described by the spring constant $K$ must be unrealistically small if the frequency is to be kept so low. For smaller cell elements with less mass, the spring constant must be even smaller if the element is to oscillate at ELF frequencies.

#### 2. Electrical resonances

But could the "observed" resonances be electrical, rather than mechanical, where the energy is transformed cyclically from storage in a magnetic field to storage in an electric field? We consider that we can describe some element of the cell by an equivalent $LC$ circuit with a resonant frequency:

$$v = \frac{\omega}{2\pi} \quad \text{where} \quad \omega = \left[ \frac{1}{LC} \right]^{1/2} . \tag{18}$$

Such a circuit will be incited thermally such that the mean total energy of $kT$ will oscillate between storage in magnetic and electric fields. We note that if the frequency is to be low, the product $LC$ must be large. The capacitance is limited by the size of the cell. The largest capacitance that would seem to be evident is the capacitance between the inner and outer surface of the cell membrane. Taking the thickness of the membrane as 50 Å and the dielectric constant as 2.5, $C_{\text{mem}} \approx 6 \times 10^{-12}$ F. Then, for a resonant frequency of $v = 60$ Hz, the inductance must be approximately equal to $10^6$ H.

It is difficult to design an ideal paradigmatic cell inductance. However, we note that in the absence of ferromagnetic materials in cells and in the absence of a natural source of many current turns, we should expect that the characteristic cell inductance should be of a magnitude such that $L \approx \mu_0 r \approx 10^{-11}$ H, too small by 17 orders of magnitude. (There are mechanical processes that lead to current phase lags in biological material of an inductive nature that follow from the inertial mass of the ions that carry currents or to the viscous resistance to the ion motion but neither of these mechanisms leads to the substantial energy storage requisite for a resonance.) Truly, Nature may be much more clever than we think, but not by a factor of $10^{17}$. There can be no 60-Hz $LC$ cell resonances.

#### 3. Cyclotron resonances

Bawin and Adey interpreted the results of an experiment[11] as indicating that the passage of calcium ions through chick-brain cell walls was reduced when the cells were subject to weak 16-Hz electromagnetic fields. Then, Liboff and McLeod[12] noted that under a magnetic field $B = 50$ $\mu$T, the size of the earth's field, the cyclotron resonance frequency $v$

$$2\pi v = \omega = \frac{qB}{m} \tag{19}$$

for a calcium ion of mass $m = 40$ amu, carrying a charge $q = e$, was equal to 16 Hz. Hence, they suggested that the cyclotron resonance of the calcium ion might be responsible for the effect reported by Bawin and Adey.

Unlike the mechanical resonance, energy in the cyclotron resonance is wholly stored in the kinetic energy of the circulating ion. The energy is transferred from the kinetic energy of motion in one direction to the energy of motion in an orthogonal direction—all in the plane of the orbit but the energy-amplitude relations stated in the last section still hold. Hence, quite generally, the orbit of such a resonance must be larger than the size of the cell by five orders of magnitude.

Nevertheless, Liboff and McLeod proposed a specific cyclotron resonance of the calcium ion where the energy of the ion was expected to be about 3.5 eV. But such an ion travels in an orbit with a diameter of 80 m.

But, of course, the ion could be traveling much slower, slow enough to travel around at 5-$\mu$ radius orbit that might be fitted into a cell. But the resultant ion energy is then only about $5 \times 10^{-14}$ eV and very, very much less than the mean thermal energy of $kT = \frac{1}{40}$ eV. Indeed, an estimate suggests that the Brownian effect would typically move the ion randomly 5 $\mu$m in any $\frac{1}{100}$ of a second that the ion is to travel to that distance about its circuit. Hence, the thermal Brownian-like motion overwhelms any orbital motion.

### 4. Nuclear magnetic resonances

The interaction of an ambient magnetic field such as the earth's field $B_e$ with the magnetic moment $\mu$ of a nucleus (with nonzero spin) generates a torque on the spinning nucleus that induces the nucleus to precess about the direction of the field. Even as the rotating magnetic moment generates an oscillating magnetic field normal to the ambient field, a weak external field normal to the ambient field that oscillates with the precession frequency will generate a precession of the nuclear polarization. The frequency $\nu$ of precession is $\nu = B_e \mu / \pi$. For the earth's field this precession frequency for protons will be about 2000 Hz; for nitrogen about 20 Hz. Moreover, the nucleus of an atom is so weakly coupled to the orbital electrons—and then the material environment—that relaxation times can be of the order of 30 s and more. So we have a resonance condition at ELF frequencies with a high $Q$.

However, it seems most unlikely that there can be any biological effect of such resonances. The proportion of the nuclei that will be aligned will be about equal to $B_e \mu / kT \approx 10^{-10}$, a proportion very much smaller than the statistical fluctuations in the alignment of nuclei in the cell. Moreover, as reflected in the large $Q$, that energy is coupled to the environment of the nucleus very, very, weakly. It is this weak coupling of the nucleus to the atomic structure—and hence to the chemical and biological environment—that makes nuclear magnetic resonance imaging (MRI) such a safe and noninvasive medical procedure though the patient is bathed in magnetic fields approximately equal to 4 T, about 100 000 times the earth's field.

### IV. SUMMARY

#### A. Experimental record

Though the theoretical considerations that represent extrapolations and interpolations of tested observations must serve as a reliable guide to our understanding of Nature, such analyses cannot supplant a well-established contrary observation. Hence we must defer to observations that are *established* through the scientific process of review and replication. But are there any such well-established observations that demonstrate effects of weak ELF fields on the biology of cells?

There are very many (of the order of 100) reports of experiments that purport to demonstrate that weak ELF

fields affect cells. A U.S. Congress Office of Technological Assessment (OTA) report[1] places the experiments in four categories: modulation of ion flows; interference with DNA synthesis and RNA transcription; interaction with the response of normal cells to various agents and biochemicals such as hormones, neurotransmitters, and growth factors; and interaction with the biokinetics of cancer cells. There is no near-consensus among those who work in the field to the effect than *any* of the reports of effects in any of these areas is valid; none have been satisfactorily replicated, many of the more substantial results have been contradicted. The problems with the research are stated succinctly in the OTA "background paper," which characterizes the experiments by noting that ". . . findings at the cell level display considerable complexity including resonant responses of "windows" in frequency and field strength, complex time dependencies, and dependence on the ambient *DC* magnetic field created by the earth . . . ELF fields appear to be an agent to which there is no known analog." The unwitting indictment is severe.

It is, perhaps, the intensity windows that are reported that makes it most difficult to accept the experimental results. It is an almost firm rule of the behavior of systems that, above an action threshold, the response to a perturbing signal increases at least linearly with the incremental signal. This linear increase will generally be terminated only when the signal is so large that it can no longer be considered a perturbation. Since it is very difficult to consider that the small signals in question are sufficiently large to have any effect at all, the view that they can be so large as to dampen out a response is even more troubling.[13] Moreover, the windows seem almost maliciously defined (by man or by Nature) to thwart simple verification of the effects. If such windows did not exist, the verification of the effects of small fields would be simple as the experiment could be conducted with much larger fields to elicit a much larger and more easily detected response.

### B. Conclusions

It does not appear to be possible for weak external ELF electromagnetic fields to affect biological processes significantly at the cell level. ELF electric fields are so completely shielded by the conductivity of the body tissues that the interaction of external fields with a strength less than 300 V/m with cells is far weaker than fundamental thermal noise.

ELF magnetic fields may act through static interactions with magnetic dipole moments of biological material or through the induced electric fields generated by changes in the magnetic fields. Since the static effects of ELF fields of 50 $\mu$T are no greater than the earth's field, it is difficult to believe that the intensity is harmful. Since the maximum induced electric field in the body induced by 60-Hz 4-$\mu$T magnetic fields is no greater than the electric field induced by walking through the earth's field, it is difficult to believe that such changing ELF magnetic fields are harmful. Also, both the static and kinetic effects of ELF fields as great as 50 $\mu$T at the cell level are, again, smaller than that from thermal noise. The impulses from weak less than 50-$\mu$T fast-rise-time ELF magnetic fields—such as from a 20-kHz sawtooth waveform—are also shown to be small compared to thermal effects.

The experimental record lacks coherence and credibility. After 20 years of experimentation, no significant effect of weak ELF fields at the cell level has been firmly established.

In summary, there are very good reasons to believe that weak ELF fields can have no significant biological effect at the cell level—and no strong reason to believe otherwise.

## ACKNOWLEDGMENTS

In the course of preparation of this paper, I found essential encouragement and technical information in many, many conversations with Eleanor R. Adair. I owe a great deal to the papers of Herman Schwan and Ken Foster and to their help and criticism. And I want to thank William Pickard, Robert Pound, Charles Bean, Jack Sandweiss, Dean Astumian, James Weaver, and Richard Setlow for the benefit of conversations and correspondence as well as too many others to name.

[1]I. Nair, M. G. Morgan, and H. K. Florig, U.S. Congress, Office of Technological Assessment for the Office of Technological Assessment, *Biological Effects of Power Frequency Electric and Magnetic Fields—Background Paper*, Report No. OTA-BP-E-53 (U.S. GPO, Washington, D.C., 1989).

[2]K. R. Foster and H. P. Schwan, in *CRC Handbook of Biological Effects of Electromagnetic Fields*, edited by C. Polk and E. Postow (Chemical Rubber Co., Boca Raton, 1986).

[3]This relation holds specifically for an isolated sphere of tissue but is an adequate approximation for other geometries such as that of the human body. However, appreciably higher internal fields can result in the body under special conditions. In particular, fields as much as 500 times greater can be induced in the ankles of a man standing on a ground place subject to a vertical field; M. W. Miller, in *CRC Handbook* (Ref. 2), p. 139.

[4]W. F. Pickard, IEEE Trans. Biomed. Eng. **35**, 243 (1988).

[5]These results are in accord with a more extensive discussion by Frank S. Barnes, in *CRC Handbook* (Ref. 2), p. 121.

[6]Cellular effects have been reported by K. J. McLeod, R. C. Lee, and H. P. Ehrlich, Science **236**, 1465 (1987) and are noted at field strengths in tissues as small as $5 \times 10^{-3}$ V/m. But these fields correspond to fields generated by external fields in air of $\approx 2.5 \times 10^5$ V/m. These fields of 0.005 V/m in the tissue lead to potential differences of about $7.5 \times 10^{-8}$ V across the membrane of the cells we consider and that is about 33 times smaller than the noise potential $2.5 \times 10^{-6}$ V we calculate. However, since the signal-to-noise ratio varies as the square of the cell radius and the large bovine fibroblast cells that were studied are effectively about three times the size of our canonical cell, we gain a factor of 9. There is an uncertainty of an order of magnitude in the effective resistivity of membrane material. If we assume that the true resistivity is four times less than our canonical value of $10^6$ $\Omega$ m, we gain another factor of 2. Furthermore, it seems that there is a low-frequency cutoff at about 10 Hz and if we take that as the band width rather than 100 Hz we gain another factor of 3 giving us an overall signal-to-noise ratio greater than one and we do not categorically reject the possibility that the purported effects are real.

[7]R. P. Blakemore, Science **190**, 377 (1975).

[8]R. B. Frankel, in *CRC Handbook of the Biological Effects of Electromagnetic Fields* (Ref. 2), p. 169.

[9]P. W. Atkins, Chem. Br. **12**, 214 (1976). The subject is reviewed by R. B. Frankel (Ref. 8).

[10]J. C. Weaver and R. D. Astumian, Science **247**, 459 (1990).

[11]S. M. Bawin and W. R. Adey, Proc. Nat. Acad. Sci. **73**, 1999 (1976).

[12]A. R. Liboff and B. R. McLeod, Bioelectromagnetics **9**, 39 (1988) and earlier papers.

[13]Intensity windows are not impossible. C. H. Durney, C. K. Rushforth, and A. A. Anderson, Bioelectromagnetics **9**, 315 (1988), have constructed an ingenious system of cyclotron— and betatron—ion dynamics that would seem to display both intensity and frequency windows but they emphasize that their model cannot describe biological effects.

Reprinted with permission from *Phys. Rev. A* **46**, 2178-2184 (1992). Copyright 1992 by the American Physical Society.

# COMMENTS

*Comments are short papers which criticize or correct papers of other authors previously published in the* **Physical Review**. *Each Comment should state clearly to which paper it refers and must be accompanied by a brief abstract. The same publication schedule as for regular articles is followed, and page proofs are sent to authors.*

## Comment on "Constraints on biological effects of weak extremely-low-frequency electromagnetic fields"

Joseph L. Kirschvink

*Division of Geological and Planetary Sciences, The California Institute of Technology, Pasadena, California 91125*
(Received 26 July 1991; revised manuscript received 20 January 1992)

In a recent paper, Adair [Phys. Rev. A **43**, 1039 (1991)] concludes that weak extremely-low-frequency (ELF) electromagnetic fields cannot affect biology on the cell level. However, Adair's assertion that few cells of higher organisms contain magnetite ($Fe_3O_4$) and his blanket denial of reproducible ELF effects on animals are both wrong. Large numbers of single-domain magnetite particles are present in a variety of animal tissues, including up to a hundred million per gram in human brain tissues, organized in clusters of tens to hundreds of thousand per gram. This is far more than a "few cells." Similarly, a series of reproducible behavioral experiments on honeybees, *Apis mellifera*, have shown that they are capable of responding to weak ELF magnetic fields that are well within the bounds of Adair's criteria. A biologically plausible model of the interaction of single-domain magnetosomes with a mechanically activated transmembrane ion channel shows that ELF fields on the order of 0.1 to 1 mT are capable of perturbing the open-closed state by an energy of $kT$. As up to several hundred thousand such structures could fit within a eukaryotic cell, and the noise should go as the square root of the number of independent channels, much smaller ELF sensitivities at the cellular level are possible. Hence, the credibility of weak ELF magnetic effects on living systems must stand or fall mainly on the merits and reproducibility of the biological or epidemiological experiments that suggest them, rather than on dogma about physical implausibility.

PACS number(s): 87.50.Eg, 87.22.Bt

Recently, Adair [1] presented a well-argued case covering the constraints on biological effects of weak extremely-low-frequency (ELF) electromagnetic fields, and concludes that many biological effects that have been reported could not possibly be real. His paper includes numerous statements such as "Hence, any biological effects of weak ELF fields on the cellular level must be found outside the scope of conventional physics," and "··· there are very good reasons to believe that weak ELF fields can have no significant biological effect at the cell level—and no strong reason to believe otherwise."

Although it is clear that many of the mechanisms considered by Adair are implausible on first principles, there is a gaping hole in the discussion concerning the biological precipitation of ferromagnetic minerals (e.g., magnetite, $Fe_3O_4$). Adair's discussion implies that only the magnetotactic bacteria are able to precipitate single-domain crystals of magnetite, and he states, "Hence, with the aid of ferromagnetic materials, a cell can—barely—sense a 50-$\mu$T field. But $Fe_3O_4$ is found in few other cells. And without the crafting of such compasses, we cannot expect the effects of magnetic fields on cells to compete with thermal fluctuations."

This is an unfortunate flaw in an otherwise reasonable discussion. *Humans and many other organisms also pre-cipitate magnetite* in a wide variety of tissues [2]. And in the nervous system or immune system, signals transduced by a minute fraction of the total cells can have global consequences.

Three goals of this present comment are as follows: First, for background, I review briefly the evidence for magnetite biomineralization in higher organisms. Second, Adair asserts that there are no good reasons to believe weak ELF fields have biological effects at the cellular level in terrestrial animals. I therefore review the recent literature which links incontrovertibly weak magnetic fields and behavior, providing a clear counterexample to his assertion. Of the eight magnetic effects on bees described in the literature, six have been replicated independently, and three by more than one other group. Good evidence links the transduction mechanism to the motion of magnetite in specialized receptor cells. Finally, a simple calculation shows that the motions of magnetosomes in response to a weak ELF magnetic field would be capable of opening or closing transmembrane ion channels. This provides one plausible mechanism for triggering a number of significant biological effects.

*Magnetite biomineralization.* Lowenstam [3] discovered the process of magnetite biomineralization in the teeth of a primitive group of mollusks, the chitons, and his subsequent work has provided one of the clearest examples of this mineralization process in any higher organism [4,5]. Each tooth contains up to 1 mg of single-domain magnetite [6], enough so that the entire tongue plate (the radula) will stick to an ordinary hand magnet [3]. So far, chiton radulae are the only macroscopic biological structures known to contain visible quantities of biogenic magnetite, although as discussed below it is present commonly in the ppm to ppb levels in a variety of other species and tissues.

Adair's discussion of the magnetotactic bacteria, while technically correct, is based largely on the analysis of one species, *Aquaspirillum magnetotacticum,* which has been studied extensively because it can be grown in pure culture [7]. This organism makes relatively small magnetosomes (membrane-bound structures containing a single-domain crystal of magnetite [8]), the chains of which have total magnetic-to-thermal energy ratios between about 10 and 20 [9] in the earth's field. Other natural magnetotactic bacteria have been discovered which contain hundreds of magnetosomes, and have magnetic-to-thermal energy ratios of several thousand [10]. Similar magnetotactic abilities also exist in the eukaryotic kingdom Proctista (the protists). Torres de Araujo *et al.* [11] describe an algae of the genus *Anisonema (Euglenophyceae)* which makes several thousand magnetosomes aligned in hundreds of magnetosome chains, which collectively give the cell a magnetic-to-thermal energy ratio of several thousand. Hence, Adair's [1] statement that magnetite-containing cells can barely detect the 50-$\mu$T geomagnetic field is not generally true. Many of these cells are not just "barely" detecting the field, they are responding *strongly* to it.

In higher animals other than the chitons, the discovery of magnetite biomineralization was made largely through the use of moment magnetometers based on superconducting quantum interference devices developed initially for use in rock and mineral magnetism [12]. If these are used in clean-lab conditions, the threshold sensitivity for the detection of magnetite can be a few parts in $10^{12}$. The initial detection of magnetite in honeybees [13] and homing pigeons [14] triggered a flurry of discoveries in other animal groups (reviewed in Ref. [2]), and led eventually to the development of gentle extraction techniques which did not disrupt the chainlike organization of the magnetosomes. Magnetosome chains extracted from the anteriordorsal (ethmoid) region of salmon [15,16] possess many of the features also found in the magnetotatic bacteria, including size and shapes within the single-domain stability region, and the alignment of the {111} crystallographic axes along the chain length. Hence, in direct contradiction to the assertion of Adair [1], some cells of higher animals do indeed craft biological bar magnets which enable them to respond strongly to weak ELF magnetic fields.

Related studies of other tissue types often reveal lower but reproducible levels of background ferromagnetic material [2]. Although efficient techniques for extracting the ferromagnetic crystals and identifying them are only now being perfected, the results are intriguing. Soft tissues of the human brain, for example, contain the equivalent of several million magnetosomes per gram [17], serving as-yet unknown biological functions. Although this implies that less than 0.1% of brain cells contain magnetite, the potential number of such cells is quite large. Two strains of mouse tumor, YC-8 lymphoma and Lewis lung carcinoma, make between five and ten crystals per cell [18].

*No ELF effects on living systems? A counter example.* Adair's [1] assertion that "After 20 years of experimentation, no significant effect of weak ELF fields at the cell level has been firmly established" is also inaccurate. In neurobiology, all known sensory modalities transduce their signals in specialized sensory cells. Hence, if an animal responds behaviorally to an external magnetic field, the stimulus to neural activity will originate at the cellular level, presumably in cells specialized for its transduction. Thus, a convincing demonstration of behavioral sensitivity to weak magnetic fields in *any* animal is enough to falsify Adair's assertion. The honeybee *(Apis mellifera)* is one of several animals which exhibit magnetically influenced behavior.

Table I shows a summary of the known magnetic effects on honeybee behavior, as well as the independent attempts to replicate them. I know of no attempts to replicate these effects that were not eventually successful (some apparently took practice). As Towne and Gould [19] provide a thorough and critical review of this literature prior to 1985 [effects (1)–(4) in Table I], a complete discussion of them is not necessary here. However, note that the horizontal dance experiment of Lindauer and Martin [20] and Martin and Lindauer [21] [effect (2) in Table I] has proven to be particularly easy to replicate [22]. Kirschvink [23] noted that the accuracy of the dance orientation data in varying strength background fields published by Martin and Lindauer [21] followed closely the Langevin function, and from the least-squares match to it predicted that the average honeybee compass receptor had a magnetic-to-thermal energy ratio in the geomagnetic field of about 6, equivalent to a single-domain cube of magnetite about 0.1 $\mu$m in size in the 50-$\mu T$ geomagnetic field.

In a series of papers, Walker and Bitterman [24–26] and Walker, Baird, and Bitterman [27] have shown recently that individual foraging honeybees will learn to discriminate weak magnetic anomalies superimposed against the background geomagnetic field [effects (5)–(7) in Table I]. Given the appropriate experimental situation, honeybees learn to discriminate magnetic cues as easily as they do visual cues [27]. In addition to our replication of the Walker-Bitterman extinction test [(5) in Table I] [28], we have recently replicated their two-choice paradigm as well [29]. We have also discovered that it can be used to map out the frequency response of the honeybee magnetoreceptor, and that honeybees will condition to powerline frequency magnetic fields [29]. The basic experiments are simple and direct.

The measurement of Walker and Bitterman [25] of the threshold sensitivity of the bees to a small static anomaly superimposed upon the background field is the most dramatic result of such conditioning experiments. By starting with a moderately strong anomaly (3 mT) in the two-choice training experiment, and by reducing the am-

TABLE I. Summary of magnetic effects on honeybee behavior.

| Effect | Original reports | Similar replications |
|---|---|---|
| (1) Misdirection in the waggle dance influenced by weak magnetic fields | Lindauer and Martin [51,20] Martin and Lindauer [21] | Hepworth *et al.* [52] Towne and Gould [19], Kilbert [53] |
| (2) Dances on horizontal comb align with points of magnetic compass | Lindauer and Martin [20] Martin and Lindauer [21] | Brines [54]; Gould *et al.* [22] (Also see Kirschbink [23]) |
| (3) Magnetic orientation of comb building | Lindauer and Martin [20] Martin and Lindauer [56] | De Jong [55]; Towne and Gould [19] |
| (4) Time sense of bees influenced by geomagnetic variations | Lindauer [57] | Partially by Gould [58] |
| (5) Extinction test conditioning experiment | Walker and Bitterman [24] | Kirschvink and Kobayashi-Kirschvink [28] |
| (6) Two-choice threshold conditioning experiment | Walker and Bitterman [25] | Kirschvink *et al.* [29] |
| (7) Small magnets on anteriordorsal abdomen interfere with conditioning experiments | Walker and Bitterman [26] | No attempts reported yet |
| (8) Pulse remagnetization converts north-seeking into south-seeking bees | Kirschvink and Kobayashi-Kirschvink [28] | No attempts reported yet |

plitude of the anomaly in small exponential steps, the threshold sensitivity could be determined by the point at which the bees were no longer able to discriminate correctly. Nine bees were tested in this procedure; the median threshold was 250 nT *in the presence of the earth's field*, a relative sensitivity of 0.6%. Their best bee lost the ability to discriminate in fields *below* 25 nT (0.06% of background). Similar, but less direct, estimates of the magnetic sensitivity of bees were obtained from both the misdirection and circadian rhythm experiments (effects (1) and (4) in Table I, reviewed by Towne and Gould [19]). This astounding sensitivity, however, is not physically unreasonable for a magnetite-based sensory system. Estimates for the number of discrete sensory organelles per bee, based on the measured magnetic moments, are on the order of several million [13,23]. Several analyses have shown that the ultimate sensitivity of such an array will improve by the square root of the number of receptors, and that nT-level sensitivity should be obtained easily [30–32]. Similar neurological averaging schemes are well known in the auditory and electroreception systems of many other animals.

Two of the experiments listed in Table I have a direct bearing on the nature of the magnetic sensory receptors in the honeybee. First, Walker and Bitterman [26] found that small magnetized wires glued to the anteriordorsal abdomen interfered with the ability of the bees to discriminate magnetic anomalies, whereas copper wires had no effect. Magnetic wires in other locations similarly

had no effect. Magnetite biomineralization in the anteriordorsal abdomen was discovered previously by Gould, Kirschvink, and Deffeyes [13]. Second, Kirschvink and Kobayashi-Kirschvink [28] were on occasion able to elicit magnetic north-seeking behavior in bees trained to visit a simple *T* maze. A short magnetic pulse with a peak amplitude of 100 mT (stronger than the coercivity of most biogenic magnetites) was able to convert north-seeking exit responses into south-seeking ones. This same experiment works on the magnetotactic bacteria [33,34], and is a unique fingerprint of a ferromagnetic compass receptor.

It is thus clear that the initial reports of magnetic behavioral effects on honeybees, although met with intense skepticism, have survived the acid tests of replication. They have led progressively to more refined experiments which illuminate the nature and sensitivity of the receptor system. The honeybee data provide clear and reproducible evidence that at least one terrestrial animal is influenced at the cellular level by weak ELF magnetic fields. Hence, the existence of similar effects in other magnetite containing cells cannot be dismissed *a priori* as done by Adair [1].

*A biophysical model of magnetite and ELF magnetic fields.* Adair [1] is correct to stress that biophysical models of interaction must be examined *quantitatively*. Thus, it is necessary to present here a biologically plausible but quantitative sketch model showing how ELF magnetic effects at the cellular or subcellular levels might lead to significant effects; the model presented here is adapted from a similar biophysical analysis developed for the magnetite-based sensory system of honeybees [29]. The existence of this sketch shows that it is wrong to reject the ELF bioeffect data, including recent epidemiological [35–37] studies, merely because Adair [1] could not construct a physically plausible linkage.

Several biological constraints are as follows. First, studies of biogenic magnetites indicate that they are coated usually by a thin veneer of organic material [2,16], which is usually a thin phospholipid membrane [8,10]. Only in the chiton teeth is there evidence for magnetite crystals embedded in a larger, more rigid structure [3–5]. Second, many of the particles in fresh tissues move relatively freely *in situ,* as shown by the poor ability of unfixed or unfrozen tissues to hold a remanent magnetization [2]. Third, because most intracellular components in eukaryotic cells are held in place relative to cellular membranes by proteinaceous filaments of the cytoskeletal system, similar attachments probably exist for the magnetosomes, as they do in magnetotactic bacteria [10].

Hence, it is reasonable to suggest that magnetic ELF biological effects could arise from membrane deformations produced by magnetosome-induced cytoskeletal tension. In fact, mechanically sensitive *trans*-membrane ion channels are present in almost every organism and tissue, including bacteria, yeast, invertebrates, higher plants, and vertebrates, and are known from oocytes, epithelia, endothelial cells, skeletal muscles, smooth muscles, and neurons [38]. In higher organisms there is good evidence that they are linked to the cytoskeletal system through spectrinlike proteins, and their number densities can be many per square $\mu$m [39]. Biophysical properties of such channels are understood fairly well, largely through their identification on the stereocilia of hair cells. Opening of a single channel for a few milliseconds can lead to the firing of an action potential, and the sensitivity of these structures is such that they can sense the Brownian motion of the ciliary bundles [40]. Howard and Hudspeth [41] have made estimates of the single-channel gating force, the difference between the force exerted on the ionic gate when it is open and that when it is closed, which are in the range between 0.2 and 0.4 pN. Similarly, the gating distance for these channels is about 4 nm [41]. These structures operate essentially at the kT limit, and an external input of mechanical energy of $\Delta E$ will change the probability of a channel being open or closed by a Boltzmann factor of $\exp(-\Delta E/kT)$. If coupled perfectly, a magnetosome with a magnetic-to-thermal energy ratio of 10 in the geomagnetic field (which "barely" responds to the field according to Adair [1]) could act to change the probability of a gate being closed by a factor of $\exp(-10)$ (e.g., the probability at any time of the gate being closed could shift from a value near 0.999 99 to a value of 0.000 05). $Ca^{2+}$ ions, in particular, move easily through this type of channel, and this ion also controls many phosphorylation cascades which are chemical systems of very high "gain." Hence, the question posed above reduces to finding the level of external ELF magnetic fields that would be required to supply enough torque on a magnetosome to allow it to open a mechanically sensitive ion channel.

Figure 1 is a sketch of a configuration which fits these biological constraints. A cytoskeletal filament anchors a magnetosome to the membrane via a mechanically sensitive ion channel as shown. The background geomagnetic field, $B_{\text{earth}}$, of 50 $\mu$T is aligned perpendicular to the membrane, and we apply an ELF magnetic field, $B_{\text{ELF}}\cos(\omega t)$, parallel to the membrane and perpendicular to $B_{\text{earth}}$. We wish to determine the minimum strength of the ELF magnetic field (as a function of fre-

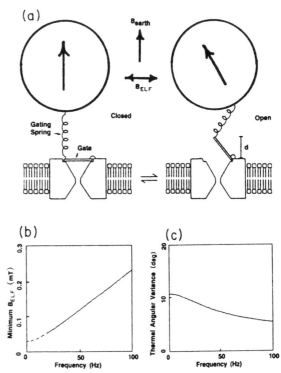

FIG. 1. A schematic diagram for how a magnetosome might act to open or close a mechanically sensitive *trans*-membrane ion channel, and order-of-magnitude estimates of the field levels required. (a) shows a magnetosome connected to an ion channel gate via a cytoskeletal filament (a gating spring), adapted from Howard and Hudspeth [41], but not drawn to scale as the magnetosome should be larger than shown. The geomagnetic field $B_{\text{earth}}$ is perpendicular to the plane of the membrane, whereas the ELF component, $B_{\text{ELF}}\cos(\omega t)$, is parallel to it. As discussed in the text, rotation of the magnetosome in response to the oscillating external field should be capable of opening and closing the ion gate. (b) shows an order-of-magnitude estimate for the minimum fields to switch the gate as a function of frequency for a magnetosome of 0.1-$\mu$m radius in a fluid with a viscosity of 1 poise, and (c) shows the magnitude the rms angular deviation produced by Brownian motion; this is below the 16° needed to open the gate. This rms angular deviation decreases slightly with increasing frequency because the minimum value of $B_{\text{ELF}}$, shown in (b), increases. These calculations are made assuming that other cytoskeletal links prevent the magnetosome from drifting sideways while allowing it to rotate freely. Note also that this model should not apply at frequencies below about 10 Hz due to the phasic nature of mechanically sensitive ion channels and the elastic properties of membranes.

quency) necessary to open periodically the ionic gate. To be conservative, assume that the gate opens through the distance, $d$ of 4 nm with an applied force, $F$, of 1 pN. To open the gate using a spherical magnetosome of radius, $r$, equal to 0.1 $\mu$m, this grain will need to rotate through an angle $\theta_{min}$ of $\arccos(1 - d/r)$, or about 16°. A magnetosome of this size and shape will be a single magnetic domain [42]. Although somewhat larger than the *A magnetotacticum* particles considered by Adair [1], magnetite crystals of this size have been extracted from the human brain and other organisms [2,10,43].

Under most circumstances, a magnetosome in a fluid medium will be overdamped critically by viscous forces (e.g., the low Reynolds number intracellular environment described by Purcell [44]). Hence, inertial terms can be neglected, and the equation of motion is similar to that of a forced, over-damped torsional pendulum. In the situation shown in Fig. 1, the torque on the magnetosome from the cytoskeletal filament (the "gating spring" [41]) acts with the same $\sin(\theta)$ dependence as does the magnetic torque from the earth's field. The equation is then

$$C\dot{\theta} + (Fr + \mu B_{earth})\sin(\theta) = \mu B_{ELF}\cos(\theta)\cos(\omega t) , \quad (1)$$

where $C$ is the coefficient of rotational friction about the center of the magnetosome, $\theta$ is the angle between the static background field and the magnetic moment of the magnetosome, $\dot{\theta}$ is the angular velocity, $\mu$ is the total magnetic moment of the particle, $\omega$ is the frequency, and $t$ denotes time. The magnetic moment for a magnetite particle of this radius is $2 \times 10^{-15}$ A m$^2$. For a sphere of this size, the coefficient of rotational friction is given by $6\eta V$, where $V$ is the volume and $\eta$ is the viscosity of eukaryotic cellular protoplasm, which is about 100 times more than water [45]. The stochastic rotations produced by Brownian motion are not included here, as they act independently of the other forces; for our purposes we note that the angular variance of motion, $\langle \theta_{therm} \rangle^2$ is given by the thermal-to-magnetic energy ratio, $kT/\mu B_{total}$, and its rms value should be less than the 16° estimated above for opening the ionic channel gate.

Although Eq. (1) is a first-order equation, it does not have closed-form solutions for $\theta(t)$ due to the presence of the $\sin(\theta)$ and $\cos(\theta)$ terms, and the small angle approximation is not always appropriate in this situation. However, a close approximation can be found easily by the following approach. In the case where $\theta$ is small, $\sin(\theta)$ and $\cos(\theta)$ are approximately $\theta$ and 1, respectively. Equation (1) then becomes linear, and the solution for long times becomes

$$\theta(t) = \theta_{max}\cos(\omega t + E) , \quad (2)$$

where

$$\theta_{max} = \frac{\mu B_{ELF}}{\sqrt{(rF + \mu B_{earth})^2 + c^2\omega^2}} \quad (3)$$

and $E$ is a small phase delay. Although this works for small $\theta$, if the value of $B_{ELF}$ is much larger than $B_{earth}$, $\theta_{max}$ may become much larger than its maximum possible value of $\pi/2$. In the low-frequency limit where $\omega$ approaches zero, $\theta_{max}$ should reduce simply to the

arctangent of $B_{ELF}/B_{earth}$, so it is reasonable to replace $\theta_{max}$ with $\text{Arctan}(\theta_{max})$. This modification also works for low values of $\theta$ because $\text{Arctan}(\theta)$ is also $\theta$ in this limit. Numerical approximations for Eq. (1) confirm that this modification gives the correct values for $\theta_{max}$ to within a few percent for a wide range of frequencies and field strengths.

Figure 1(b) shows the minimum values for $B_{ELF}$ needed to make $\theta_{max}$ just equal to the 16° rotation for opening the ion gate as a function of frequency, and Fig. 1(c) shows the expected angular deviation of the particle produced by Brownian motion, $\langle \theta \rangle_{therm}$. At the powerline frequency of 60 Hz, the critical ELF field for opening the channel is 0.14 mT (1.4 G), and $\langle \theta \rangle_{therm}$ is well below 16°.

One obvious problem with the sketch model as shown is that a 90° rotation of the magnetic field would cause the gate to open permanently. Humans move around in the magnetic field and natural selection would have removed any harmful effect of such motion long ago. However, two factors should act to mitigate this at very low frequencies. First, mechanically sensitive *trans*-membrane ion channels are phasic, closing on their own with an exponential time constant of about 0.1 s after sudden onset of a unidirectional membrane stress [46]. Second, a small force on a biological membrane will cause it to deform, with a characteristic time constant also of about 0.1 s [47]. These effects may be related, as closure of the channels may be a result of membrane deformation relieving stress in the cytoskeleton. Hence, at frequencies below about 10 Hz there should be minimal effects of alternating fields of virtually any strength, as the ion channels and membranes have enough time to respond. At higher frequencies the membranes and channels should behave in the manner assumed in the model. Because humans do not typically spin themselves at 60 Hz in the geomagnetic field for extended periods of time, alternating fields of earth strength are not something which cells have been exposed to during most of the past 3.5 billion years of organic evolution.

Hence, in direct contradiction to the statements of Adair [1], it may indeed be possible for weak, ELF magnetic fields to produce biological effects at the cellular level through a nonsensory process. If sensory processes are involved which integrate over large numbers of magnetosomes, effects at lower-field strengths are possible [29]. Although the minimum threshold field levels required for this type of nonsensory effect at 60 Hz are well above the 0.3-$\mu$T (3-mG) levels inferred from some of the early epidemiological correlations between electric power wiring configurations and leukemia, those levels have not withstood subsequent replication attempts [37]. On the other hand, the studies of Savitz, John, and Kleckner [36] and London *et al.* [37] (and several others) show a consistent pattern of increased risk from the regular use of household electrical appliances, like electric blankets and hair dryers, which do expose users to fields of this strength [48]. Because the mechanically sensitive ion channels allow Ca$^{2+}$ to pass easily when opened, and intracellular Ca$^{2+}$ orchestrates many aspects of the cell-division process [49], the model outlined above could lead plausibly to occasional chromosome nondisjunction and consequences of this sort [50].

In summary, there are very good reasons to believe that weak ELF fields can and do have significant biological effects at the cell level, and the process of magnetite biomineralization provides at least one viable mechanism through which such things can happen. The credibility of weak ELF magnetic effects on living systems must therefore stand or fall mainly on the merits and reproducibility of the biological or epidemiological experiments which suggest them, rather than on dogma about physical implausibility.

Supported in part by NIH Grant No. GM-41635 and the Electric Power Research Institute (EPRI) Contract No. RP2965-8. I thank S. J. Kirschvink, J. Diaz-Ricci, C. Rafferty, and J. J. Hopfield.

[1] R. K. Adair, Phys. Rev. A. **43**, 1039 (1991).

[2] *Magnetite Biomineralization and Magnetoreception in Organisms: A New Biomagnetism,* edited by J. L. Kirschvink, D. S. Jones, and B. J. MacFadden (Plenum, New York, 1985), p. 682.

[3] H. A. Lowenstam, Geol. Soc. Am. Bull. **73**, 435 (1962).

[4] K. M. Towe and H. A. Lowenstam, J. Ultrastructur. Res. **17**, 1 (1967).

[5] M. H. Nesson and H. A. Lowenstam, in *Magnetite Biomineralization and Magnetoreception in Organisms: A New Biomagnetism* (Ref. 2), pp. 333–363.

[6] J. L. Kirschvink and H. A. Lowenstam, Earth Planet. Sci. Lett. **44**, 193 (1979).

[7] R. P. Blakemore, D. Mareta, and R. S. Wolfe, J. Bacteriol. **140**, 720 (1979).

[8] Y. A. Gorby, T. J. Beveridge, and R. P. Blakemore, J. Bacteriol. **170**, 834 (1988).

[9] R. B. Frankel, and R. P. Blakemore, J. Magn. Magn. Mater. **15-18**, 1562 (1980).

[10] H. Vali and J. L. Kirschvink, in *Iron Biomineralization,* edited by R. P. Frankel and R. P. Blakemore (Plenum, New York, 1990), pp. 97–115.

[11] F. F. Torres de Araujo, M. A. Pires, R. B. Frankel, and C. E. M. Bicudo, Biophys. J. **50**, 375 (1985).

[12] M. Fuller, W. S. Goree, and W. L. Goodman, in *Magnetite Biomineralization and Magnetoreception in Organisms: A New Biomagnetism* (Ref. 2), pp. 103–151.

[13] J. L. Gould, J. L. Kirschvink, and K. S. Deffeyes, Science **202**, 1026 (1978).

[14] C. Walcott, J. L. Gould, and J. L. Kirschvink, Science **184**, 180 (1979).

[15] M. M. Walker, T. P. Quinn, J. L. Kirschvink, and T. Groot, J. Exp. Biol. **140**, 51 (1988).

[16] S. Mann, N. H. C. Sparks, M. M. Walker, and J. L. Kirschvink, J. Exp. Biol. **140**, 35 (1988).

[17] J. L. Kirschvink, A. Kirschvink, and B. Woodford, Proc. Intl. IEEE Conf. on Eng. Medicine Biol. **12**, 1089 (1990).

[18] J. L. Kirschvink, F. Tabrah, and S. Batkin, J. Exp. Biol. **101**, 321 (1982).

[19] W. F. Towne and J. L. Gould, in *Magnetite Biomineralization and Magnetoreception in Organisms: A New Biomagnetism* (Ref. 2), pp. 385–406.

[20] M. Lindauer and H. Martin, in *Animal Orientation and Navigation,* edited by S. R. Galler, K. Schmidt-Koenig, G. J. Jacobs, and R. E. Belleville (NASA, U.S. Government Printing Office, Washington, D.C., 1972) pp. 559–567.

[21] H. Martin and M. Lindauer, J. Comp. Physiol. **122**, 145 (1977).

[22] J. L. Gould, J. L. Kirschvink, K. S. Deffeyes, and M. L. Brines, J. Exp. Biol. **86**, 1 (1980).

[23] J. L. Kirschvink, *BioSystems* **14**, 193 (1981).

[24] M. M. Walker and M. E. Bitterman, J. Comp. Phys. A **157**, 67 (1985).

[25] M. M. Walker and M. E. Bitterman, J. Exp. Biol. **145**, 489 (1989).

[26] M. M. Walker and M. E. Bitterman, J. Exp. Biol. **141**, 447 (1989).

[27] M. M. Walker, D. L. Baird, and M. E. Bitterman, J. Comp. Psychol. **103**, 62 (1989).

[28] J. L. Kirschvink and A. Kobayashi-Kirschvink, Amer. Zool. **31**, 169 (1991).

[29] J. L. Kirschvink, T. Kuwajima, S. Ueno, S. J. Kirschvink, J. C. Diaz-Ricci, A. Morales, S. Barwig, and K. Quinn, J. Gen. Physiol., Supplement on Sensory Transduction, pp. 225–240 (1992).

[30] J. L. Kirschvink and J. L. Gould, Biosystems **13**, 181 (1981).

[31] E. D. Yorke, J. Theor. Biol. **89**, 533 (1981).

[32] J. L. Kirschvink and M. M. Walker, in *Magnetite Biomineralization and Magnetoreception* in Organisms: A New Biomagnetism (Ref. 2), pp. 385–406.

[33] A. J. Kalmijn and R. P. Blakemore, in *Animal Migration, Navigation and Homing,* edited by K. Schmidt-Koenig and W. T. Keeton (Springer-Verlag, Berlin, 1978), pp. 354–355.

[34] J. C. Diaz-Ricci, B. J. Woodford, J. L. Kirschvink, and M. R. Hoffman, Appl. Environ. Microbiol. **57**, 3248 (1991).

[35] N. Wertheimer and E. Leeper, Ann. NY Acad. Sci. **502**, 43 (1987).

[36] D. A. Savitz, E. M. John, and R. C. Kleckner, Am. J. Epidem. **131**, 763 (1988).

[37] S. J. London, D. C. Thomas, J. D. Bowman, E. Sobel, and J. M. Peters, *Am. J. Epidemiol.* **134**, 923 (1991).

[38] M. Sokabe, F. Sachs, and A. Jing, Biophys. J. **59**, 722 (1991).

[39] F. Sachs, Mol. Cell. Biochem. **104**, 57 (1991).

[40] W. Denk and W. W. Webb, Phys. Rev. Lett. **63**, 207 (1989).

[41] J. Howard and A. J. Hudspeth, Neuron **1**, 189 (1988).

[42] M. E. Evans and M. W. McElhinny, J. Geomag. Geoelect. **21**, 757 (1969).

[43] J. L. Kirschvink, Bioelectromagn. **10**, 239 (1989).

[44] E. M. Purcell, Am. J. Phys. **45**, 3 (1977).

[45] A. D. Keith and W. Snipes, Science **183**, 666 (1974).

[46] W. J. Moody and M. M. Bosma, J. Membrane Biol. **107**, 179 (1989).

[47] R. M. Hochmuth and R. E. Waugh, Ann. Rev. Physiol. **49**, 209 (1987).

[48] R. Pool, Science **249**, 1096 (1990).

[49] R. B. Silver. Ann. NY Acad. Sci. **582**, 207 (1990).

[50] E. Solomon, J. Borrow, and A. D. Goddard, Science **254**, 1153 (1991).

[51] M. Lindauer and H. Martin, Z. Vgl. Physiol. **60**, 219 (1968).

[52] D. Hepworth, R. S. Pickard, and K. J. Overshott, J. Apic. Res. **19**, 179 (1980).

[53] K. Kilbert, J. Comp. Physiol. **132**, 11 (1979).

[54] M. L. Brines, Ph.D. thesis, Rockefeller University, 1978.

[55] D. De Jong, J. Comp. Phys. **147**, 495 (1982).

[56] H. Martin and M. Lindauer, Fortschr. Zool. **21**, 211 (1973).

[57] M. Lindauer, Proc. Int. Congr. Entomol. **15**, 450 (1977).

[58] J. L. Gould, Am. Scientist **68**, 256 (1980).

Reprinted with permission from *Phys. Rev. A* **46**, 2185-2187 (1992). Copyright 1992 by the American Physical Society.

PHYSICAL REVIEW A                    VOLUME 46, NUMBER 4                    15 AUGUST 1992

# Reply to "Comment on 'Constraints on biological effects of weak extremely-low-frequency electromagnetic fields'"

Robert K. Adair

*Department of Physics, Yale University, P.O. Box 6666, New Haven, Connecticut 06511*

(Received 6 March 1992)

Kirschvink [preceding Comment, Phys. Rev. A **46**, 2178 (1992)] objects to my conclusions [Phys. Rev. A **43**, 1039 (1991)] that weak extremely-low-frequency (ELF) electromagnetic fields cannot affect biology on the cell level. He argues that I did not properly consider the interaction of such fields with magnetite ($Fe_3O_4$) grains in cells and that such interactions can induce biological effects. However, his model, designed as a proof of principle that the interaction of weak 60-Hz ELF fields with magnetite domains in a cell can affect cell biology, requires, by his account, a magnetic field of 0.14 mT (1400 mG) to operate, while my paper purported to demonstrate only that fields smaller than 0.05 mT (500 mG) must be ineffective. I then discuss ELF interactions with magnetite generally and show that the failure of Kirschvink's model to respond to weak fields must be general and that no plausible interaction with biological magnetite of 60-Hz magnetic fields with a strength less than 0.05 mT can affect biology on the cell level.

PACS number(s): 87.50.Eg, 87.22.Bt

Kirschvink [1] argues that I have left a "gaping hole" in my didactic paper [2], titled "*Constraints on biological effects of weak extremely low-frequency (ELF) electromagnetic fields*" inasmuch as he considers my discussion of the interaction of such fields with biologically produced magnetite ($Fe_3O_4$) inadequate. In fact there are no factual errors of commission in the two paragraphs that I devote to that subject and I hold that there are no substantive errors of omission—or gaping holes. My paper, generally, addressed the interaction of the weak 60-Hz fields of our environment with human cells and concluded that such interactions are much too weak to have biological consequences. I defined *weak magnetic fields* in my paper as "field strengths no greater than 50 $\mu$T (or 0.5 G), the strength of the earth's field." Kirschvink's arguments that the interaction of three-times larger fields (of 0.14 mT) with biological magnetite may affect biology at the cell level are then not in contradiction to my findings.

I first diverge from consideration of Kirschvink's model calculations, which I consider the heart of his *Comment,* to respond to some of his specific criticisms. In the second paragraph of his *Comment* he says, "Adair's discussion implies that only the magnetotactic bacteria are able to precipitate $\cdots$ magnetite." Such an implication can only follow from a misreading of my two paragraphs devoted to this subject. The material in those paragraphs was largely derived from my study of the review by Frankel [3] (Ref. [8] in my paper) which addressed the evidence for magnetite in other life forms at length.

Then, Kirschvink views, as "inaccurate," my statement, written in a context which refers to the weak 60-Hz fields in the environment; "After 20 years of experimentation, no significant effect of weak ELF fields at the cell level has been firmly established." He continues: "Thus, a convincing demonstration of behavioral sensitivity to weak magnetic fields in *any* animal is enough to falsify Adair's assertion" and goes on to refer to the mag-netically influenced behavior of the honeybee which he says is well established and, hence, "falsifies" my statement. In my paper, I discuss known effects on the behavior of magnetotactic bacteria induced by moderately weak constant magnetic fields and refer to the effect of very weak constant electric fields on the behavior of sharks. I chose to discuss, as an example, the behavior of magnetotactic bacteria instead of honeybees for reasons that Kirschvink himself states clearly in another paper [4], "many responses $\cdots$ like honeybee waggle dances $\cdots$ have [not] yet approached the level of clarity and simplicity displayed in experiments with the magnetotactic bacteria, which is the best example of geomagnetic sensitivity in any living organism."

I find Kirschvink's section, "*Biophysical Model of Magnetite and ELF Magnetic Fields*" more to the point. Here he proposes a specific model (his Fig. 1) of biological effects of the interactions of ELF fields with cellular magnetite in an attempt to forge a proof-of-principle of his thesis that "ELF magnetic fields at the cellular or subcellular level might lead to significant effects." But his model, designed such that the interaction of an ELF field on a magnetosome will open an otherwise closed ion channel in a cell membrane, requires moderately strong fields. As he comments, "At the powerline frequency of 60 Hz, the critical ELF field for opening the channel is 0.14 Mt (1.4 G)." But I have never claimed to *prove* that fields of this magnitude cannot induce biological effects; 0.14 mT is larger by about a factor of 3 than the canonical field of 0.05 mT that I used in my paper as a representative maximum for my ineffectivity arguments and is typically 100 times larger than environmental fields that have concerned some.

Moreover, I note that Kirschvink has used some assumptions in his model that raise doubts as to whether even 0.14-mT fields can affect biology and suggests that the design of a more sensitive model will be difficult indeed. In particular, he uses as a gate opener a very large magnetosome with a very large magnetic moment of $2 \times 10^{-15}$ A m$^2$. This is about a factor of 10 greater than that for the largest stable magnetite single domain as calculated by Butler and Bannerjee [5]. Also, the energy difference between the open and closed-gate configuration is only about $1.85kT$. Hence, in the absence of an external ELF, one might expect that the gate would be open about $e^{-1.85}/(1+e^{-1.85}) \approx 13\%$ of the time, which is comparable to the open time of about 25% that might be expected from the action of the ELF field on the model system with no noise.

Since the energy of displacement varies as the square of the magnitude of the external ELF field in Kirschvink's model, the mean energy will be equal to about $0.13kT$ for an ELF field equal to the earth's field of 0.5 mT. For a field of 10 $\mu$T (or 100 mG), which is near the maximum, one ordinarily finds in the environment [6] that the interaction energy is about $0.005kT$. Hence, his model supports the thesis that thermal noise can be expected to overwhelm the interactions of the weak fields of the environment with any magnetite to be found in human cells.

Therefore, the results of Kirschvink's calculations contradict his remark to the effect that his model shows that, "in direct contradiction to the statements of Adair, it may be possible for weak, ELF magnetic fields to produce biological effects at the cellular level through a nonsensory process." Indeed, in light of differences greater than 1000 between the interaction energies required for this model and the interaction energies from the environmental fields of about 5 $\mu$T—or less—that have been of concern, his statements implying that he has shown that weak environmental fields "could lead plausibly to $\cdots$ chromosome nondisjunction and consequences of this sort" are misleading.

By considerations that include Kirschvink's model as a special case, I show generally that no plausible interaction of a weak 60-Hz magnetic field with magnetite in cells or other small structures can be expected to have biological consequences. I proceed in the manner of Kirschvink by considering the kinetic and potential energies induced in a magnetite structure by the interaction of a perturbing field where the $kT$ noise is neglected. If those energies are very much smaller than $kT$, I conclude that the thermal noise will overwhelm the signal and the interaction cannot be expected to have any biological effect. This procedure has the advantage of simplicity of exposition and should be adequate to set lower limits on the magnitude of fields that might affect biology through interaction with biological magnetite.

So as to consider a maximum effect, I assume that the unbound magnetite structure is aligned by the earth's field and is subject to a 60-Hz field of amplitude $B_{ELF}$ directed at right angles with respect to the earth's field. That field will induce an alternating torque on the magnetosome structure that will cause it to oscillate. If the alternating field is to generate biologically significant signals, the field must perturb the magnetite system to an extent greater than the natural perturbations from thermal fluctuations. In particular, either the kinetic or potential energies generated by the action of the imposed

field must be as large as $kT$.

The torque on a free magnetic element with a magnetic moment $\mu$ will be made up of a resistive torque, $T_r = -C\dot{\theta}$, a binding torque, $T_b = -B_{earth}\mu\theta$, and a driving torque, $T_d = B_{ELF}\mu \cos\omega t$, where $\theta$ is the angle of rotation and $\omega = \dot{\theta} = 377$ radians per second. (I use Kirschvink's notation.) The equation of motion, valid for small vibrations, takes the form

$$I\ddot{\theta} = -C\dot{\theta} - B_{earth}\mu\theta + B_{ELF}\mu \cos\omega t , \qquad (1)$$

where $I$ is the moment of inertia of the element. Writing $\theta(t) = \theta_0\cos(\omega t + \phi)$, for $\theta_0 < 20°$, which will generally hold for the small fields $B_{ELF}$ we are considering,

$$\theta_0^2 = \frac{(B_{ELF}\mu)^2}{(B_{earth}\mu - I\omega^2)^2 + C^2\omega^2} . \qquad (2)$$

This equation is fundamentally the same as Kirschvink's Eq. (3) though I use a small angle approximation and retain the inertial effect of $I$.

Neglecting the inertial effects, which is a good approximation for the situations considered here, Eq. (2) can be written

$$\theta_0^2 = \left[\frac{B_{ELF}}{B_{earth}}\right]^2 \frac{1}{1+(\omega\tau)^2} ,$$

where

$$\tau = \frac{C}{B_{earth}\mu} \qquad (3)$$

is a relevant time constant. If the time constant is long compared to $\frac{1}{60}$th of a second, the response of the magnetite system to the perturbing field will be severely damped.

The mean kinetic energy $W_T$ and mean potential energy $W_V$ can be written as

$$W_T = \frac{I\omega^2\theta_0^2}{4} ,$$

and

$$W_V = \frac{B_{earth}\mu\theta_0^2}{4} . \qquad (4)$$

It is important to couch conclusions in term of some particular simple structure in order to provide insights into general behaviors. Hence, I state energies in units of $kT$ and magnetic moments $\mu$ in terms of the magnetic energies $B_{earth}\mu$, also in units of $kT$. For moments of inertia and viscous effects I use a sphere of radius $r$ as a surrogate for more generally shaped bodies of a given volume. I take the density of the nonmagnetite material of the sphere as that of water and, for purposes of estimating the moment of inertia, assume the heavy magnetite is spread evenly through the sphere. The resistive torque is taken as $C = 6\eta v$, where $v$ is the volume of the body and $\eta$ the viscosity. With this evaluation of $C$, the characteristic time constant $\tau$ can be written as $\tau = (6\eta v)/(B_{earth}\mu)$.

Here, I discuss two different models of the effects of 60-Hz magnetic fields on magnetite elements. Following

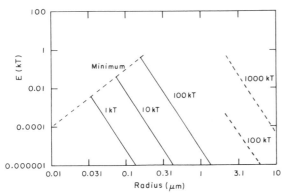

FIG. 1. The potential energy, measured in units of $kT$, induced by the interaction of 60 Hz, 50 $\mu$T, fields with magnetite elements that might be found in cells. The solid lines show the energies as a function of radius for spherical magnetic elements that are assumed to act internal to the cell where the viscosity of the cytoplasm is taken as $\eta \approx 0.1$ N s/m$^2$. Each line presents the values of the potential energy for elements with different magnetic moments expressed as $B_{earth}\mu$. The dashed lines are meant to describe the rotations of whole spherical cells which hold magnetite elements rigidly within the cell. Here the viscosity is assumed to be that of water, $\eta = 0.001$ N s/m$^2$. The line labeled minimum defines the limiting size when the magnetite occupies the whole volume.

Kirschvink [1], I consider the motion of single-domain magnetosomes within the cell and assume that such structures will generally be smaller than $r = 0.5$ $\mu$m and will have a magnetic moment $\mu$ such that $B_{earth}\mu < 50kT$. For this environment , I take the effective viscosity as that of cytoplasm taken [1,7] as $\eta = 0.1$ N s/m$^2$. Then I use Eqs. (2) and (4) to calculate the energies induced by perturbative 60-Hz magnetic fields, $B_{ELF}$. The solid lines of Fig. 1 show the variation of potential energy as a function of $r$ for different magnetic moments $\mu$, expressed in terms of energies $B_{earth}\mu$ in units of $kT$, and for a perturbing field $B_{ELF} = 50$ $\mu$T $= B_{earth}$, which is the limiting value used in my paper [2]. The line labeled "minimum" shows the limit of sizes reached when the structure is wholly Fe$_3$O$_4$. The kinetic energies are much smaller and are not plotted.

The small values for the induced energies can be under-stood in terms of the large magnitudes of the time constants $\tau$. For example, for a magnetite system in the interior of the cell with a radius of 0.5 $\mu$m carrying a large magnetic moment $\mu$ such that $B_{earth}\mu = 25kT$, the time constant, calculated from Eq. (4), will be 3 s, and $(\omega\tau)^2 = 1.33 \times 10^6$.

Although we plot the calculated energies for single-domain elements with magnetic moments as large as $B_{earth}\mu \rightarrow 100kT$, we note that the magnetostatic energy for single-domain systems such that $B_{earth}\mu > 3kT$ is such as to favor the division of such large magnetite domains into several nonaligned domains, thus sharply reducing the magnetic moment of the magnetosome.

In some cases, strings of magnetosomes, aligned magnetically, are rigidly held in cells and the field can then cause the whole cell to rotate. These strings of separated individual domains are not subject to the magnetostatic energy factors that constrain the size of single domains hence large total magnetic moments $\mu$ such that $B_{earth}\mu \approx 1000kT$ may occur. For the rotation of these cells, I assume that the viscosity of the cell medium may be as small as that of water and take $\eta = 0.001$ N/m$^2$ Generally, the cell will be of the size $r > 5$ $\mu$m. For such a cell, with $r = 5$ $\mu$m and $B_{earth}\mu = 1000kT$, rotating in a medium with the viscosity of water, $\tau \approx 0.75$ s. The dashed lines show the potential energies generated by 60 Hz, 50 $\mu$T, fields in the excursions of these cells. Again, the kinetic energies are insignificant.

From the plots of Fig. 1, the induced energies are seen to be smaller —and excepting the implausible very large single-domain elements presumed to act within the cell, very much smaller— than $kT$. Hence, I conclude that 60-Hz magnetic fields weaker than 50 $\mu$T cannot generate significant biological effects through action on magnetite. However, since the induced energies vary as $B_{ELF}^2$, these simple arguments do not preclude biological effects for 60-Hz fields appreciably larger than the earth's field, $B_{earth} = 50$ $\mu$T. Conversely, energies induced by maximal long-time environmental fields of 5 $\mu$T are 100 times smaller.

Hence, these calculations, including Kirschvink's results, support my statement, quoted in his *Comment*, that, "There are very good reasons to believe that weak ELF fields can have no significant effect at the cell level—and no strong reason to believe otherwise."

[1] J. L. Kirschvink, preceding paper, Phys. Rev. **46**, 2178 (1992).
[2] R. K. Adair, Phys. Rev. A **43**, 1039 (1991).
[3] R. B. Frankel, in *CRC Handbook of the Biological Effects of Electromagnetic Fields*, edited by C. Polk and E. Postow (Chemical Rubber Co., Boca Raton, FL, 1986).
[4] J. L. Kirschvink and A. Kobayashi-Kirschvink, Am. Zool. **31**, 169 (1991).
[5] R. F. Butler and S. K. Banerjee, J. Geophys. Res. **80**, 4049 (1975).
[6] The magnetic-field strengths in the environment from common sources are discussed—with references—in I. Nair, M. G. Morgan, and H. K. Florig, U.S. Congress, Office of Technology Assessment Report No. OTA-BP-E53, 1989 (unpublished). Typical maximum fields listed in Table 2-2 are from: house wiring,—10 mG; ground currents, 5 mG; distribution lines, 10 mG. It is these—largely unavoidable— fields that have been linked by the OTA, in this report, and by others, to health effects. The electric motors in appliances generate fields as great as 25 G very near the stator magnets but these fields fall off sharply with distance to levels less than 25 mG at 1 m. Hence, exposure to such fields are characteristically limited in spatial extent as well as duration and are generally avoidable.
[7] W. J. Moody and M. M. Bosma, J. Membrane Biol. **107**, 179 (1989).

Reprinted by permission from *Proc. Nat. Acad. Sci.* **91**, 9422-9425 (1995). Copyright 1995 by the National Academy of Sciences, U.S.A.

*Proc. Natl. Acad. Sci. USA*
Vol. 91, pp. 9422–9425, September 1994
Biophysics

# Biological responses to weak 60-Hz electric and magnetic fields must vary as the square of the field strength

ROBERT K. ADAIR

Department of Physics, Yale University, New Haven, CT 06511

*Contributed by Robert K. Adair, June 6, 1994*

**ABSTRACT**     Under quite general conditions, the biological response $j(G)$ to a very weak continuous 60-Hz electric or magnetic field $G$ is shown to be proportional to the square of the field strength. This conclusion follows from the continuity of the function $j(G)$ and the first three derivatives of $j(G)$ with respect to $G$ over the amplitude of $G$. That continuity is ensured in nominally discontinuous systems by the presence of thermal noise. I argue the validity of the conjecture that all plausible biological responses to weak 60-Hz fields vary with the square of the field strength. A specific model is used to illustrate characteristic dependencies of biological responses to exposure times.

## The Measure of Exposure

The interpretation of some classes of exploratory experiments that address the question of biological effects of weak fields depends on the variable chosen to define those fields. This is especially true of epidemiological studies of health effects of weak 60-Hz magnetic fields. Here, the at-risk groups and control groups have often been classified in terms of the mean fields to which they have been subjected (1–3). Also, in the analysis of some data (1), weight has been placed on what has been purported to be evidence of a dose–response variation that is roughly linear in the field strength. If the salient variable were the energy density, proportional to the square of the field, both the classification of subjects and the dose–response variation would be changed considerably. Indeed, the proper design of such a study may depend critically on the variable chosen to describe the exposure.

The choice of field strength as the proper variable to parameterize possible biological effects of weak 60-Hz electromagnetic fields seems to have been made by default with no guidance from biophysical models. I argue here that if there are any biological effects of such fields, they should be expected to be proportional to the square of the field strength—which is proportional to the energy density of the field. The bases for the argument are fundamentally simple. For any biological response that varies sufficiently smoothly with the field, that response can be expressed as the sum of a term that is linear and a term that is quadratic with the field for a sufficiently small field. The mean response over time to the linear term must be 0—the effect of the positive excursions will be canceled by the negative excursions—and the time-average response will then vary with the square of the field where there is no cancellation. I then show that thermal noise smooths responses that would otherwise vary discontinuously with field strength.

## Taylor's Theorem

We consider that we can describe the biological response to a weak electric or magnetic field $G$ by a functional relationship $j(G)$, where $dj/dG = j_G$, $d^2j/dG^2 = j_{GG}$, and $d^3j/dG^3 = j_{GGG}$ are continuous in a small region, $a < G < b$. Then, for any value of $G$ in that region we can express $j(G)$ by Taylor's formula

$$j(G) = j(a) + j_G(a)g\left(\frac{\Delta G}{g}\right)$$
$$+ \frac{1}{2}j_{GG}(a)g^2\left(\frac{\Delta G}{g}\right)^2 + \frac{1}{6}j_{GGG}(\xi)g^3\left(\frac{\Delta G}{g}\right)^3, \qquad [1]$$

where $\Delta G = G - G(a)$, $g$ is a natural scale factor determined by physical conditions, with the dimensions of the field $G$ and $\xi(G)$, where $a < \xi(G) < b$ is a value of the field, in the region $a - b$, which depends on the imposed field $G$.

If the last term, the Lagrangian remainder, is sufficiently small, $j(G)$ can be expressed as a second-degree polynomial in $(\Delta G/g)$. If $j_{GGG}$ is bounded, that remainder must be sufficiently small over an appropriately small interval $a - b$.

The interjection of the scale field $g$ is artificial. The response $j(G)$ is independent of the value chosen for $g$. But the utility of any application will depend on the range of validity of the equation and the explicit introduction of that scale has a heuristic value. With that insertion the coefficients $j_{nG}g^n$ have the same dimensions as $j(G)$ and, with the proper choice of $g$, can be expected to be of the same magnitude. Also, the expansion variable, $G/g$, is dimensionless and $g$, if properly chosen, is an explicit measure of the range of convergence of the equation.

With the Lagrangian remainder set to 0, Eq. **1** can be rewritten in terms of an expansion about an interior point $G'$, $a < G' < b$, of the interval $a - b$. The expansion factor will then be $G - G'$. Since we will usually be interested in situations such that $G' = 0$, and $j(0) = 0$, we simplify the equations by making those choices and

$$j(G) = j_G g\left(\frac{G}{g}\right) + \frac{1}{2}j_{GG}g^2\left(\frac{G}{g}\right)^2, \qquad [2]$$

where $j_G$ and $j_{GG}$ are evaluated at $G = 0$. Then, writing $G = G_0\cos\omega t$, where, typically, $\omega = 2\pi \times 60$ and taking the time average

$$\overline{j(G)} = \frac{1}{4}j_{GG}g^2\left(\frac{G_0}{g}\right)^2, \qquad [3]$$

and the response is proportional to the square of the field strength as we have postulated.

The suppression of the first term upon averaging over time follows from the oscillatory form of $G = G_0\cos\omega t$. If the same arguments were made using the field energy density, $W = \alpha G_0^2\cos^2\omega t$, where $\alpha$ is an appropriate constant, as the salient variable, the time-average biological response, $\overline{j(W)}$, to the field energy density, $W$, would be linear in $W$ and in $G_0^2$, consistent with Eq. 3.

The publication costs of this article were defrayed in part by page charge payment. This article must therefore be hereby marked "*advertisement*" in accordance with 18 U.S.C. §1734 solely to indicate this fact.

9422

Biophysics: Adair

*Proc. Natl. Acad. Sci. USA* 91 (1994)     9423

One might ask if a secondary biological response $k(j)$ to the primary response $j(G)$ might not be nonlinear in $j$—perhaps $k(j) \propto \sqrt{j}$ and the overall linearity with $G$ would be returned. But the general argument holds for $k(G)$ also, and $\overline{k(G)}$ must vary quadratically with $G$ independent of the complexity of the biology for sufficiently small values of $G$. In detail, if $\overline{j(G)}$ is small, $\bar{k} \propto \bar{j}$.

The time-average operation implies that we are considering responses $j$ that are limited by natural time constants longer than 1/60th of a second. For many plausible mechanisms, biological effects on whole organisms will be proportional to the integral of the square of the field strength over time.

## Time Rates of Change

For completeness, we address biological effects that may depend on both the field and the rate of change of the field. Since changing magnetic fields induce electric fields through Faraday's law, and changing electric fields induce magnetic fields through Ampere's law, such completeness is formally justified, although at frequencies as low as 60 Hz the electric and magnetic fields can generally be considered separately.

However, we can describe changing fields more completely by a generalization of Eq. 2

$$j(G, \dot{G}, \ddot{G}, \cdots) = j_G g \left( \frac{G}{g} \right) + j_{\dot{G}} \dot{g} \left( \frac{\dot{G}}{\dot{g}} \right) + j_{G\dot{G}} g \dot{g} \left( \frac{G}{g} \right) \left( \frac{\dot{G}}{\dot{g}} \right)$$
$$+ j_{GG} g^2 \left( \frac{G}{g} \right)^2 + j_{\dot{G}\dot{G}} \dot{g}^2 \left( \frac{\dot{G}}{\dot{g}} \right)^2 + \cdots, \quad \textbf{[4]}$$

where $j_{G\dot{G}} = \partial^2 j / \partial G \partial \dot{G}$, etc., and we have introduced an additional scale factor $\dot{g}$.

Taking, again, $G = G_0 \cos \omega t$, upon taking a time average, the first three terms at the right of Eq. 4 drop out and both of the remaining terms vary with the square of the field strength $G$; hence, the results of the previous section are preserved.

The higher time derivatives of $G$ vary with time as $G$ or $\dot{G}$; hence, any dependence of the response $j$ on those factors can be subsumed into the functional dependencies of $G$ and do not affect matters.

## Continuity of $j(G)$

Eq. 1 is useful only if the function $j$ and its derivatives are continuous over the interval $a - b$ and if that interval is sufficiently large. We first address the continuity issue.

**Electric Fields.** There are plausible models of the biological response, $j(G)$, to the field $G$ that are not mathematically well behaved in the sense required for the validity of Eq. 1. For example, we consider a biological response to the electric field $j(E)$ such that

$$\text{for } E < E', j(E) = 0 \quad \text{and for} \quad E > E', j(E) = j_0, \quad \textbf{[5]}$$

where $j_0$ is a constant. Physically, this could be a representation of a molecular current, $j(E)$, through a gate in the cell membrane where $E$ is the electric field strength in the tissue near the cell. For fields less than $E'$, the gate is closed and no current flows; for fields greater than $E'$, the gate is open and a current, $j_0$, passes through the gate; the current $j_0(E)$ is discontinuous at $E = E'$. Models of such an opening of a gate in the membrane through a configuration change in a gate protein in the membrane induced by an electric field in the membrane have been discussed (4). Such a change will generally take place in a time, $\tau_{op}$, that is very short compared to characteristic 60-Hz times; that is, $\tau_{op} \ll 1/\omega$. An open gate model of the interaction of magnetic fields has also been proposed (5).

But the simple model can operate as suggested in Eq. 5 only at absolute zero. We show that thermal noise will modify the form of $j(E)$, smoothing out the discontinuity.

We begin by assuming simply that there are two states of the gate, closed ($\psi_{cl}$) and open ($\psi_{op}$), where an energy, $w_{op}$, is required to open the gate in the absence of the field $E$. We express the probability of the gate being closed as $P_{cl}$ and the probability of the gate being open as $P_{op}$ from the partition as

$$P_{cl} = \frac{1}{1 + e^{-w/kT}} \quad \text{and} \quad P_{op} = \frac{e^{-w/kT}}{1 + e^{-w/kT}}, \quad \textbf{[6]}$$

where $w = w_{op} - dw$, where $dw$ is the energy supplied by the field, and $w$ is the energy difference between the open and closed states of the gate. We write $dw = ED$, where $D$ has the dimensions of an electric dipole moment.

In this formulation, the current that passes through the gate, $j_{in}$, will be proportional to the probability that the gate is open. However, at equilibrium, with $E = 0$ and $w = w_{op}$, although there will be some probability that the gate is open through thermodynamic fluctuations, the net current must still be 0. Hence, there must be a countercurrent $j_{out}$ that cancels $j_{in}$ at 0 field;

$$j_{in} = j_0 \frac{e^{-w/kT}}{1 + e^{-w/kT}} \quad \text{and} \quad j_{out} = j_{in} \overset{w = w_{op}}{=} j_0 \frac{e^{-w_{op}/kT}}{1 + e^{-w_{op}/kT}}. \quad \textbf{[7]}$$

If there is a change in the gate energy $dw = w_{op} - w = ED$ generated by the field, the net current $j(E) = j_{in} - j_{out}$ that will flow will be a continuous function of $dw$ even as the probability of the gate being open will be a continuous function of $dw$.

It is interesting to carry this reasoning further by applying it to a relatively realistic model. We take $dw = ED$, where $D = qr_d$ is a characteristic transition dipole moment of a gate membrane protein written here as the product of a characteristic charge, $q < 10e$, and a characteristic length, $r_d$. The effective field in the membrane $E_{mem} \approx E r_{cell}/d_{mem}$, where $r_{cell}$ is the cell radius, $d_{mem}$ is the membrane thickness, and $E$ is the electric field in the tissue about the cell. Hence, $dw/kT = E/g$, where $g = (kT/qr_{cell}) \times (d_{mem}/r_d)$ and $d_{mem}/r_d \approx 1$.

With some algebraic manipulation for $E \ll g$ (or $dw \ll kT$) and $w_{op} \gg kT$, the net current $j(E)$ is

$$j(E) = j_{in} - j_{out} = j_d(e^{E/g} - 1)$$

where

$$j_d = j_0 \frac{e^{-w_{op}/kT}}{1 + e^{-w_{op}/kT}}, \quad \textbf{[8]}$$

and the discontinuity has been removed and $j(E)$ is analytic in $E$.

For smaller values of $w_{op}$, the functional relation $j(E)$ is more complicated but is still analytic:

$$j(E) = j_d \left[ \alpha \frac{E}{G} + \beta \frac{1}{2} \left( \frac{E}{g} \right)^2 + \cdots \right], \quad \textbf{[9]}$$

where $A = \exp(-w_{op}/kT)$ and $\alpha = 1 - A/(1 + A)$ and $\beta = 1 - 3A/(1 + A) + 2A^2/(1 + A)^2$.

In the absence of noise—e.g., $T = 0 - j_d = 0$—no current will flow; the transition is driven by noise in a manner that is similar to processes described (see *Resonance Activation* and *Stochastic Resonance* in ref. 6).

Since only $E$ enters Eq. 9, the functional dependence of $j(E)$ on $E$ is independent of the energy spacing of the gates, $w_{op}$, or the field, $E_{op} = w_{op}/D$, necessary to open the states. Hence, with no noise, or $T = 0$, there can be discontinuities in $j(E)$ at many points, $E_i$, physically representing other gates, with different gate-opening energies, $w_i$, which may allow either positive or negative flows, $j_i'$, to pass when open. Then, with the noise turned on, the current will be

$$j = \sum_i j_{di} \left[ \alpha_i \frac{E}{g} + \beta_i \frac{1}{2} \left( \frac{E}{g} \right)^2 + \cdots \right]. \quad [10]$$

Then, writing $E = E_0 \cos \omega t$ for a 60-Hz field and taking the time average, we have a net current

$$\overline{j(E)} = J_d \frac{1}{4} \left( \frac{E_0}{g} \right)^2, \quad [11]$$

where $J_d = \Sigma j_{di} \beta_i$.

**Magnetic Fields.** If a 60-Hz magnetic field, **B**, is to affect biology directly (i.e., not through the electric field induced through the Faraday effect), it must act through a torque applied to an organic element with an effective magnetic dipole moment, $\mu$. For molecular transitions, the interaction energy can be expressed as $dw = B\mu$, in parallel to the measure of interaction of the electric field $dw = ED$. Taking $g = kT/\mu$, discontinuities are again bridged for $B/g \ll 1$ and Eqs. **8–10** hold with the notational change from $E$ to $B$.

The magnetic moments of molecular elements, such as protein molecules, are small (7) and for plausible values of these moments, $B\mu \ll kT$ and $B/g \ll 1$ for $g = kT/\mu$ even for large magnetic fields. However, domains of ferrimagnetic magnetite ($Fe_3O_4$), in a form called magnetosomes, have been found in human tissues (8) and cells containing large numbers of these domains secured to the cell structure may have large magnetic moments, $\mu_m$. For such systems, the energy transfer, $dw$, is limited by the viscosity of the medium in which the elements rotate under the torque applied by the field. In general, $dw < B\mu_m \times (\tau_{60}/\tau)$, where $\tau$ is the time constant for rotation of the element and $\tau_{60} = 1/\omega$ is the characteristic 60-Hz time constant. For typical systems with volume $v$, $\tau = 6\eta v/\kappa$, where $\eta$ is the viscosity of the medium in which the element rotates and $\kappa$ is the binding force; for many systems, $\kappa \approx B_e \mu_m$, where $B_e$ is the magnetic field of the earth.

Then, for large systems, such as cells, containing secured magnetosomes, Eqs. **8–10** also hold taking $g = (kT/\mu_m) \times \omega\tau$.

**Expansion Scale Factors**

Aside from continuity, Eq. **1** is useful only if the interval $a - b$ is sufficiently large. The size of the interval depends on physical factors and can be estimated from the magnitude of the physically defined proper scale factors $g$, which ideally are chosen so that $g = |a - b|$, where $g$ is then the largest region over which Eq. **1** is valid. The best choice of $g$ will be made differently for electric and magnetic fields. Hence, we consider estimates of $g$ for the two fields separately.

**Electric Fields.** A natural value of the scale factor $g$ for biological effects of electric fields in the body acting on individual cells will be set by taking $g$ equal to the field that, multiplied by a characteristic length and a characteristic charge, would equal the characteristic thermal energy $kT$ (7). Hence, $g = kT/qr_{cell} \approx 25$ V/m, where $r_{cell} = 100$ $\mu$m is the radius of a large cell and $q = 10e$ is a large characteristic charge. It is possible that large aggregates of cells connected electrically through gap junctions may respond as an entity to electric fields (9). For such a system with a radius $R$, $g = kT/qR$ may be an appropriate scale factor. For $R = 1$ cm, $g = 250$ mV/m.

The magnetic fields in residential areas from power lines are typically less than $B_0 = 1$ $\mu$T (10 mG). Such 60-Hz magnetic fields induce electric fields in the body $E_0$ as large as 0.02 mV/m through the Faraday effect. Among appli-

ances, the electric fields from electric blankets of the order of 200 V/m may induce similar electric fields in the body. Since such fields are very small compared to $g = 250$ mV/m ($E_0/g < 10^{-4}$), we can expect that the representation of Eq. **3** will hold for such fields.

**Magnetic Fields.** If a 60-Hz magnetic field, **B**, affects biology through the torque applied through the field to an element with a magnetic moment, $\mu$, that torque will be **L** = (**B** × $\mu$) and the interaction energy will be $w = ($**B** × $\mu)$. Assuming an orientation that maximizes the energy, $w = B\mu$ where $B_0\mu\cos\omega t$.

Since the earth's field $B_e$ is $\approx 50$ $\mu$T, a much smaller 60-Hz magnetic field can be significant biologically only through its oscillatory character. The moments $\mu_a$ of atoms, molecules, and nuclei are small and for such elements, $g = kT/\mu_a > 0.2$ T.

However, ferrimagnetic magnetite ($Fe_3O_4$) domains have been found in human tissues. For plausible sets of domains bound to cells, such as have been seen in other organisms, the magnetic moments $\mu_m$ can be quite large and the natural scale $g = kT/\mu_m < 5 \times 10^{-2}$ $\mu$T can be very small. However, the rotary oscillation of elements carrying magnetite is constrained by dissipative effects so that the rotational energies are appreciably smaller than $B_e\mu$ for 60-Hz fields (5, 10–12). When the effects of viscosity are considered, the energy transfers will be less than $B\mu_m(\tau_{60}/\tau)$ and the scale field can be taken conservatively as $g = (kT/\mu_m)(\tau/\tau_{60})$. Here $\tau_{60} = 1/\omega$ and $\tau \approx 6\eta v/B_e\mu$, where $\eta$ is the viscosity of the medium in which the system rotates and $v$ is the volume of the element, taken as approximately a sphere. For a cell of radius 10 $\mu$m, in a medium of the viscosity of water, $\eta = 7 \times 10^{-4}$ N·s/m$^2$, $g \approx 0.06$ T (600 G), and Eq. **3** should be valid for fields of the magnitude of $B_0 = 1$ $\mu$T (10 mG).

Although quasi-free individual magnetosomes have not been observed in cells, we must consider that such systems may exist and affect cell biology. For typical single magnetosomes with magnetic moments, $\mu_m \approx 10^{-16}$ Am, $g = kT/\mu \approx 50$ $\mu$T (500 mG). While magnetosomes with larger moments have been observed, the energy transfers are further constrained by the large viscosity of the cellular cytoplasm (13, 14) so that the value of $g = 50$ $\mu$T can be retained.

**Variation of Response with Exposure Times**

We examine a specific, plausible model of the interaction of the field to gain general insights into the variation of biological responses to exposure times.

In particular, we assume that the imposition of a field $G(t) = G_0(t)\cos\omega t$ on an organism generates a net current, $j$, through the cell membrane of some specific molecular species or ion, which varies with the square of the field strength as expressed in Eq. **11**. Then, for times significantly greater than $1/\omega$,

$$j = j_0 G_0^2, \quad [12]$$

where $j_0$ is a proportionality constant.

The current, acting for time $t$, will change the equilibrium concentration $Q_0$ of the molecule or ion in the cell cytoplasm by an amount $dQ/Q_0 = \Delta \propto jt$. In the absence of the perturbing field, the system must be held at an equilibrium by homeostatic processes that counter random statistical drifts in the concentrations. We describe that equilibrium process for $\Delta \ll 1$ by a relation of the kind

$$\frac{d\Delta}{dt} = -\sum_{n=1} \frac{\Delta_n}{\tau_n} \approx -\frac{\Delta}{\tau}, \quad [13]$$

Biophysics: Adair

*Proc. Natl. Acad. Sci. USA 91 (1994)*    9425

where the $\tau_n$ are proportionality constants. Then, for small deviations from equilibrium, we might expect the concentration change to vary with time, over times $t \gg 1/\omega$ as,

$$\frac{d\Delta}{dt} = k\overline{G^2} - \frac{\Delta}{\tau},$$ [14]

where $\tau$ is the homeostatic relaxation time of the system and $k$ is a constant defined by the specific character of the system. For a constant signal $G_0$ and a time $t \gg \tau$, $\Delta = kG_0^2\tau/2$. For *in vitro* experiments that measure changes in the concentration of an ion of some other product, or a response that depends directly on such a change in concentration, upon the initiation of the field, the signal will vary as the square of the field strength and the time during which the signal was applied.

Through the change in the interior cell environment, the probability $P(\Delta)$ of a genetic insult that initiates a malignancy may be changed correspondingly. The biological signal may be the cumulative probability of the initiation of the malignancy, which can be expected to vary as

$$P = \int P_0(t)\Delta(G_0, t)dt,$$ [15]

where $P_0(t)$ is a proportionality factor that may vary slowly with time even as other biological parameters of the organism can be expected to change in time.

With this model, if $G_0(t)$ is generally constant for periods $\delta t > \tau$, the probability of the generation of a malignancy can be expected to vary as

$$P = \int P_0'(t)G_0(t)^2 dt \approx \overline{P_0'(t)}\int G_0^2(t)dt,$$ [16]

where $\overline{P_0'(t)}$ is an average value of the proportionality constant. If $G_0(t)$ changes often in times $\delta t \le \tau$, $P$ will generally be smaller than the value expressed by Eq. 16.

The analysis of epidemiological data that considers effects of fields over long periods of time may then be complicated by variations of biological factors with time that may modify any promotions initiated by the fields as well as by latencies in detection. However, any effects can still be expected to be proportional to $G_0^2$.

## Summary

The arguments presented here show that for sufficiently small 60-Hz electric and magnetic fields, any biological effect of the fields must vary as the square of the field strength. In general, "sufficiently small" is defined as a region no larger than that where thermal noise plays an important role. Unless the range of validity so defined is sufficiently large to be interesting, the argument is empty. In previous work, I have argued that there can be no significant effects from electric fields in the body smaller than 1 mV/m (7) or from magnetic fields smaller than 5 $\mu$T (10–12) as a consequence of effects of thermal noise. Without abandoning that conclusion, those arguments can be taken as indicating that if there is a biological effect from such small fields, that effect must be small and then proportional to the square of the field strength or the equivalent—the effect must be proportional to the field energy density.

For plausible systems, the cumulative probability of the generation of genetic insults that might lead to malignancies is sensibly taken as the time integral of the square of the field strength, and such an integral will then be an appropriate measure of exposure.

1.  Feychting, M. & Ahlbom, A. (1993) *Am. J. Epidemiol.* **138,** 467–472.
2.  Olsen, J. H., Nielsen, A. & Schulgen, G. (1993) *Br. Med. J.* **307,** 891–895.
3.  Verkasalo, P. K., Puĸkala, E., Honisto, M. Y., Valjus, J. E., Heikela, K. V. & Koskenvuo, M. (1993) *Br. Med. J.* **307,** 895–898.
4.  Weaver, J. C. & Astumian, R. D. (1990) *Science* **247,** 459–461.
5.  Kirschvink, J. L. (1992) *Phys. Rev. A: Gen. Phys.* **46,** 2178–2184.
6.  Hänggi, P., Talkner, P. & Borkovec, M. (1990) *Rev. Mod. Phys.* **62,** 251–342.
7.  Adair, R. K. (1991) *Phys. Rev. A: Gen. Phys.* **43,** 1039–1048.
8.  Kirschvink, J. L., Kobayashi-Kirschvink, A. & Woodford, B. J. (1992) *Proc. Natl. Acad. Sci. USA* **89,** 7683–7687.
9.  Weaver, J. C. & Astumian, R. D. (1992) *Bioelectromagnetics (NY) Suppl.* **1,** 119–122.
10. Adair, R. K. (1992) *Phys. Rev. A: Gen. Phys.* **46,** 2185–2188.
11. Adair, R. K. (1993) *Bioelectromagnetics* **14,** 1–4.
12. Adair, R. K. (1994) *Proc. Natl. Acad. Sci. USA* **91,** 2925–2929.
13. Keith, A. D. & Snipes, W. (1974) *Science* **183,** 666–668.
14. Pollard, E. C. (1979) *The Aqueous Cytoplasm*, ed. Keith, A. D. (Dekker, New York), pp. 9–15.

Reprinted by permission from *Proc. Nat. Acad. Sci.* **92**, 3740-3743 (1995). Copyright 1995 by the National Academy of Sciences, U.S.A.

*Proc. Natl. Acad. Sci. USA*
Vol. 92, pp. 3740–3743, April 1995
Biophysics

# Rectification and signal averaging of weak electric fields by biological cells

R. Dean Astumian*, James C. Weaver†, and Robert K. Adair‡

*Departments of Surgery and of Biochemistry and Molecular Biology, University of Chicago, Chicago, IL 60637; †Harvard–MIT Division of Health Sciences and Technology, Massachusetts Institute of Technology, Cambridge, MA 02139; and ‡Department of Physics, Yale University, New Haven, CT 06520

*Contributed by Robert K. Adair, January 17, 1995*

**ABSTRACT** Oscillating electric fields can be rectified by proteins in cell membranes to give rise to a dc transport of a substance across the membrane or a net conversion of a substrate to a product. This provides a basis for signal averaging and may be important for understanding the effects of weak extremely low frequency (ELF) electric fields on cellular systems. We consider the limits imposed by thermal and "excess" biological noise on the magnitude and exposure duration of such electric field-induced membrane activity. Under certain circumstances, the excess noise leads to an increase in the signal-to-noise ratio in a manner similar to processes labeled "stochastic resonance." Numerical results indicate that it is difficult to reconcile biological effects with low field strengths.

In previous papers (1, 2) we considered the signal-to-noise ratio expected for a weak external extremely low frequency (ELF) signal field applied to a biological cell subject to thermal (Johnson–Nyquist) noise voltage across the membrane, where the membrane is treated as a resistor and capacitor in parallel. The basic hypothesis is that a biological system cannot in principle be influenced by an applied electromagnetic field if the biological signal (i.e., the change in some parameter away from the unperturbed condition) resulting from the field is smaller than the root-mean-square (rms) noise in that parameter in the absence of the field.

We considered the signal to be the change in the instantaneous membrane potential $\delta V$, which leads to the condition $\overline{\delta V^2} \geq 4 R_{mem} k_B T \Delta f$ to achieve a signal-to-noise ratio (S/N) greater than unity, where $R_{mem}$ is the membrane resistance, $k_B$ is the Boltzmann constant, $T$ is the absolute temperature, and $\Delta f$ is the relevant frequency bandwidth.

Since both $\delta V$ and $R_{mem}$, as well as the electrical properties that set a limit to $\Delta f$, can be written in terms of the size of the cell as well as the membrane electrical properties, estimates for the minimum electric field necessary to at least overcome the effects of thermal noise in terms of the physical parameters of biological cells were obtained.

In the present paper we explicitly treat signal averaging in terms of a general model of field-induced membrane activity that includes the rectification of currents transmitted through the membrane and the rectification of catalytic action by enzymes subjected to fields in the membrane. Also, unlike the previous papers (1, 2), where only the fundamental limit on detection imposed by thermal ($k_B T$) noise was treated, we consider S/N as a function of a general "white noise" intensity, since there are sources of noise in biological membranes other than Johnson–Nyquist (thermal) noise which may act to effectively increase the temperature. We find that S/N can increase with increasing noise under biologically relevant

conditions in a manner similar to the phenomenon of "stochastic resonance" known for many physical systems (3–5).

**The Rectifier Equation**

Biological cells operate most often near steady state. Molecules that are generated through some process are eliminated at approximately the same rate as they are produced. For example, many metabolic processes (including decarboxylation by ornithine decarboxylase) produce oxidizing radicals, such as superoxide, as by-products. These oxidizing agents can diffuse to the nucleus and oxidize DNA, possibly causing deleterious mutations. The effects of such agents are limited by the action of enzymes such as superoxide dismutase that scavenge these oxidants and convert them to harmless materials. At a steady state, the average rate of production of superoxide equals the rate of degradation, $\overline{J}_{creation} = \overline{J}_{destruction}$, where the overline indicates a time average. However efficient the scavenging mechanism, some radicals will escape the scavengers and be eliminated in the process of oxidizing the genetic material, thus damaging that material. In this picture, DNA acts as a sink for unscavenged radicals, which are turned into damaged sites that accumulate over time.

Through effects on membrane proteins, an applied ELF electric field may increase the average rate of production of superoxide. Specifically, the change in field could affect superoxide production by changing the chemical equilibrium in the cell. That equilibrium could be modified through the field-induced opening of protein gate channels in the membrane, thus changing the membrane transmission properties, or through field-induced changes in the catalytic properties of enzyme proteins associated with the membrane. Such an increase in production will result in an increase in the concentration of the oxidants in the cell and an increased superoxide concentration, leading to an increased damage rate. The biologically important "signal" generated by the field-induced change in membrane activity is the total damage accumulated during exposure to the field.

As is the case for certain models of damage from radioactivity, the important parameter is the accumulated dose and not the maximum instantaneous intensity. To obtain a quantitative relationship between the various relevant parameters (applied field strength, cell size, normal rate of catalysis, noise intensity, and time of exposure) we consider a simple model shown in Fig. 1. Moreover, for clarity, we consider specifically a model for the transmission of a substance S through the membrane where S can enter the cell only through a protein gate or channel. For simplicity, we assume that there are two states of the protein, $\psi_{open}$ and $\psi_{closed}$. (If the modification follows from a change in the catalytic effect of an enzyme protein imbedded in the membrane, we could label the protein states $\psi_{active}$ and $\psi_{inactive}$ and proceed with the same general argument.)

---

The publication costs of this article were defrayed in part by page charge payment. This article must therefore be hereby marked "*advertisement*" in accordance with 18 U.S.C. §1734 solely to indicate this fact.

Abbreviations: ELF, extremely low frequency; S/N, signal-to-noise ratio.

---

Biophysics: Astumian *et al.*

*Proc. Natl. Acad. Sci. USA* 92 (1995)     3741

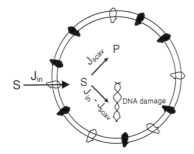

FIG. 1. Schematic illustration of our model. A substance S can enter the cell only through a protein gate. The filled structures indicate closed channels, while the unfilled ones denote open channels through which S can pass. The transition between closed and open state is governed by the membrane potential (see text). After S enters the cell, there are two possible fates—either it is "scavenged" and converted to P or it diffuses to the nucleus and reacts with DNA, causing a damage site. An external electric field will bias the probability for the channel to be open, and hence the current of S into the cell, but the protein responsible for scavenging the S that enters is a cytosolic molecule and not influenced by the field. Thus a relatively small interaction acting over a long period of time can cause accumulation of damaged DNA sites.

The dynamical behavior of the system can be described in terms of diffusion on a one-dimensional potential surface such as depicted in Fig. 2. The equilibrium between the open and closed forms depends on the energy difference between the two states according to a Boltzmann equation $P_{open}/P_{closed} = e^{-U/D}$. The probability for a channel to be open is thus given by the partition equation,

$$P_{open} = \frac{e^{-U/D}}{1 + e^{-U/D}}, \qquad [1]$$

where $U$ is the difference in energy between the closed and open states and $D$ is the amplitude of white noise acting on the channel. At thermal equilibrium, $D = k_B T$ is the characteristic Boltzmann thermal noise energy. For some cells, there may be significant additional stochastic fields of biological origin, we take $D \geq k_B T$, thus approximating the effects of such excess fields as an effective increase in membrane temperature. The number of open channels is $N_{open} = P_{open} \cdot N_{tot}$, where $N_{tot}$ is the total number of channels in the cell membrane.

The average rate of entry of S into the cell, $\overline{J}_{in}$, is proportional to the number of open channels,

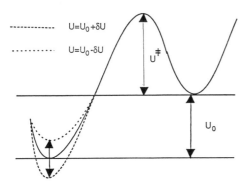

FIG. 2. Illustration of the "free energy" vs. reaction coordinate for the open–closed transition of the membrane channel. When the energy of the closed state is lower than that of the open state, the equilibrium will be shifted toward the closed state. In this case, an applied ac field will cause a net dc increase in the probability for the channel to be open, relative to the unperturbed state.

$$\overline{J}_{in} = k[S]_{out} N_{open}, \qquad [2]$$

where $k$ is a bimolecular rate constant and $[S]_{out}$ is the concentration of S outside of the cell. We take the concentration of S inside the cell to be much less than that outside the cell so the backflow through the open channel can be neglected. The maximum inflow can be defined as $J_{max} = k[S]_{out} N_{tot}$.

We presume a coupling between the gate protein such that an external ELF electric field $E(t) = E_0 \cos(\omega t)$ modulates the energy difference between the closed and open states such that $U = U_0 + \delta U$, where $U_0$ is the energy difference between the states in the absence of a perturbing electric field. At ELF frequencies, where the capacitive admittance of the membrane is very small, $\delta U = 1.5zE_0 r_{cell} \cos(\theta) \cos(\omega t)$, where $r_{cell}$ is the radius of the spherical cell, $z$ is the displacement charge of the voltage-gated channel, and $\theta$ is the angle between the imposed electric field and the normal to the membrane. We consider $\omega \ll \tau^{-1}$. Here $\tau^{-1} = k_{open} + k_{closed}$ is the inverse relaxation time of the channel, where $k_{open}$ and $k_{closed}$ are the rate constants for opening and closing the channel.

At steady state in the absence of the applied field the average absorption of S in the cell counterbalances the average rate of entry; for $U = U_0$, $\overline{J}_{abs} = \overline{J}_{in}$.

We consider two processes that act to eliminate S, an absorption by scavengers at an average rate, $\overline{J}_{scv}$, and an absorption by an oxidation insult to the DNA with a rate, $\overline{J}_{dna}$, where $J_{dna} + J_{scv} = J_{abs}$. We assume efficient scavenging under equilibrium conditions, so the ratio, $R_0(U = U_0) = J_{dna}/J_{scv} \ll 1$.

In the presence of the applied field, the rate of entry of S into the cell may be increased and the level of S in the cell will increase. But we consider that that increase is small and absorption efficiency will not be changed; hence, $R = R_0$ will be the relevant efficiency parameter for all conditions that we consider.

When the energy $U_0$ is perturbed by an amount, $\delta U$, such that $U = U_0 + \delta U$, $J_{in}$ will be modified and a net current, $J$, will be generated such that

$$J = J_{in} - J_{in}(0) = J_{max}\left[\frac{e^{-U/D}}{1 + e^{-U/D}} - \frac{e^{-U_0/D}}{e^{-U_0/D}}\right]. \qquad [3]$$

Expanding to second order in $\delta U/D$, for $\delta U \ll D$, we find

$$J \approx J_{max}\frac{e^{-U_0/D}}{(1 + e^{-U_0/D})^2}\left[-\frac{\delta U}{D} + \left(\frac{1}{2} - P_0\right)\left(\frac{\delta U}{D}\right)^2 + \cdots\right]. \qquad [4]$$

Eq. 4 is of the same general form as that describing the properties of a diode rectifier (6). The effect of an oscillating field is always to bring the average ratio between the open and closed states of the channel closer to unity. Thus, if $P_0 < \frac{1}{2}$ (where $P_0 \equiv P(U = U_0)$), the number of open channels, and hence the average rate of entry of S into the cell increases due to the applied field.

Averaging over time and $\theta$ gives the change in the average rate of accumulation over the surface of a spherical cell (7);

$$\overline{J} \approx \frac{e^{-U_0/D}}{D^2}AJ_{max}(zE_{rms}r_{cell})^2, \qquad [5]$$

where we use $E^2_{rms} = E^0_2/2$ for simpler comparison of the results with the conventional description of measured fields and we have defined

$$A = \frac{3(\frac{1}{2} - P_0)}{32(1 + e^{-U_0/D})^2},$$

which is bounded between $-0.002$ and $0.05$.

When $U_0$ is zero, the system is symmetric, and $P_0$ the second-order term in Eq. **4**, as well as $\bar{J}$, are identically zero. When $U_0$ is not zero, the imposition of the ELF electric field generates a rectified excess flow of S across the membrane, $\bar{J}$. That increased flow will result in a commensurate increase in the absorption, and a portion $R$ of those absorption events will result in injury to DNA. In a time $t$ we expect an accumulation of $(\bar{J}t \cdot R)$ injury events due to the applied field. Because both the inflow and the scavenging processes are stochastic, there will also be a "noise" flow which is the variance of the sum of the two processes. If we express the flow in molecules per second, the net noise drift across the membrane is equal to the square root of the number of molecules passing through the membrane plus the number absorbed. At steady state—with no external field—the probable drift in a time $t$ is

$$Q_{\text{noise}} = (2Rk[\text{S}]_{\text{out}}N_{\text{open}}t)^{1/2} \qquad [6]$$

molecules. This "noise" is to be compared with the signal—i.e., the molecular transport induced by the ELF field in a time $t$; $Q_{\text{sig}} = \bar{J}t$. After straightforward algebra we find

$$\text{S/N} \approx \frac{e^{-U_0/2D}}{D^2}A'(J_{\text{max}}Rt)^{1/2}(zE_{\text{rms}}r_{\text{cell}})^2, \qquad [7]$$

where $A' = (0.5A^2)^{1/2}(1 + e^{-U_0/D})^{1/2}$, which is bounded between 0 and 0.025.

This equation is of the same general form as that given by McNamara and Wiesenfeld in their theory of stochastic resonance (5), but with a time dependence indicative of the second-order rectification process on which we focus in this paper. This is perhaps not surprising, since the fundamental picture motivating our model is a double-well potential (Fig. 2) similar to that considered by McNamara and Wiesenfeld. In our case, however, the potential is not necessarily symmetric (i.e., the energy at the bottom of one well is different than at the bottom of the other well).

In Fig. 3 we show a plot of S/N vs. $D$, for a value of the energy gap, $U_0 = 8k_\text{B}T$, which shows the increase in S/N with noise, at small values of noise, characteristic of stochastic resonance. When the two canonical states are separated by an energy, $U_0$, greater than the energy of the applied field, $zE_{\text{rms}}r_{\text{cell}}$, that field cannot bridge the energy gap and induce a transition in the absence of noise. For noise amplitudes less than about $1/e$ of the gap, the value of S/N will increase with the noise, for larger values of the noise, S/N will fall off with increasing noise.

To obtain an estimate for the combination of time of exposure and applied field amplitude necessary to achieve a S/N of unity, we solve Eq. **7** for the applied field amplitude $E_{\text{o,min}}$, such that the field-altered net transport will equal the probable uncertainty in the transfer through noise in a time $t$ to find

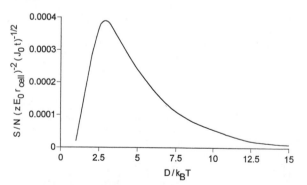

FIG. 3. Plot of S/N vs. the noise intensity, $D$, calculated from Eq. **7** with $U_0 = 8k_\text{B}T$.

$$E_{\text{min}} \approx \frac{De^{U_0/4D}}{zr_{\text{cell}}}(A'RJ_{\text{max}}t)^{-1/4}. \qquad [8]$$

**Homeostatic Constraints.** Eqs. 3–8 take the form presented in the absence of homeostatic constraints. In some circumstances, cell physiology will dictate a steady-state value of $Q$ in the cell, $Q_{\text{equil}}$, such that, to first order in $\Delta Q = Q - Q_{\text{homeostasis}}$,

$$J_{\text{homeostasis}} = \frac{dQ}{dt} = -\frac{1}{\tau_{\text{homeostasis}}}(Q - Q_{\text{equil}}), \qquad [9]$$

where $\tau_{\text{homeostasis}}$ is a time constant for the return to steady state of a perturbed cell. In such a case, a term like that on the left of Eq. **9** should be added to Eq. **3** for a complete description of the change in S (or $Q$) in the cell.

In the continuous presence of the perturbation, a new steady state will be defined. If that steady-state situation is such as to generate a higher level of stochastic insult to the cell—e.g., as injury to DNA—the probability of additional insults will be proportional to the time under which the perturbation is imposed and no pertinent homeostasis may be relevant. We have proceeded in the conservative approximation that homeostatic effects are not important.

## Numerical Results

There are four parameters to consider. These are the product of the applied field $E$ and the coupling factor $zr_{\text{cell}}$; the product of a maximum background flow $J_{\text{max}}$ and time $t$; the unperturbed energy difference between open and closed states $U_0$; and the "white" noise intensity $D$. As an explicit example, consider a 100-$\mu$m cell exposed to a 1-mV/cm rms field in the aqueous medium surrounding the cell.

If we take $U_0 = 8k_\text{B}T$, $J_{\text{max}} = 10^{12}/\text{sec}$ and $z = 10$, we find that S/N = 1 is reached after 10,700 sec (= 3 hr) for $D = k_\text{B}T$. If instead, $D = 4k_\text{B}T$ ($D = U_0/2$ minimizes $E_{\text{min}}$ in Eq. **8**), we find that S/N = 1 is reached after 3000 sec (1 hr).

The minimum field necessary to cause an effect in a reasonable period of time is greater than predicted previously. This is principally due to the fact that in ref. 1 the field itself was compared to the thermal Johnson–Nyquist noise field, and the signal averaging was incorporated into that picture. Here, we have looked at a specific mechanism involving interaction between an applied field and a membrane protein more realistically.

The change in the average behavior of the protein depends on the square of the applied field. Also, since we adopt the viewpoint that the effect of the field is to change the rate of entry or production of some molecule, we compare our "signal" with the shot noise arising from the discreteness of the molecular events. The number of such events at the membrane cannot possibly be greater than the total diffusive flux of the substrate to the membrane surface. For reasonable parameters, this flux is about $10^{12}$ events per second at most, so the shot noise is about $\pm 10^6/\text{sec}$. Although the limits imposed by the present theory are higher than those of Weaver and Astumian, they are still within an order of magnitude of the experimental data used as benchmarks in ref. 1.

Other experiments, principally those using magnetic fields, have reported effects at very low field intensities, however. For example, a 5-mG 60-Hz field (such as implicated in epidemiological studies) produces an electric field of 0.23 $\mu$V/cm at the widest girth of a human form. This may seem very small, but from the structure of the equations we see that we only have to wait in order for the field to be rectified and produce a signal larger than noise. How long must we wait? From Eq. **7**, we find that a 0.23-$\mu$V/cm field will give rise to a S/N of unity only after $4 \cdot 10^{18}$ sec, which is a long time. Thus, it seems difficult to reconcile effects with low field strengths in the context of the present theory.

## Conclusion

We have discussed two mechanisms that may be relevant for understanding possible effects of weak electric fields on biological cell-rectification by enzymes and transporters, which allows a dc response to be generated by an ac signal, and stochastic resonance, which allows "white" noise acting on a system to give rise to a larger signal (and S/N) than would be the case if only thermal ($k_BT$) noise were acting on the system. We focused on a specific model of field-induced membrane activity where a substance flows through a membrane voltage-gated channel, but the basic principles apply to a much wider array of physical and chemical systems (8). The nonmonotonic dependence of S/N on noise strength can be expected in any system that must surmount an activation barrier to make a transition resulting in a response to an external signal. Rectification requires in addition an asymmetry. In the case of the channel, the asymmetry is provided by $U_0 \neq 0$.

In conclusion, the two major results of this paper are (*i*) that rectification provides a mechanism by which signal from an external ac electric field can be accumulated; and (*ii*) that "noise" larger in magnitude than expected at equilibrium does not necessarily lead to a higher threshold for response of a system to a weak ELF field, and indeed can increase the ability of the system to respond. Despite these conclusions, we must remember that the field strengths predicted as thresholds for response, while small, are still larger than fields likely to arise from typical environmental sources.

Further, it is important to emphasize that even if an external field is larger than our threshold value, this does not imply that the field will cause an effect, but only that an effect is possible within the context of a straightforward thermodynamic perturbation–response analysis.

1. Weaver, J. C. & Astumian, R. D. (1990) *Science* **247,** 459–462.
2. Adair, R. K. (1991) *Phys. Rev. A* **43,** 1039–1048.
3. Benzi, R., Sutera, A. & Vulpiani, A. (1981) *J. Phys. A.* **14,** 453–460.
4. Douglas, J. K., Wilkens, L., Pantazelou, E. & Moss, F. (1993) *Nature (London)* **365,** 337–340.
5. McNamara, B. & Wiesenfeld, K. (1989) *Phys. Rev. A.* **39,** 4854–4869.
6. Serway, R. A. (1990) *Physics for Scientists and Engineers* (Saunders, Philadelphia), 3rd Ed.
7. Astumian, R. D. & Robertson, B. (1989) *J. Chem. Phys.* **91,** 4891–4901.
8. Astumian, R. D. & Robertson, B. (1993) *J. Am. Chem. Soc.* **115,** 11063–11068.

Reprinted with permission from Joseph L. Kirschvink, Atsuko Kobayashi-Kirschvink, and Barbara J. Woodford. Copyright 1992.

*Proc. Natl. Acad. Sci. USA*
Vol. 89, pp. 7683–7687, August 1992
Biophysics

# Magnetite biomineralization in the human brain

(iron/extremely low frequency magnetic fields)

Joseph L. Kirschvink, Atsuko Kobayashi-Kirschvink, and Barbara J. Woodford*

Division of Geological and Planetary Sciences, The California Institute of Technology, Pasadena, CA 91125

*Communicated by Leon T. Silver, May 7, 1992*

**ABSTRACT** Although the mineral magnetite ($Fe_3O_4$) is precipitated biochemically by bacteria, protists, and a variety of animals, it has not been documented previously in human tissue. Using an ultrasensitive superconducting magnetometer in a clean-lab environment, we have detected the presence of ferromagnetic material in a variety of tissues from the human brain. Magnetic particle extracts from solubilized brain tissues examined with high-resolution transmission electron microscopy, electron diffraction, and elemental analyses identify minerals in the magnetite–maghemite family, with many of the crystal morphologies and structures resembling strongly those precipitated by magnetotactic bacteria and fish. These magnetic and high-resolution transmission electron microscopy measurements imply the presence of a minimum of 5 million single-domain crystals per gram for most tissues in the brain and >100 million crystals per gram for pia and dura. Magnetic property data indicate the crystals are in clumps of between 50 and 100 particles. Biogenic magnetite in the human brain may account for high-field saturation effects observed in the T1 and T2 values of magnetic resonance imaging and, perhaps, for a variety of biological effects of low-frequency magnetic fields.

In past studies of iron storage and magnetic resonance imaging (MRI), it has been assumed universally that there are no permanently magnetized (ferromagnetic) materials present in human tissues (1, 2). Similar assumptions have been made in virtually all biophysical assessments of human risk associated with exposure to static and extremely low-frequency magnetic fields (3) and by critics (4) of epidemiological studies that suggest links between weak power-line-frequency magnetic fields and various human disorders (5, 6). These analyses have focused on the side effects of electrical induction or possible diamagnetic and paramagnetic interactions. However, the ferromagnetic mineral magnetite ($Fe_3O_4$) is formed biochemically by many living organisms. Because ferromagnetic crystals interact more than a million times more strongly with external magnetic fields than do diamagnetic or paramagnetic materials of similar volume, earth-strength magnetic fields can yield many responses that stand above thermal noise (7). Hence, the assumption implicit in past studies that human tissues are free of ferromagnetic material needs to be reassessed critically and tested experimentally.

Previous searches for biogenic magnetite in human tissues have not been conclusive (8, 9). Despite this, extensive research over the past 30 years has demonstrated that many organisms have the biochemical ability to precipitate the ferrimagnetic minerals magnetite ($Fe_3O_4$) (10–16) and greigite ($Fe_3S_4$) (17). In terms of its phyletic distribution, magnetite biomineralization is particularly widespread, having been documented in monerans (10), protists (11), and animals (12–16), with a fossil record extending back into Precambrian time (18). Within Kingdom Animalia, it is known within the

mollusks (12), arthropods (13), and chordates (14, 15) and is suspected in many more groups (16). In the microorganisms (10, 11) and fish (15), linear chains of membrane-bound crystals of magnetite (magnetosomes) form structures best described as "biological bar magnets."

We report here that human tissues possess similar crystals of biogenic magnetite, with minimum estimates between 5 and 100 million single-domain crystals per gram in the tissues of the human brain. Magnetic particle extracts from solubilized tissues examined with high-resolution transmission electron microscopy (TEM) and electron diffraction identify minerals in the magnetite–maghemite solid solution, with many crystal morphologies and structures resembling those precipitated by magnetotactic bacteria and fish.

## MATERIALS AND METHODS

**Tissue Samples.** Human brain material was obtained 12–24 h postmortem from the Alzheimer's Disease Research Center Consortium of Southern California. Samples of brain and meninges were dissected using acid-cleaned ceramic or Teflon-coated instruments. These tissues were placed into 70% ethanol [made with deionized water and filtered through a 200-nm (pore-size) Millipore filter] in containers that had previously been cleaned with 2 M HCl. Samples from seven brains were obtained from patients whose ages averaged 65 years and ranged from 48 to 88 years. Four of these were from suspected Alzheimer disease patients. Cerebral cortical areas and cerebellum were included for all seven brains. In one case, brain and spinal dura, basal ganglia, and midbrain and, in another case, olfactory bulbs, superior sagittal sinus, and tentorium of the dura were obtained in addition to the above tissues.

**Magnetometry.** Subsamples for magnetic measurements were removed from the tissues by using similar tools in a magnetically shielded dust-free clean laboratory (19). Measurements of ferromagnetic materials were made using a magnetometer employing Rf-biased superconducting quantum interference devices (SQUIDs), designed to measure the total ferromagnetic *moment* of samples placed within a Helmholtz-coil pickup loop (20). Samples were fastened to a thin acid-washed monofilament string, and a stepping motor moved the sample vertically between the magnetization and demagnetization coils and the measurement region of the SQUID magnetometer. Several magnetic analyses borrowed from the field of rock and mineral magnetism (21–23) were performed routinely on frozen tissue samples to determine the concentration, mineralogy, and packing geometry of any ferromagnetic materials present.

---

Abbreviations: MRI, magnetic resonance imaging; SQUID, superconducting quantum interference device; TEM, transmission electron microscopy; IRM, isothermal remanent magnetization; ARM, anhysteretic remanent magnetization.
*Present address: Department of Anatomy and Cell Biology, University of Southern California, 1333 San Pablo Street, Los Angeles, CA 90033.

The publication costs of this article were defrayed in part by page charge payment. This article must therefore be hereby marked "*advertisement*" in accordance with 18 U.S.C. §1734 solely to indicate this fact.

**Sample Preparation for the Magnetometer.** Pia and blood vessels were removed from all samples of the meninges before analysis in the SQUID magnetometer. Two preparation methods were used. Large intact samples of the cerebral cortex and cerebellum were frozen directly in liquid nitrogen. Brain tissues that fractured upon freezing or dissection were placed into a previously acid-cleaned ice-cube mold and frozen into blocks with small quantities of nonmagnetic deionized water. Either the frozen piece of brain or the ice/brain block was attached by a slip knot to the monofilament line and then centered within the column of the SQUID magnetometer. Background instrument noise and the levels of laboratory contaminants were monitored with blank 15-g ice cubes of distilled deionized water; typical ice-cube background noise levels were in the range of $2 \times 10^{-8}$ A·m$^2$·kg$^{-1}$. All aqueous solutions used in sample handling were passed through 200-nm filters. All solutions, including the toluene and tissue solubilizers, were cleaned magnetically by storing for at least 2 weeks prior to use in containers with large high-intensity NdFeB magnets strapped to their base to aid in the removal of any preexisting ferromagnetic contaminants.

**Extraction and Electron Microscopy.** Extraction devices made from Pyrex weighing vials were used to remove the magnetic particles from the brain tissues. The ground-glass caps were modified by glass blowing to make a thin-walled cylindrical finger, sealed on the bottom, extending from the cap about ⅔ of the distance into the vial. Tissues were digested in magnetically cleaned commercial solutions of toluene/quaternary ammonium hydroxide (e.g., Beckman tissue solubilizer), ≈1:5 (vol/vol) for a minimum period of 1 week while exposed to the strong field of a NdFeB magnet inserted within the finger. The vial cap and magnetic finger were then rinsed in clean toluene, the magnetic aggregates were redispersed mechanically in 0.25 ml of toluene, and small drops were placed on carbon-coated copper grids for high-resolution TEM analysis. Samples were examined at high resolution on a Phillips model 430 300-kV high-resolution TEM with an energy-dispersive x-ray analysis system for elemental determinations. Mineralogic assignments were made by indexing the spot patterns produced by selected-area electron diffraction on individual mineral grains and on rings from powder patterns, with calibration against a gold film standard. An estimate of the grain-size distribution was made by measuring the length and width of 70 crystal shadows from a large clump. Control samples consisting of the solutions without brain tissues, as well as the solutions spiked with known quantities of bacterial magnetite, were run to check for contaminants in the solvents as well as to determine their effect, if any, on the well-studied morphology of bacterial magnetites.

## RESULTS

**Magnetometry.** All of the tissues examined had isothermal remanent magnetizations (IRMs) that saturated in applied fields of ≈300 mT, a characteristic property of the magnetite–maghemite series. The ability to gain and lose remanent magnetization in these experiments is a definitive characteristic of ferromagnetic materials. Table 1 shows the mean values for each brain. The average magnetization indicates the equivalent of ≈4 ng of magnetite per gram of tissue. In contrast, average values for the meninges from three brains (Table 1) are nearly 20 times higher, or ≈70 ng/g. For comparison, measurements of IRM from triple-distilled deionized ice cubes yield a background "noise" of ≈0.5 ng/g.

There was remarkable consistency in the IRM measurements for both the brain tissue and the meninges. There was little difference in IRM from one area of cerebral cortex to another or in the cerebral versus the cerebellar cortex. Differences between tissues from the normal brains versus those suspected or confirmed to be Alzheimer disease cases were negligible. Areas of the brain previously reported to have high iron content include the dentate nucleus, the basal ganglia, and areas of the midbrain (24). Samples of these areas had no greater content of magnetic particles than did the cerebellar or cerebral cortex.

Fig. 1 shows magnetic properties for representative tissues, including coercivity determinations (20) (Fig. 1A) and a test for intergrain interaction effects using the anhysteretic remanent magnetization (23) (ARM, Fig. 1B). Median coercivity values were ≈30 mT, but ranged from 12 (pia from cerebellum) to 50 (basal ganglia) mT, well within the coercivity range for single-domain magnetite. The shift in coercivity distributions, as measured by IRM acquisition and its demagnetization, and the relatively slow tendency to acquire an ARM suggest that the particles *in situ* are in small interacting clumps. Comparison with bacterial control samples suggests between 50 and 100 particles per clump.

**Extraction and Electron Microscopy.** When viewed under low power through an optical dissecting microscope, black strings of aggregated particles extracted from brain tissues are seen collected at the focus of the magnetic finger device. In shape and morphology, these aggregations are indistinguishable from similar aggregates from the magnetotactic bacterial controls. No magnetic aggregates were observed to collect in the blank tissue-free control samples. Rough volume estimates of the extracted material, made by measuring the length and width of the aggregates and totaling for each chain, agree to within an order of magnitude with estimates from the IRM measurements, implying that the extraction technique was reasonably efficient.

Fig. 2 shows two representative crystal morphologies of the extracted magnetic particles. Grain sizes were bimodal, with 62 of the 70 measured crystals in the 10- to 70-nm range and the remaining 8 with sizes ranging from 90 to 200 nm. Measurements of the TEM shadows from 62 of the smaller particles in one aggregate yielded an average size of 33.4 ± 15.2 nm. Note that this mean value must be biased toward

Table 1. Mean saturated IRM for cerebral cortex and cerebellum tissues from each brain

| Tissue | Saturated IRM, $\mu$A·m$^2$·kg$^{-1}$ | Magnetite, ng/g | No. of subsamples |
|---|---|---|---|
| Brain | | | |
| 1 | 0.14 ± 0.08 | 3.0 ± 1.4 | 11 |
| 2 | 0.18 ± 0.10 | 3.9 ± 2.2 | 5 |
| 3 | 0.14 ± 0.05 | 3.0 ± 1.1 | 5 |
| 4 | 0.27 ± 0.21 | 5.9 ± 4.6 | 6 |
| 5 | 0.20 ± 0.09 | 4.3 ± 2.0 | 3 |
| 6 | 0.19 | 4.1 | 1 |
| 7 | 0.33 ± 0.19 | 7.2 ± 4.1 | 2 |
| Meninges | | | |
| 1 | 2.5 ± 1.8 | 54 ± 39 | 8 |
| 2 | 2.5 ± 1.5 | 54 ± 33 | 8 |
| 6 | 5.0 | 109 | 1 |

Data for saturated IRM are expressed as $\mu$A·m$^2$·kg$^{-1}$ (wet weight) (mean ± SD). Occipital samples were from Brodman areas (B.A.) 17, 18, and 19; temporal samples were from B.A. 20, 21, and 22; parietal samples were from B.A. 3, 1, 2, 5, and 7; and frontal samples were from B.A. 4 and 6. Sample sizes ranged from 0.5 g to 22 g. The meninges from samples of brains 1, 2, and 6 were analyzed separately. The ice-cube technique was used for all of the meninges, and on the tissues from brain 2, and for 7 of the 11 samples from brain 1; no difference in results was seen with this technique. Magnetite concentrations were estimated by noting that the saturation remanence should be exactly half of the saturation magnetization for a dispersion of single-domain crystals (21). Brains 1–4 were from normal patients, brains 5 and 6 were confirmed Alzheimer patients, and brain 7 was a suspected Alzheimer patient.

Biophysics: Kirschvink *et al.*

*Proc. Natl. Acad. Sci. USA* 89 (1992)    7685

larger sizes because the extraction procedure will discriminate against very small particles that move more slowly through the liquid. Size and shape relationships for all measured particles fall within the single-domain and superparamagnetic fields for magnetite (25). Crystal volume estimates, done by assuming equant particle shapes, imply that the larger particles compose a maximum of ≈85% of the magnetite. Using this distribution data, we estimate that brain tissues contain a minimum of ≈5 million crystals per gram, distributed in 50,000–100,000 discrete clusters. Similarly, the meninges contain a minimum of 100 million crystals per gram, in 1–2 million clusters.

Energy-dispersive x-ray analyses of the crystals gave consistent peaks of Fe, with variable Cu peaks (from the copper TEM grids) and minor Si, Ca, and Cl (probably contaminants from the glassware). Mixed Fe-Ti oxides, which are usually present at least in trace amounts in geologically formed magnetic minerals, were not detected in any of the brain crystals examined. Indexed electron microdiffraction patterns from individual crystals and particle aggregates yield the d-spacings characteristic of magnetite ($Fe_3O_4$), with smaller particles showing variable oxidation toward the ferrimagnetic solid-solution end member, maghemite ($\gamma$-$Fe_2O_3$). This oxidation probably occurred during the extraction process, as is observed commonly in very fine grained magnetites (22).

Fig. 2A is a TEM image of a clump of small particles from the cerebellum, and Fig. 2B shows a high-resolution TEM image of a well-ordered single-domain maghemite crystal imaged in the [211] zone. It displays several intersecting sets of crystal lattice fringes that appear as fine stripes that run across the image (and are viewed best at a low angle relative to the page). The most prominent set, which runs across the width of the crystal, corresponds to the 4.85-Å spacing of the {111} plane; another set perpendicular to this, running the length of the crystal, has the 2.95-Å spacing of the {02$\bar{2}$} planes. Note that the [111] direction of the crystal, which is the easy direction of magnetization (22), is parallel to the particle length and that the {111} fringes go completely across the width of the particle without disruption. A superimposed "graininess" is present, along with somewhat ill-defined edges. These are typical features of magnetite crystals formed within magnetosome membranes (26, 27) and are very similar to the single-domain particles in the magnetosome chain structures present in the dermethmoid tissues of salmon (15). Fig. 2C shows the indexed electron-diffraction spot pattern from this crystal.

Fig. 2D shows one of the larger particles, which is ≈200 nm in size. Other particles range up to 600 nm in diameter. Electron microdiffraction indicates that these particles are dominated by a single crystal, with occasional smaller particles adhering to their surface. Their measured size and shapes place them within the single-domain stability field (25). These particles have magnetic orientation energies in the geomagnetic field 20–150 times higher than the background thermal energy $kT$.

## DISCUSSION

Results from these studies indicate that human brain and meninges contain trace amounts of ferromagnetic material. These magnetic particles in the human brain are diffusely and homogeneously distributed over all cerebral lobes, the cerebellum, basal ganglia, and midbrain. The consistency of our magnetic property data from piece to piece of brain tissue and from piece to piece of meninges suggests that the observed moments were not produced by occasional contamination from the environment but were *in situ* ferromagnetic materials distributed in a tissue-characteristic fashion. The magnetic material was in the tissues *prior* to the chemical

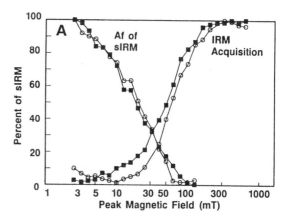

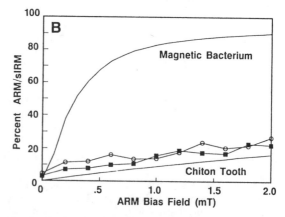

FIG. 1.    Rock magnetism of human brain tissues. (*A*) The curves labeled IRM acquisition show the relative magnetic moments remaining in the samples after a brief exposure to a magnetic pulse of the indicated strength. The tendency of the curves to flatten at high field levels is characteristic of the magnetite–maghemite solid solution series; most other ferromagnetic iron minerals saturate in fields >1 T. The curves labeled Af of sIRM show the progressive alternating-field demagnetization of the saturation IRM. The magnetic field value at which these two curves cross is the best measure of the average coercivity. The ordinate of the intersection point for noninteracting particles occurs at the 50% value; a depression or shift in this position is an indication of particle clumping effects. (*B*) The acquisition of ARM. The upper control curve shows data from a sample of magnetotactic bacteria in which the magnetite crystals are aligned in linear chains and have few interparticle interactions, whereas the lower control curve is from a sample of magnetite from chiton teeth, which are single-domain crystals but are highly interacting. Solid squares are data from pia from the frontal lobe, whereas the open circles show data from the cerebellum. sIRM, saturated IRM.

digestion steps, which are of the most concern for potential contamination. An external inorganic source is also unlikely because of the lack of particles containing mixed Fe-Ti oxides, which are common in igneous and metamorphic magnetites. Surface textures and crystallographic features for the smaller particles are remarkably similar to biogenic magnetites studied in bacteria (27) and fish (15). The {111} crystal alignment has been interpreted as a biological mechanism for maximizing the magnetic moment per particle, as the {111} direction yields ≈3% higher saturation magnetizations than do other directions (15, 27, 28). This prismatic particle shape is also uncommon in geological magnetite crystals of this size, which are usually octahedra. Hence, these magnetite crystals probably form within human tissues by a similar biologically controlled process. Unfortunately, the tissue digestion and extraction process destroys the

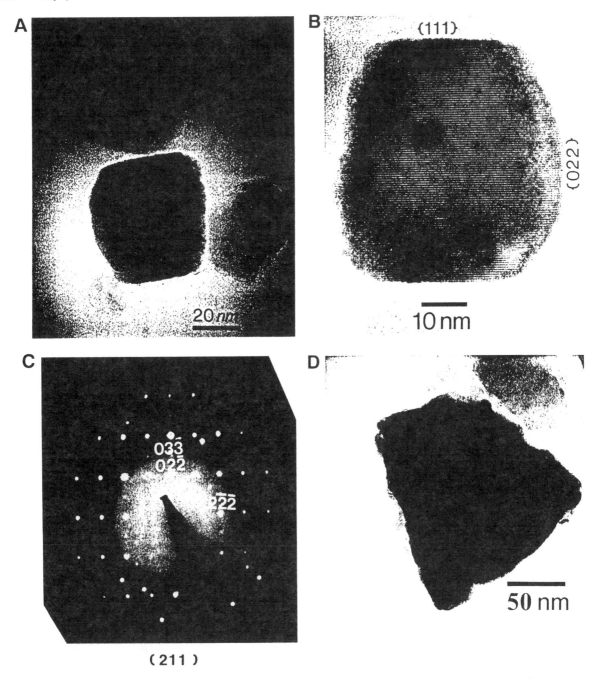

FIG. 2.    TEM images and diffraction patterns of representative magnetite and maghemite crystals from the human cerebellum. (*A*) A clump of small particles. The high-resolution TEM image of the maghemite crystal in *B* shows the pattern of intersecting {111} and {02$\bar{2}$} fringes, with particle elongation in the [111] lattice direction. (*C*) The indexed selected-area electron diffraction pattern of this crystal, taken in the ⟨211⟩ zone. (A few miscellaneous spots are also present from the adjacent crystals seen in *A*, and the faint row of spots midway between the bright rows are [01$\bar{1}$] and equivalent reflections that indicate the oxidation to maghemite.) The diffraction rings from an aggregate of small crystals confirms the magnetite–maghemite identification. These measured values/$\gamma$-Fe$_2$O$_3$ standards/and [indexed] d-spacings for the rings are, respectively, 4.0 Å/4.18 Å [200], 4.8 Å/4.82 Å [111], 3.2 Å/3.41 Å [211], 2.8 Å/2.95 Å [220], 2.6 Å/2.78 Å [221], 2.2 Å/2.23 Å [321], 1.8 Å/1.87 Å [420], 1.7 Å/1.70 Å [422], 1.5 Å/1.61 Å [511], and 1.3 Å/1.32 Å [620]. The tetragonal reflections [211], [221], and [321] are present in maghemite, and not in magnetite, and the pattern from the aggregate is a mixture of the two. One of the large magnetite particles is shown in *D* (diffraction pattern not shown).

cellular organization of the particles. Only the ARM results yield clues to the *in situ* grouping in small clumps.

In recent years, several medical groups have claimed that MRI images weighted by T1 and T2 values correlated with the observed distribution of stainable ferric iron in human brain tissue (2, 29, 30). These anomalous values have been inter-

preted as arising from irregular distributions of paramagnetic iron (deoxyhemoglobin, ferritin, and hemosiderin). Iron distributions measured in this fashion increased with age, as is known from extensive histological work (24). However, this interpretation was challenged subsequently by Chen *et al.* (31), who found generally poor correlation between iron concentration and T2 relaxation, and by Bizzi *et al.* (32), who discovered that the iron-correlated spin echo effects did not have the quadratic variation with increasing magnetic field strength predicted by the paramagnetic hypothesis. All of these results are more compatible with the presence of trace levels of magnetite.

The presence of magnetite in human tissues has potential implications for at least two biomedical issues that have been discussed extensively in the literature; these include human exposure to the strong static fields used in MRI studies (3) and the much weaker 50- and 60-Hz fields produced by the electric power system and appliances in industrialized countries (4–7). (*i*) MRI systems are now being used routinely in clinical applications that subject patients to static background magnetic fields in excess of 1.5 T, 30,000 times stronger than typical geomagnetic fields. Under these conditions the maximum magnetostatic orientational potential energies for the magnetic particle clumps are between $10^3$ and $10^7$ times higher than the thermal energy $kT$ at body temperature. Hence, the energies are much larger than the chemical energies present in covalent bonds, which typically are on the order of 100 $kT$. (*ii*) The magnetic torque from external alternating fields will induce mechanical oscillations in the particles, and the potential exists for such motions to have effects like opening transmembrane ion channels. Two separate analytical approaches suggest that fields of 50 or 60 Hz with peak intensities slightly stronger than that of the earth would be required to make these effects stand above $kT$ (7, 33), but the large numbers of crystals might allow averaging to yield effects at lower levels. Although peak alternating magnetic fields generated by most electric transmission lines are well below this level, some electric appliances produce stronger fields (34). Unfortunately, without more knowledge of the cellular location, ultrastructure, or biological function of these particles, it is impossible to predict whether magnetomechanical effects of this sort pose a human health hazard.

We thank Dr. Carol Miller of the University of Southern California Medical School for providing access to brain materials, Drs. Juan Diaz-Ricci, Derek H. Fender, and Leon T. Silver for helpful support and discussions, and Dr. C. C. Patterson for ultrapure water. Dr. Brent Fultz and Ms. Carol Garland of the Caltech Materials Research Center provided essential help with the high-voltage electron microscopy. Drs. K. M. Towe and R. B. Frankel provided critical and useful reviews of the manuscript. This work was supported by National Institutes of Health Grant GM-41635, and the Caltech Materials Research Facility is supported by National Science Foundation Grant DMR-8811795. This is contribution 5068 from the Division of Geological and Planetary Sciences of the California Institute of Technology.

1. Brittenham, G. M., Farrell, D. E., Harris, J. W., Feldman, E. S., Danish, E. H., Muir, W. A., Tripp, J. H. & Bellon, E. M. (1982) *N. Engl. J. Med.* **307**, 1671–1675.
2. Gomori, J. M., Grossman, R. I., Goldberg, H. I., Zimmerman, R. A. & Bilaniuk, L. T. (1985) *Radiology* **157**, 87–93.
3. Tenforde, T. S. & Budinger, T. F. (1986) in *NMR in Medicine: Instrumentation and Clinical Applications*, eds. Thomas, S. R. & Dixon, R. L. (Am. Assoc. of Physicists Med., New York), pp. 493–548.
4. Adair, R. K. (1991) *Phys. Rev. A* **43**, 1039–1048.
5. Savitz, D. A., Wachtel, H., Barnes, F. A., John, E. M. & Tvrdik, J. G. (1988) *Am. J. Epidemiol.* **128**, 21–38.
6. London, S. J., Thomas, D. C., Bowman, J. D., Sobel, E. & Peters, J. M. (1991) *Am. J. Epidemiol.* **134**, 923–937.
7. Kirschvink, J. L. (1992) *Phys. Rev. A* **46**, in press.
8. Kirschvink, J. L. (1981) *J. Exp. Biol.* **92**, 333–335.
9. Baker, R. R., Mather, J. G. & Kennaugh, J. H. (1983) *Nature (London)* **301**, 78–80.
10. Frankel, R. B., Blakemore, R. P. & Wolfe, R. S. (1979) *Science* **203**, 1355–1356.
11. Torres de Araujo, F. F., Pires, M. A., Frankel, R. B. & Bicudo, C. E. M. (1985) *Biophys. J.* **50**, 375–378.
12. Lowenstam, H. A. (1962) *Geol. Soc. Am. Bull.* **73**, 435–438.
13. Gould, J. L., Kirschvink, J. L. & Deffeyes, K. S. (1978) *Science* **202**, 1026–1028.
14. Walcott, C., Gould, J. L. & Kirschvink, J. L. (1979) *Science* **184**, 180–182.
15. Mann, S., Sparks, N. H. C., Walker, M. M. & Kirschvink, J. L. (1988) *J. Exp. Biol.* **140**, 35–49.
16. Kirschvink, J. L., Jones, D. S. & MacFadden, B. J. (1985) *Magnetite Biomineralization and Magnetoreception in Organisms: A New Biomagnetism* (Plenum, New York).
17. Heywood, D. R., Bazylinski, D. A., Garrattreed, A., Mann, S. & Frankel, R. B. (1990) *Naturwissenschaften* **77**, 536–538.
18. Chang, S. R. & Kirschvink, J. L. (1989) *Annu. Rev. Earth Planet. Sci.* **17**, 169–195.
19. Walker, M. M., Kirschvink, J. L., Perry, A. S. & Dizon, A. E. (1985) in *Magnetite Biomineralization and Magnetoreception in Organisms: A New Biomagnetism*, eds. Kirschvink, J. L., Jones, D. S. & MacFadden, B. J. (Plenum, New York), pp. 154–166.
20. Fuller, M., Goree, W. S. & Goodman, W. L. (1985) in *Magnetite Biomineralization and Magnetoreception in Organisms: A New Biomagnetism*, eds. Kirschvink, J. L., Jones, D. S. & MacFadden, B. J. (Plenum, New York), pp. 103–151.
21. O'Reilly, W. (1984) *Rock and Mineral Magnetism* (Blackie, London).
22. Stacey, F. D. & Banerjee, S. K. (1974) *Physical Principles of Rock Magnetism* (Elsevier, New York).
23. Cisowski, S. (1981) *Phys. Earth & Planet. Inter.* **26**, 56–62.
24. Hallgren, B. & Sourander, P. (1958) *J. Neurochem.* **3**, 41–51.
25. Butler, R. F. & Banerjee, S. K. (1975) *J. Geophys. Res.* **80**, 4049–4058.
26. Gorby, Y. A., Beveridge, T. J. & Blakemore, R. P. (1988) *J. Bacteriol.* **170**, 834–841.
27. Vali, H. & Kirschvink, J. L. (1990) in *Iron Biomineralization*, eds. Frankel, R. P. & Blakemore, R. P. (Plenum, New York), pp. 97–115.
28. Kirschvink, J. L. (1992) *Automedica* **14**, 257–269.
29. Drayer, B. P., Burger, P., Darwin, R., Riederer, S., Herfkens, R. & Johnson, G. A. (1986) *Am. J. Neuroradiol.* **7**, 373–80.
30. Drayer, B. P., Olanow, W., Burger, P., Johnson, G. A., Herfkens, R. & Riederer, S. (1986) *Radiology* **159**, 493–498.
31. Chen, J. C., Hardy, P. A., Clauberg, M., Joshi, J. G., Parravano, J., Deck, J. H. N., Henkelman, R. M., Becker L. E. & Kucharczyk, W. (1989) *Radiology* **173**, 521–526.
32. Bizzi A., Brooks, R. A., Brunetti A., Hill J. M., Alger, J. R., Miletich R. S., Francavilla, T. L. & Di Chiro, G. (1990) *Radiology* **177**, 59–65.
33. Adair, R. K. (1992) *Phys. Rev. A* **46**, in press.
34. Pool, R. (1990) *Science* **249**, 1378–1381.

Reprinted with permission from *Nature* **374**, 123 (1995). Copyright 1995 Macmillan Magazines Limited.

# Ferromagnetism and EMFs

SIR — The question of whether weak, extremely low-frequency electromagnetic fields (EMFs) can cause cancer always generates heated debate (see, for example, refs 1–3). In addition to epidemiological studies, a substantial body of literature exists on EMF stimulation of cells grown *in vitro* (for example, refs 4, 5). Although numerous effects have been reported, many have been difficult to replicate (see refs 6, 7), and no clear biophysical mechanism has emerged. Many of the proposed mechanisms, like ion cyclotron resonance[8], have drawn criticism for being physically unrealistic (see ref. 9).

From developments in a totally unrelated field, there may be a much simpler, as yet overlooked, mechanism for explaining many of these *in vitro* EMF cellular effects. For the past two decades, the study of the biologically precipitated ferrimagnetic mineral magnetite ($Fe_3O_4$) has relied heavily on the use of ultrasensitive superconducting quantum interference device (SQUID) magnetometers to quantify trace levels of magnetite in various biological and laboratory materials[10,11]. It rapidly became clear that unique clean-laboratory techniques were required for this work because of the ubiquitous presence of ferromagnetic contamination. This contamination included ferromagnetic particulates present not only in the dust in the air, but also adsorbed onto the surfaces of laboratory equipment, present within glass and plastics, and even in reagent-grade laboratory chemicals and water.

We have encountered the same problem in our recent attempts to grow cells in tissue culture for an investigation of their magnetic properties. It is customary to use disposable, pre-sterilized plastic labware (flasks, pipettes, centrifuge tubes, and so on) and commercially prepared culture media in tissue-culture experiments because of their convenience and the assumption of a high level of quality control and cleanliness. We have found that none of these materials is free of ferromagnetic particulate contamination. Liquid-transfer manipulations, typical of cell-culture protocols, wash these particles from the surfaces of flasks and pipettes, and concentrate them with the cells during centrifugation. As an example, in a sham experiment we used 50 ml of leukocyte culture medium to rinse ten plastic T-250 flasks, ten 10-ml pipettes and ten 50-ml centrifuge tubes. After final centrifugation, we detected the equivalent of 160 ng magnetite in the rinsate, and the magnetic data indicated that the contaminants are small particles, usually in the sub-100-nm size range. As 160 ng magnetite equates to about 32 million 100-$nm^3$, this can be compared to the approximately 1 million cells that would have been produced in an equivalent culture volume.

Magnetite particles, 100 nm in diameter, either naked or coated with bovine serum albumin, are readily taken up by human white blood cells, including nonphagocytic lymphocytes as well as phagocytes[12]. Because the ferromagnetic particles interact strongly with magnetic fields, their presence in cell cultures, at a number density far higher than that of the cells, may provide a simple mechanism to account for links between EMF exposure and *in vitro* biological effects. A simple calculation shows that the mechanical energy present in a single 100-nm magnetite crystal exposed to a 60-Hz, 0.1-mT magnetic field is many times the thermal background noise[13]. Such particles, if adsorbed on cell surfaces or ingested by the cells, could conceivably transfer this energy to contiguous cell structures such as mechanically activated ion channels (which operate with a gating force close to the thermal noise limit[14,15]), and thereby alter cytoplasmic ion concentrations sufficiently to produce the observed biological effects.

We are not aware that the authors of any of the published studies of *in vitro* EMF effects have either controlled for, or attempted to reduce the levels of, ferromagnetic contamination. Although this is understandable, because the particles are difficult to detect and quantify except by sensitive magnetometry, their existence should not be ignored. *In vitro* studies may ultimately provide the information that will explain the connection between EMF exposure and biological effects, and as such they constitute roughly half of the projects at present being sponsored by the 5-year, $65 million NIEHS/DOE research programme on the biological effects of EMF. However, any effect of EMF exposure on cultured cells, if it is due to the presence of ferromagnetic contaminants, would have no relevance to *in vivo* biology. Data used to establish human exposure standards to electromagnetic fields must rely on properly controlled experiments.

**Atsuko K. Kobayashi**
**Joseph L. Kirschvink**
*Division of Geological & Planetary Sciences,*
*California Institute of Technology,*
*Pasadena,*
*California 91125, USA*
**Michael H. Nesson**
*Department of Biochemistry & Biophysics,*
*Oregon State University,*
*Corvallis,*
*Oregon 97331, USA*

1. Pool, R. *Nature* **349**, 554 (1991).
2. Florig, H.K. *Science* **257**, 468 (1992).
3. Hilemann, B. *Chem. Engng News* **71**, 15–29 (1993).
4. Goodman, R., Wei, L-X., Bumann, J. & Shirley-Henderson, A. *Bioelectrochem. Bioenerget.* **29**, 185–192 (1992).
5. Blackman, C.F., Benane, S.G. & House, D.E. *Bioelectromagnetics* **12**, 173–182 (1991).
6. Lacy-Hulbert, A., Wilkins, R., Metcalfe, J.C. & Hesketh, R. *Bioelectromagnetics Soc. 16th a. meet.* (abstr.) 52 (Bioelectromagnetics Soc., Copenhagen, 1994).
7. Saffer, J.D. & Thurston, S.J. *Bioelectromagnetics Soc. 16th a. meet.* (abstr.) 54 (Bioelectromagnetics Soc., Copenhagen, 1994).
8. Liboff, A.R. *J. Biol. Phys.* **13**, 99–102 (1985).
9. Adair, R.K. *Phys. Rev.* **A34**, 1039–1048 (1991).
10. Walker, M.M., Kirschvink, J.L., Perry, A.S. & Dizon, A.E. in *Magnetite Biomineralization and Magnetoreception in Organisms: A New Biomagnetism* (eds Kirschvink, J.L., Jones D.S. & MacFadden, B.J.) 154–166 (Plenum, New York, 1985).
11. Kirschvink, J.L., Kobayashi-Kirschvink, A. & Woodford, B.J. *Proc. natn. Acad. Sci. U.S.A.* **89**, 7683–7687 (1992).
12. Matsunaga, T., Hashimoto, K., Nakamura, N., Nakamura, K. & Hashimoto, S. *Appl. Microbiol. Biotechnol.* **31**, 401–405 (1989).
13. Kirschvink, J.L. *Phys. Rev.* **A46**, 2178–2184 (1992).
14. Denk, W. & Webb, W.W. *Phys. Rev. Lett.* **63**, 207–210 (1989).
15. Howard, J. & Hudspeth, A.J. *Neuron* **1**, 189–199 (1988).

**123**

*Biological Effects of Low-Frequency Electromagnetic Fields*

Reprinted by permission from *Proc. Nat. Acad. Sci.* **91**, 2925-2929 (1994). Copyright 1994 by the National Academy of Sciences, U.S.A.

# Constraints of thermal noise on the effects of weak 60-Hz magnetic fields acting on biological magnetite

Robert K. Adair

Department of Physics, Yale University, New Haven, CT 06511

*Contributed by Robert K. Adair, December 20, 1993*

**ABSTRACT** Previous calculations of limits imposed by thermal noise on the effects of weak 60-Hz magnetic fields on biological magnetite are generalized and extended to consider multiple signals, the possibility of anomalously large magnetosome structures, and the possibility of anomalously small cytoplasm viscosities. The results indicate that the energies transmitted to the magnetite elements by fields less than 5 $\mu$T, characteristic of the electric power distribution system, will be much less than thermal noise energies. Hence, the effects of such weak fields will be masked by that noise and cannot be expected to affect biology or, therefore, the health of populations.

Biological magnetite, $Fe_3O_4$, a ferrimagnetic metallic compound, with a saturation magnetism about 30% of that of iron, is usually found in single-domain units covered with a thin membrane, called magnetosomes. Low-frequency magnetic fields induce a torque on these domains that might affect biology in a manner that could result in consequences important to public health (8, 14, 15). However, if that field is so small that the induced torques are much less than the stochastic Brownian-motion torques from thermal agitation, the torques from the fields will be masked by that noise and cannot be expected to be biologically significant. In particular, we consider affects of a canonical 60-Hz 5-$\mu$T field, one-tenth of the earth's DC field, but appreciably greater than the maximum exposures to populations from the electric power distribution system. In considering the details of the interactions and the limits on the effects of such fields, it is convenient to consider two kinds of magnetite elements, composite systems and single magnetosomes.

Magnetosomes are generally found in chain-like assemblies, with their magnetic moments aligned, in the interior of cells. The individual magnetosomes are tied to cell bodies, probably through the cytoskeleton. In such an assembly, torques on the magnetosomes are transmitted to the cell body through structures that secure the magnetosome to that body. Hence the magnetic field acts to rotate the whole cell through forces on the individual magnetosomes. The movement of these composite systems, typically whole cells, is strongly constrained by the impedance of the surrounding environment that, for cells interior to the body, will not be less than that of the viscosity of water.

Although individual magnetosomes not rigidly tied to the whole cell structure do not seem to have been identified, I assume that such magnetosomes exist and, though secured to a place in the cell, may be free to rotate in that place and generate biological effects through that rotation. The rotation of these individual magnetosomes must also be constrained by the impedance of their environment that will be no less than that of the viscosity of the cytoplasm in which they are immersed. Since the energy transfers to quasi-free individual magnetosomes are less strongly constrained than that of the

composite systems, such transfers must be considered in analyses of possible biological effects of 60-Hz magnetic fields. Consequently, most of this discussion is directed toward the establishment of limits on the possible interactions of hypothetical mechanisms.

If the rotation of the composite system or single magnetosome is to affect biology, the magnetite system must be coupled to an element through some harness so that motion of the magnetite system changes the biologically sensitive conformation of that element. That transition must require an energy in excess of $kT$, where $k$ is Boltzmann's constant and $T$ is the absolute temperature, if it were not to occur regularly through thermal agitation in the absence of any coupling to the 60-Hz magnetic field. The viscous impedance of a harness and the addition of a substantial activation energy add to the minimum energy transfer required if the rotation of the magnetosome is to affect biology. But both the coupling and the minimum energy requirement are model-dependent; hence, in these limiting calculations, we treat the magnetic system as if it were free and conclude, conservatively, that the system cannot affect biology if the energy transfer to the free system from the 60-Hz magnetic field is less than $kT$.

### Energy Transfers to Biological Elements

A time-varying magnetic field, $\mathbf{B}(t) = \mathbf{B}_0\cos \omega t$, will, in general, induce varying torques on a magnetite system with a moment of inertia $I$ and a magnetic moment, $\mu$, residing in equilibrium in an environment that may not be isotropic. That driving torque will be countered by binding and resistive torques that will vary with the angular displacement, $\theta$, and its time derivative. I write the total torque as a vector with components;

$$T_i = -\kappa_{ij}\theta_j - \beta_{ij}\overset{\circ}{\theta}_j + [\mathbf{B}(t) \times \boldsymbol{\mu}]_i + \chi_i(t), \qquad j = 1, 3. \quad [1]$$

Here $\kappa$ and $\beta$ are tensors and $\kappa_{ij}\theta_j$, $\beta_{ij}\overset{\circ}{\theta}_j$, and $[\mathbf{B}(t) \times \boldsymbol{\mu}]_i$ are components of vectors that are not, in general, aligned; $\chi_i(t)$ represents the effects of thermal agitation in the direction $\hat{\mathbf{i}}$.

By taking the direction of the total torque $\mathbf{T}$ as the base direction, I write the linear equation,

$$T = I\overset{\circ\circ}{\theta} = -\beta\overset{\circ}{\theta} - \kappa\theta + B_0\mu \cos \omega t \cos \phi \sin \zeta + \chi(t), \quad [2]$$

where the terms at the right are the components of the vector torques in the direction of the resultant $\mathbf{T}$, $\kappa$ and $\beta$ are now scalar coefficients, and $\theta$, $\overset{\circ}{\theta}$, and $\overset{\circ\circ}{\theta}$ are the components of the angular displacement, angular velocity, and angular acceleration, respectively, in the direction of the total torque. The angle $\phi$ is the angle between the direction of the imposed torque and the final acceleration and $\zeta$ is the angle between the imposed field, $\mathbf{B}_0\cos \omega t$, and the magnetic moment, $\mu$, of the element.

I ignored torques proportional to higher powers of displacement and velocity. In the spirit of a Taylor's expansion, for small displacements and velocities, the linear term must dominate; for larger displacements, more complex behavior is possible. However, since $\kappa$ is left a free parameter, any

The publication costs of this article were defrayed in part by page charge payment. This article must therefore be hereby marked "*advertisement*" in accordance with 18 U.S.C. §1734 solely to indicate this fact.

2925

variation of the binding force through high-order effects cannot affect the conclusions. And, since $\beta$ cannot be less than the value derived from the linear effect of viscosity, higher-order resistive effects can only add to the resistance and decrease the energy transfer.

I consider the four terms at the right in Eq. **2**:

**The Driving Torque.** The energy transferred to the system will be greatest for $\phi = 0$ and $\zeta = \pi/2$, and I adopt those values.

An appropriate conjunction of four vectors—the 60-Hz magnetic field, the earth's field, the magnetic moment of the magnetite element, and the biologically defined direction of the effective action—must obtain if the effect of the field is to be large. If the biological effect of the torque is proportional to $\hat{\mathbf{T}} \cdot \hat{\mathbf{n}}$, where the effective direction, $\hat{\mathbf{n}}$, is randomly set with respect to the direction of the torque, the energy transfer, proportional to $(\hat{\mathbf{T}} \cdot \hat{\mathbf{n}})^2$, will be greater than 50% of the maximum for only about 15% of the elements.

Since moveable magnetosomes tend to be aligned with the earth's field and the resultant vector torque $\mathbf{T}$ is proportional to $[\mathbf{B}(t) \times \boldsymbol{\mu}]$, 60-Hz fields in the direction of the earth's field may be least effective in transferring energy to magnetic systems. Hence, fields from power lines, generally near vertical outside of the right-of-way and partially aligned with the earth's field, can be expected to have their effects reduced by factors of the order of 5 from the maximum energy transfers derived here.

**Binding Torques.** Magnetosomes secured in place, but otherwise free to rotate, will be aligned with the earth's field $B_e$ and the binding torque will be $B_e\mu \sin\theta$. Since $\sin\theta < \theta$, for large angles, in the linear approximation, $\kappa < B_e\mu$. For other plausible situations, further constraints may exist and $\kappa \geq B_e\mu$. I retain generality by leaving $\kappa$, the retaining force constant, as a free parameter.

**Resistive Torques.** Since viscosity is complex on the microscopic level, it must be incoherent with other processes; hence, the dissipation factor, $\beta$, cannot be less than that from the viscous resistance of the fluid in which the elements are immersed. Hence, we choose, minimally, $\beta = 6\eta v$, the Stokes' Law value for a sphere with a volume $v$ equal to the volume of the element, where $\eta$ is the viscosity of the medium in which the element is imbedded. For elongated bodies with the magnetic moment in the direction of the longest axis, this form is conservative inasmuch as it will somewhat understate the resistance to the rotation of the bodies about their minor axes and overstate the maximum energy transfer to such systems. For the rotation of whole cells in the tissue plasma, we take the viscosity as that of water, $\eta_w = 0.0007$ N·s/m$^2$. For the rotation of individual magnetosomes in the interior of the cell, we consider a range of viscosities from that of water to the value of about 0.1 N·s/m$^2$, measured for rotating systems in the aqueous cytoplasm of eukaryote plant and mammalian cells (1, 2). Since the energy transfer to magnetite systems is largely bounded by the local viscosity, the uncertainties in that viscosity are important.

**Thermal Noise.** The magnetosome will undergo Brownian-like thermal agitation represented by $\chi(t)$.

## Signal and Noise Amplitudes

Since Eq. **2** is linear, we can write the solution to the equation as $\theta(t) = \theta_B(t) + \theta_{kT}(t)$, where $\theta_B(t)$ is the solution in the absence of noise, $\chi(t) = 0$, and $\theta_{kT}(t)$ is the solution with noise but no perturbing field, $B(t) = 0$.

Here, $\theta_B(t) = \theta_0\cos(\omega t + \phi)$, where $\phi$ is an irrelevant phase angle, and

$$\theta_0^2 = \frac{(B_0\mu)^2}{I^2(\omega_0^2 - \omega^2)^2 + \beta^2\omega^2}, \quad \text{where} \quad \omega_0^2 = \frac{\kappa}{I}. \quad [3]$$

From statistical mechanics and the Langevin equation,

$$\overline{\cos\theta_{kT}} = \coth\left(\frac{\kappa}{kT}\right) - \frac{kT}{\kappa}, \quad \text{or} \quad \overline{\theta_{kT}^2} \xrightarrow{\kappa > kT} \frac{2\,kT}{\kappa}. \quad [4]$$

Since the noise amplitude, $\theta_{kT}$, and the signal amplitude, $\theta_B$, are orthogonal, the time-average intensities simply add; $\overline{\theta^2(t)} = \overline{\theta_B^2(t)} + \overline{\theta_{kT}^2(t)}$. We write, for convenience, $\theta_{rms}^2 = \theta_0^2/2 = \overline{\theta_B^2(t)}$ and $\theta_{kT}^2 = \overline{\theta_{kT}^2(t)}$.

The dominant role that energy plays in statistical mechanics, and in information theory (3), follows largely from the orthogonality of noise amplitudes. Hence, we define the signal-to-noise ($S/N$) ratio in terms of energies and compare the mean kinetic and potential energies the system acquires from the external "signal" magnetic field with the characteristic "noise" energy, $kT$;

$$W_T = \frac{1}{2}I\omega^2\theta_{rms}^2, \quad W_V = \frac{1}{2}\kappa\theta_{rms}^2; \quad \text{hence,} \quad \frac{W_V}{W_T} = \frac{\omega_0^2}{\omega^2}. \quad [5]$$

Since at 60 Hz, for systems of interest, $\omega_0^2 \gg \omega^2$ and $W_V \gg W_T$, we need consider only the potential energy to establish energy-transfer limits. The mean noise potential energy, $\frac{1}{2}\kappa\theta_{kT}^2 = kT$; hence, the condition that the potential energy is less than $kT$ is the same as the condition that the amplitude, $\theta_{rms}$, induced by the 60-Hz field, must be less than the mean excursion, $\theta_{kT}$, induced by thermal agitation.

Neglecting $\omega^2$ in the term $\omega_0^2 - \omega^2$, of Eq. **3**,

$$W_V < \frac{(B_{rms}\mu)^2}{2}\frac{\kappa}{\kappa^2 + \beta^2\kappa^2}, \quad [6]$$

where $B_{rms}^2 = B_0^2/2$. Since these inequalities pertain to nearly free individual magnetosomes resident in cells and the resistive effects of the biological interaction are neglected, the inequalities are strong.

From Eq. **6**, the potential energy limit will be a maximum when the natural time constant, $\beta/\kappa$, is equal to $1/\omega$. Then,

$$W_V < \frac{(B_{rms}\mu)^2}{4\beta\omega} = B_{rms}^2\mu \cdot \frac{\mu}{4\beta\omega}. \quad [7]$$

The form at the right exploits the proportionality between $\mu$ and $\beta$ for single domains of magnetite. The magnetic moment of a magnetosome will be $\mu = H'v$, where $H' \approx 4.8 \times 10^5$ A/m is the magnetic field characteristic of magnetite domains (4). As the domains are roughly spherical, we take $\beta = 6\eta v$, where $\eta$ is the viscosity of the medium about the domain and $\mu/\beta = H'/6\eta$ is independent of the size of the domain. For a value of the viscosity $\mu'$ measured in units of the viscosity of water, $\mu/4\beta\omega \approx 7.5 \times 10^4/\mu'\ T^{-1}$. The value will be smaller for magnetite imbedded in a matrix of organic material such as the magnetosome membrane, even as the volume of the whole rotating system will be greater than the volume of the magnetite.

From Eq. **7**, for a 60-Hz field, $B_{rms} = 5\ \mu$T, the maximum energy transfer to a very large single-domain magnetosome, with a magnetic moment such that $B_e\mu = 25\ kT$, in a cellular environment with a viscosity of 0.005, will be $W_V = 0.14\ kT$. I take this as the maximum plausible transfer to a single magnetosome. But other limits are interesting. If the viscosity is as large as 100 times that of water (1), $W_V > kT$ only if $B_e\mu > 5700\ kT$. For a viscosity of zero, taking $\kappa = B_e\mu$, from Eq. **6**, $W_V > kT$ only if $B_e\mu > 200\ kT$.

According to Butler and Banerjee (5), the maximum possible size of such single-domain crystals stable with respect to transitions to a specific two-domain configuration varies strongly with the length/width ratio. Though their results

Biophysics: Adair

*Proc. Natl. Acad. Sci. USA 91 (1994)*     2927

admit very large domains for highly elongated crystals, other transitions may be favored for such crystals—and very large single-domain systems have not been found in nature. Biologically formed magnetite crystals have a variety of shapes and sizes (6) but single magnetosomes have not been identified with moments $\mu$ greater than that for which $B_e\mu = 25$ $kT$—and most have moments such that $B_e\mu \approx kT$. Indeed, magnetosomes found in magnetotactic bacteria are of that size (4), which is near the maximum theoretical size of stable cubic single domains of magnetite. Hence, excepting the existence of single-domain magnetosomes much larger than have been observed, even for very small viscosities, 60-Hz 5-$\mu$T magnetic fields acting on single magnetosomes cannot be expected to affect biology—or public health.

The energy of multidomain crystals will be more strongly constrained by a factor, $\mu/\mu'$, where $\mu'$ is the moment if the domain moments were perfectly aligned—i.e., if the magnetite assembly is saturated. Multidomain magnetite grains with diameters as large as 0.6 $\mu$m have been found in the human brain (6) with orientation energies, $B_e\mu$, that could be as great as 150 $kT$. For such a crystal, $W_V < 0.18\ kT$ for 60-Hz 5-$\mu$T magnetic fields. For composite systems such as cells, for a given magnetic moment, the energy limit of Eq. 7 should be multiplied by a factor $v/v' \ll 1$, where $v$ is the volume of the aligned magnetite and $v'$ is the total volume of the system. Hence, the energy induced in such systems will be small.

Again from Eq. 6, for the very large values of $\kappa$ relevant to elements held rigidly, $W_V \propto 1/\kappa$ and will be much smaller than the maximum values defined in Eq. 7. Assemblies of aligned magnetosomes with moments such that $B_e\mu \approx 5000\ kT$ have been observed in certain microorganisms (7). Such large assemblies are known to be made up of thousands of small domains (magnetosomes) attached rigidly by cytoskeleton elements to the cell as a whole. Then whole cells will oscillate under an external 60-Hz field. From Eq. 7, the maximum energy transfer to a spherical cell with a radius of 10 $\mu$m, holding a magnetic moment $\mu$ such that $B_e\mu = 5000\ kT$, will be less than 0.04 $kT$. But that maximum energy transfer supposes a binding torque very much larger than that from the earth's field, $\kappa \gg B_e\mu$. If the restoring force is taken as $B_e\mu$, from Eq. 6, $W_V < 2.5 \times 10^{-4}\ kT$.

With the value of $\kappa = \beta\omega$ set for maximum energy transfer and $B_{rms} = 5\ \mu$T,

$$\theta_{rms}^2 < \frac{(B_{rms}\mu)^2}{4\beta^2\omega^2}, \quad \theta_{rms} < B_{rms} \cdot \frac{\mu}{2\beta\omega} \rightarrow 0.106, \quad [8]$$

and the small-angle condition used in Eq. 3 is nominally satisfied for any pure magnetite domain whatever the size. The angle of excursion will be smaller by the factor $v/v'$ for multidomain composites. However, $\theta_{kT} \approx \sqrt{2kT/\kappa}$, the mean amplitude of thermal agitation will usually be larger (e.g., for $\kappa/kT = 10$, $\theta_{kT} \approx 0.45$ radians) and, since $\sin \theta < \theta$, the linearity of Eq. 2 will be impaired and the effective value of the restraining force parameter, $\kappa$, will be reduced. Since the maximum energy transfer is largely constrained by the resistive factor, $\beta$, and not by $\kappa$, the conclusions drawn from the linear equation are not much changed. Indeed, from Eq. 6, if $\kappa < \beta\omega$, which is the case for most systems, a smaller value of $\kappa$ leads to a smaller energy transfer.

## Time Dependencies

For the earth's field, $\omega = 0$ and $B_{rms} = B_e \approx 50\ \mu$T, $W_V = B_e\mu \gg kT$ for elements with large net magnetic moments. Hence, the rotational excursions of such magnetic elements must far exceed that induced by thermal fluctuations or by a 60-Hz 5-$\mu$T field. Then the smaller 60-Hz fields can affect biology in a manner different than the ubiquitous earth's field only

through mechanisms insensitive to frequencies much lower than 60 Hz. Kirschvink (8) has pointed out that cellular processes with the perquisite long time constants are known. For example, the opening and closing of membrane channels take place over times of the order of 0.1 s (9). Hence, there may be cellular systems that accommodate to configurational changes that take place over periods as long as 0.1 s but are affected significantly by more rapid excursions.

Such mechanisms would not be affected by noise if the changes in orientation due to noise were slow. We estimate the characteristic rate of change from noise by equating the time, $t$, required for characteristic Brownian movement angular excursions, $\theta_{Br}$, to equal the angular amplitudes, $\theta_{rms}$, induced by the 60-Hz fields and comparing that time to the characteristic time, $1/\omega$.

From the relations describing Brownian rotation,

$$\theta_{Br}^2 = \frac{2kT}{6\eta v}\ t = \theta_{rms}^2 = \frac{(B_{rms}\mu)^2}{4(6\eta v\omega)^2} \quad \text{and} \quad t = \frac{(B_{rms}\mu)^2}{48\eta v\omega^2\ kT}. \quad [9]$$

Then for the very large magnetosome with a moment such that $B_e\mu = 25kT$, for a 60-Hz magnetic field, $B_{rms} = 5\ \mu$T, and using a small value of viscosity, $\eta = 0.005$ N·s/m$^2$, we find the interaction time, $t = 1.8 \times 10^{-4}$ s $\ll 1/\omega$. Since the characteristic time for single-domain magnetosomes varies as the volume of the domain, smaller elements will have even shorter characteristic noise fluctuation times. For large composites, such as cells, for a given magnetic moment, the characteristic time varies as $1/v$, where $v$ is the volume of the cell, and the characteristic noise times are always small. Hence, a low-bandwidth filter could exist that excludes effects from the earth's field but admits 60-Hz effects—and almost all noise.

## Multiple Signals

**Coherence.** If many detectors act cooperatively, or "coherently," the signal-to-noise ratio of the set may be greater than the signal-to-noise ratio of an individual detector.

We address such coherence by examining the energy transfers from the field to a system of $M$ magnetosome detectors associated as if they were tied together mechanically—and are, therefore, completely coherent—so the sum of their torques act on some biologically sensitive element. The moment of the set will then be $M\mu$, where $\mu$ is the moment of an individual magnetosome.

From Eqs. 6 and 7, in the limit of zero viscosity, $\beta = 0$, the energy transfer to the system will be $M^2/\kappa$ times the energy transfer to one magnetosome acting alone. However, if the system responds coherently to the perturbing field, it must respond coherently to the earth's field. Hence, the binding torque $\kappa = MB_e\mu$ and the energy transfer to the system will be increased only by $M$. Since the noise of the set will be $M$ times the noise from one detector, the signal-to-noise ratio of the $M$ coherent detectors, $(S/N)_M$, will be the same as $S/N$ for one detector.

If the viscosity is large, $\beta\omega \gg B_e\mu$. But since $\beta$ is proportional to the volume of the magnetosome set and then proportional to $M$, $(S/N)_M$ of the set will still be equal to $S/N$ for the individual detector.

However, if the magnetosome is strongly bound by other mechanisms, and $\kappa \gg B_e\mu$, then $(S/N)_M = M(S/N)$. (And the ratio of signal amplitudes to noise amplitudes for the set of $M$ detectors will be greater by a factor $\sqrt{M}$ than for one detector.) However, from Eq. 6, $S/N \propto 1/\kappa$ and will be small for large values of $\kappa$, and the ratio of signal energy to noise energy for $M$ coherent magnetosome detectors will never be greater than the $S/N$ for one detector where $\kappa = B_e\mu$ and $\beta = 0$. Hence, even if many magnetosomes act coherently, their interaction with the canonical fields cannot be expected to affect biology.

**Incoherent Sources.** But the summation of signals from incoherent sources, acted upon by the same 60-Hz signal, can be more important. If, from a set of $K$ detectors, a subset of $M$ elements can activate a binary (yes–no) system, such as opening and closing a gate, with a signal $S \ll kT$, only for $K = (K/M)^2(kT/S)^2$ elements, will $(S/N)_K = 1$ (*Appendix A*). In other terms, for $M$ active elements, $(S/N)_M = \sqrt{M}(S/N)$. In particular, under the canonical 5-$\mu$T 60-Hz field, if appropriate summation processes are in effect, if $S/N = S/kT$ for one element has the maximum value of 0.14 for magnetosomes that are of the maximum observed size and have moments such that $B_e\mu = 25kT$, and if (e.g.) 50% of these magnetosomes are aligned so as to trigger a transition on a binary system through torques generated by the field, then $(S/N)_K = 1$ for $K = 200$ elements. However, the total magnetite is then such that $B_e\mu = 5000kT$ for the whole cell, which is near the maximum observed in any cell.

**Multiple Signals Over Time.** In general, the maximum possible signal-to-noise ratio is increased by a factor $\sqrt{Q}$ if the detector responds coherently to a train of $Q$ pulses (the paradigm is resonance action). Hence, in principle, the signal-to-noise ratio of a detector can be increased by a factor of 60 by responding coherently to the 3600 60-Hz pulses observed in a minute. However, this requires a detector frequency selectivity or bandwidth of about 1/3600 Hz—at exactly 60 Hz—which is not possible (10).

However, "rectification" mechanisms, such as suggested by Weaver and Astumian (11) in their consideration of biological effects of weak electrical fields and by Kirschvink (8) for magnetic fields, allow a significant periodic flow of product across the membrane by actions initiated by fields that induce energy transfers smaller than $kT$. In these models, the perturbing fields, which need not be precisely periodic and thus define a narrow bandwidth, change the transmission of the cell membrane by opening gates for specific ions or neutral molecules.

For weak signals where the signal energy, $dw \ll kT$, the induced current can generally be described by the Nernst equation (*Appendix B*),

$$I = I_0 \left[ -\frac{dw}{kT} + \frac{1}{2}\left(\frac{dw}{kT}\right)^2 \cdots \right], \qquad [10]$$

where $I_0$ is a "dark current" and $dw \approx B_e\mu\theta_{kT}\theta_0\cos\omega t = dw_0 \times \cos\omega t$.

Over a time $t \gg 1/\omega$, the mean number of molecules transmitted through the membrane as a consequence of the 60-Hz field will be $Q_s = (I_0/4)(dw_0/kT)^2 t$. There will also be a "noise" transfer across the membrane equal to the square root of the number of molecules passing through the membrane (in plus out). At equilibrium—with no external field—the probable drift will be $Q_{kT} = [(I_{in} + I_{out})t]^{1/2} \approx (2I_0t)^{1/2}$ molecules in a time $t$. For $K$ gates,

$$\left(\frac{S}{N}\right)_K = \frac{Q_s}{Q_{kT}} = \sqrt{\frac{I_0t}{32}}\left(\frac{dw_0}{kT}\right)^2. \qquad [11]$$

If the number of gates were increased by $A^2$, $I_0 \to A^2I_0$, and if the magnetic signal were reduced by a factor of $A$, $\theta_0 \to \theta_0/A$ and $dw_0 \to dw_0/A$, the signal-to-noise ratio will be reduced by the factor $1/A$.

The incremental transfer with time from rectification, which varies as the $\sqrt{t}$, may be important (11). By setting $S/N = 1$, in Eq. **11**, the rectified current will equal the mean thermal noise drift in a time, $t = (32/I_0)(kT/dw_0)^4$. Taking, for example, a maximal value of the dark current through one channel, in the absence of the field with the channel nomi-

nally closed, as $I_0 = 1$ s$^{-1}$, and the value, $dw_0/kT = 0.14$, calculated for a large magnetosome, such that $B_e\mu = 25kT$ in a 5-$\mu$T field, we find a time of $8 \times 10^4/P$ seconds for $P$ activated channels. Homeostatic effects that bring cells to equilibrium in the face of normal thermal drift will ensure that no biological effects follow from so small a rate of change. If there were very many channels, the transfer could be significant, but the amount of magnetite required to generate substantial signals is much greater than that which is found, or can be expected to be found, in a cell.

**Summation of Signals from Different Cells.** The effects of weak fields on cells through the conjunction of signals from many magnetosomes are limited by the amount of magnetite the cells hold. If mechanisms exist that can sum signals from the magnetite in different cells of an organism, that limit is impeached and bees (8, 12), and probably other species, detect small static magnetic fields that induce changes in individual detectors smaller than that from thermal noise through complex sensory mechanisms that sum the signals from many individual receptors thus increasing the signal-to-noise ratio substantially.

These mechanisms have been developed and honed by evolution through the advantages in survival and propagation accorded to those individual members of the species who are able to use this facility. However, the signal from 60-Hz fields is much reduced by the viscous impedance to the rapid cycling. And, since the ability to detect 60-Hz fields, not found in nature, could not confer any survival advantage in the past, we should not expect that the complex signal processing mechanisms that allow animals such as the honeybee to detect small DC magnetic field anomalies would be developed specially to process 60-Hz signals. Indeed, while honeybees seem to detect DC magnetic field anomalies smaller than 1 $\mu$T quite reliably, they do not seem to be as good at detecting 2.2-mT 60-Hz fields, fields several thousand times greater (13).

**Summary**

(*i*) For a 60-Hz 5-$\mu$T field, acting on biological magnetite, biologically deleterious effects can be expected only through mechanisms that are insensitive to the 10-times larger DC field of the earth. (*ii*) For any magnetite system, the kinetic energy induced by the field is negligible. (*iii*) For any cell-size composite system, the potential energy induced by the field is much less than the noise energy. Hence, any biological effects must stem from energies transmitted to quasi-free single magnetosomes in cells. But there is no histological evidence for the rotation of single magnetosomes inside of the cell. (*iv*) For such magnetosome, free to rotate inside of the cell, $W_V \ll kT$ for magnetosomes of that size, $B_e\mu \approx kT$, most generally found in biological systems, and the interaction of magnetic fields on such systems cannot affect biology. (*v*) If the cytoplasm viscosity is 100 times that of water, as indicated by some measurements (1), $W_V \ll kT$ for any magnetosome and the fields cannot affect biology. (*vi*) Though theoretical signal-to-noise ratios increase with the square root of the number $M$ of independent free magnetosome detectors in a cell, $(S/N)_M \geq 1$ only for very large numbers, $M$, of very large domains, of which a high portion are properly aligned to exercise a biological function insensitive to low-frequency perturbations; moreover, a special summation mechanism must operate.

In conclusion, 60-Hz magnetic fields weaker than 5 $\mu$T cannot be expected to generate biological effects through their interaction with biological magnetite because the small effects of the fields will always be masked by thermal agitation noise. However, the arguments presented here do not preclude effects from larger 60-Hz fields.

Biophysics: Adair

*Proc. Natl. Acad. Sci. USA* 91 (1994)    2929

## Appendix A: Signal-to-Noise Ratio

From standard information theory (3), the information transfer in bits, $M$, over a period, $t$, can be written, $M \geq (Wt)\log_2(1 + P/N) + \log_2\varepsilon$, where $P/N$ is the signal-to-noise power, $W$ is the channel bandwidth, and $\varepsilon < 1$ is the error probability. The error probability per bit in the presence of thermal noise can then be taken, setting $Wt = 1$, as $\varepsilon = 0.5/(1 + S/kT)$, where $S$ is the signal energy.

Then, for detectors that select one of two conditions, the probability of the detector answer being right is $p = 1 - 0.5/(1 + S/kT)$. For a set of $K$ detectors of which $Q$ are sensitive to the signal and for $S \ll kT$, the number required so that the excess that is "right" will equal the standard error is $K = (K/Q)^2(kT/S)^2$, and, for $K = Q$, $(S/N)_K = \sqrt{K}\,(S/kT)$.

## Appendix B: The Nernst Equation

Taking the number of closed gates in the membrane as $P_0$ and the number of open gates as $P_1 = P - P_0$, from the partition,

$$P_0 = P\,\frac{1}{1 + e^{-w/kT}} \quad \text{and} \quad P_1 = P\,\frac{e^{-w/kT}}{1 + e^{-w/kT}}. \quad [12]$$

Taking the current, $I_{\text{in}}$, proportional to the number of open gates,

$$I = I_{\text{in}} - I_{\text{out}} = N\left[\frac{e^{-w/kT}}{1 + e^{-w/kT}} - \frac{e^{-w_0/kT}}{1 + e^{-w_0/kT}}\right], \quad [13]$$

where $N$ is a proportionality constant and $w = w_0 + dw$, where $dw$ is the energy added by the field. For $dw \ll kT$,

$$I = I_0\left[e^{-dw/kT} - 1\right] \rightarrow I_0\left[-\frac{dw}{kT} + \frac{1}{2}\left(\frac{dw}{kT}\right)^2\right], \quad [14]$$

where $I_0 = N(e^{-w_0/kT})/(1 + e^{-w_0/kT})^2$.

The energy of interaction, $w$, between the magnetic field **B** and the magnetic moment, $\mu$, is $w = (\mathbf{B}\cdot\mu)$ and $dw = (d\mathbf{B}\cdot\mu) - B\mu\sin\theta\,d\theta$, where $\mathbf{B} = \mathbf{B}_e$, $d\mathbf{B} = \mathbf{B}_0\cos\omega t$, $\sin\theta = \theta_{kT} \approx (2kT/B_e\mu)^{1/2}$, and $d\theta = \theta_0\cos\omega t$. For $\kappa = B_e\mu$, from Eq. **3**, $\theta_0 < B_0/B_e$ and we write $\theta_0 = B_0/B_e$.

For the systems of most interest, $(\mathbf{B}_0\cdot\mu) = 0$, and

$$dw = dw_0\cos\omega t \approx \theta_{kt}\theta_0 B_0\cos\omega t$$

$$= \sqrt{\frac{2kT}{B_e}} \cdot \frac{B_0}{B_e} B_0\cos\omega t \quad [15]$$

and $dw_0/kT \approx 0.1\cos\omega t$ for the canonical system such that $B_0 = 5\mu\text{T}$ and $B_e\mu = 25kT$.

We estimate the dark current, per "closed" channel, as $I_0 = (n/\tau)(a/4\pi r^2)$, where $n$ is the difference in the density of molecules across the membrane, $a = 25 \times 10^{-20}$ m$^2$ is the area of a passage through the membrane, and $\tau = r^2(6\pi\eta\alpha/2kT) = 0.08$ s, for is the time the molecule, with a radius $\alpha = 5 \times 10^{-10}$ m, takes to diffuse a distance equal to cellular radius, $r = 10$ $\mu$m, by Brownian motion. For $n = (dV/ed)4\pi\varepsilon_0 r^2 = 10^6$, from the concentration of singly charged ions responsible for the potential difference of about $dV = 0.1$ V across the cell membrane with a thickness $d = 10^{-8}$ m, we find $I_0 = 0.0026$ molecule per s. Though the uncertainties in the estimate are large, we consider our use of $I_0 = 1$ per s per channel conservative.

1. Keith, A. D. & Snipes, W. (1974) *Science* **183**, 666–668.
2. Pollard, E. C. (1979) in *The Aqueous Cytoplasm*, ed. Keith, A. D. (Dekker, New York), pp. 9–15.
3. Raisbeck, G. (1964) *Information Theory* (MIT Press, Cambridge, MA), pp. 30–50.
4. Frankel, R. B. (1986) in *CRC Handbook of Biological Effects of Electromagnetic Fields*, eds. Polk, C. & Postow, E. (Chemical Rubber Co., Boca Raton, FL), pp. 169–196.
5. Butler, R. F. & Banerjee, S. K. (1975) *J. Geophys. Res.* **80**, 4049–4058.
6. Kirschvink, J. L., Kobayashi-Kirschvink, A. & Woodford, B. J. (1992) *Proc. Natl. Acad. Sci. USA* **89**, 7683–7687.
7. Vasli, H. & Kirschvink, J. L. (1990) in *Iron Biominerals*, eds. Frankel, R. B. & Blakemore, R. P. (Plenum, New York), pp. 97–115.
8. Kirschvink, J. L. (1992) *Phys. Rev. A* **46**, 2178–2184.
9. Moody, W. J. & Bosma, M. M. (1989) *J. Membr. Biol.* **107**, 179–188.
10. Adair, R. K. (1991) *Phys. Rev. A* **43**, 1039–1048.
11. Weaver, J. C. & Astumian, R. D. (1990) *Science* **247**, 459–462.
12. Walker, M. M. & Bitterman, M. E. (1985) *J. Comp. Physiol.* **157**, 67–73.
13. Kirschvink, J. L., Kuwajima, T., Ueno, S., Kirschvink, S. J., Diaz-Ricci, J. C., Morales, A., Barwig, S. & Quinn, K. (1992) *J. Gen. Physiol., Suppl.*, 225–240.
14. Adair, R. K. (1993) *Bioelectromagnetics* **14**, 1–5.
15. Adair, R. K. (1992) *Phys. Rev. A* **46**, 2185–2188.

Reprinted with permission from *Phys. Today* **47**, 30-37 (1994). Copyright 1994 American Institute of Physics.

# ELECTROSENSORY ORGANISMS

## By detecting weak electric fields from animate or inanimate sources, many aquatic animals acquire information used for orientation, communication and other critical behavior.

Joseph Bastian

Many aquatic animals have the ability to sense very weak electric fields. This electric sense is found in numerous species of marine and freshwater fish and in several amphibian species. Electrosensory abilities have also been reported in "higher" animals including the platypus and a semiaquatic mole.[1-3]

The sensitivity of the electrosensory systems responsible for this ability can be impressively high. Freshwater catfish respond to electric field gradients as low as 1 microvolt per centimeter, and marine sharks and rays are sensitive to gradients of less than 5 nanovolts per centimeter. This high sensitivity enables electrosensitive animals to locate prey using the weak fields due to current leakage from aquatic organisms. The animals with the highest sensitivities, marine sharks and rays, can navigate using the voltage gradients induced by ocean currents flowing in Earth's magnetic field as well as voltage gradients induced by their own movements.[4]

A subset of fish with electrosensory systems also possess electric organs, and these animals generate electric fields. In a few species, such as the Nile catfish and the South American electric eel, the electric organ can produce outputs of hundreds of volts. These fish use their strong discharges defensively to ward off predators as well as offensively to stun prey. Two large groups of so-called weakly electric fish, the South American Gymnotiformes and the African Mormyriformes, produce discharges in the millivolt range. These weak discharges, coupled with electroreceptors that are preferentially sensitive, or "tuned," to the discharges' frequency charac-

**Joseph Bastian** is a George Lynn Cross Research Professor in the zoology department at the University of Oklahoma, in Norman.

teristics, make up an "active" sensory system analogous to the echolocation system used by many species of bat. Active electrosensory systems provide the fish with a communication channel as well as a means of detecting the presence and quality of objects, or "electrolocation targets," in their immediate vicinity.[5,6]

### Electric organ discharges and fields

The signals generated by electric fish are amazingly diverse not only in amplitude but also in their temporal characteristics. Species are characterized as having "pulse" electric organ discharges or "wave" electric organ discharges depending on the frequency and regularity of the discharges. Figure 1 shows the South American weakly electric fish *Gymnotus carapo* and *Apteronotus leptorhynchus*, examples of "pulse" and "wave" fish, respectively, along with their electric organ discharge waveforms and spectra.

The discharges of pulse fish (figure 1a) consist of brief waveforms separated by longer intervals. Each species produces a characteristic pulse shape; the shapes range from simple monophasic waveforms to complex events consisting of several sequential phases, such as the triphasic discharge of *Gymnotus* (inset in figure 1a). The discharges of various species of pulse fish range[5] in width from about 100 microseconds to about 10 milliseconds. Although the pulse waveform for a given species is typically very constant, male and female pulses can differ, providing a cue for sex recognition, as discussed later.

The amplitude spectrum of the electric organ discharge of pulse fish is broad, having energy spread over a wide range of frequencies; however, the dominant frequency components vary among species. These spectral

© 1994 American Institute of Physics

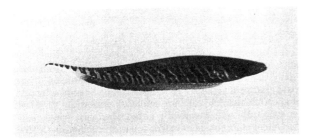

**a** Gymnotus carapo ('pulse' fish)

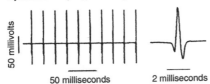

50 millivolts

50 milliseconds    2 milliseconds

**c** Apteronotus leptorhynchus ('wave' fish)

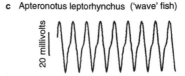

20 millivolts

2 milliseconds

**b**

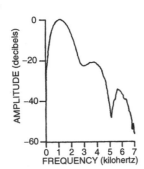

AMPLITUDE (decibels)

FREQUENCY (kilohertz)

**d**

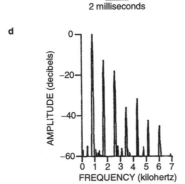

AMPLITUDE (decibels)

FREQUENCY (kilohertz)

**e**

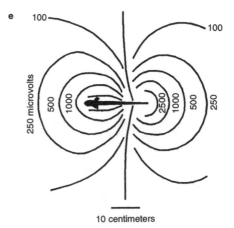

10 centimeters

**'Pulse' and 'wave' fish** and their electric signals.
**a–d:** Waveforms and amplitude spectra of the electric
organ discharges of a 12-cm-long *Gymnotus carapo* (left
side of figure) and of a 14-cm *Apteronotus leptorhynchus*
(right side of figure). Head-positive voltages are plotted
as upward deflections. **e:** Map of the electric organ
discharge field of *Apteronotus albifrons*, a species closely
related to *Apteronotus leptorhynchus*. Potential
measurements were made relative to a reference electrode
150 cm lateral to the fish. (Adapted from ref. 8.) **Figure 1**

differences, as well as time-domain differences in the
discharges, facilitate recognition by individuals of the
same species and minimize confusion resulting from the
occupation of a given habitat by many species.[5]

Wave fish produce continuous, quasisinusoidal waveforms of very constant frequency. The discharge frequencies of individuals of a given species are confined to a
"species range" (500–900 Hz for *Apteronotus leptorhynchus*), and within a species individuals typically have
different frequencies. The amplitude spectra of wave
discharges (figure 1d) consist of narrow peaks at the
fundamental frequency and at several higher harmonics.
When only a few species of wave fish occupy the same
habitat, the species' frequency ranges usually overlap

only minimally, insuring clear communication and electrolocation channels for each group.[5] However, when
larger numbers of species coexist, communication and
electrolocation may at times be compromised because the
species' electric organ discharge frequencies overlap significantly.[7] Although the discharge frequency of individual wave fish is usually very constant, they do sometimes
modulate their frequency, as do pulse fish; both groups
engage in electrical signaling behavior during mating and
aggressive encounters.

The geometry of the field resulting from the electric
organ discharge is roughly dipole-like, as figure 1e shows.
The field surrounding the rostral (headward) portion of
the animal is expanded in the headward direction, with

the result that equipotential lines near the animal are approximately parallel to the body surface. Beyond about 10 cm from the fish, the field potential and gradient fall off as the inverse second and third power of distance, respectively, as expected for a dipole source.[8] Closer to the animal, however, the field decays much more slowly; the potential falls off approximately as the −0.5 power of distance.

Plots of field geometry such as figure 1e are typically based on peak-to-peak or rms values and provide a somewhat simplified view because they ignore the temporal variations in the electric organ discharge. Recent studies show that in *Apteronotus* the discharge waveforms measured at various sites along the body are not in phase. Discharge maxima and minima propagate over the surface of the animal in a cyclic fashion, with the result that the shape of the field varies as a function of time within the discharge cycle.[9]

## Mechanism of electric discharge

Figure 2 illustrates the operation of a relatively simple electric organ—that of the electric eel. The organ, located within the animal's long trunk and tail, is composed of flattened cells (red) known as electrocytes. The electrocytes, which are modified muscle cells that have over evolutionary time lost the ability to contract, are arranged in series within several parallel columns occupying most of the volume of the trunk and tail. The electrocytes are similar to other "excitable" tissues, such as nerve or muscle cells, in that they can produce transient electrical events.

When an electrocyte is inactive, its interior is at a negative potential relative to the surrounding body fluids, as indicated in figure 2 for the resting electrocyte. The internal negativity results from unequal concentrations of ions in solution inside and outside the cells and unequal permeability of the membrane to these ions. Sodium ions are more concentrated outside the cell, and potassium ions are more concentrated inside the cell. These concentration gradients are maintained by metabolically driven ion pumps within the cell membrane.

The cell membrane also contains several categories of ion channels. These can be very specific with respect to the types of ions that can pass through them; by changing their permeability, the channels can act as "gates" for these ions. For example, the voltage-sensitive sodium channel is relatively impermeable to Na$^+$ ions when a cell's internal potential is at its resting negative value—about −90 mV for the eel electrocyte. But the channel conductance increases dramatically when the

cell's internal potential becomes less negative or depolarized. In addition to voltage-sensitive channels, there exist channels sensitive to the intracellular concentration of specific ions (the calcium-activated potassium channel, for example) and chemically gated channels, whose conductances change when neurotransmitter substances bind to receptor molecules on the surface of the membrane.

The eel's electric organ discharge is initiated when nerve impulses originating in the brain and conducted along spinal motor neurons cause the neurotransmitter acetylcholine to be liberated from the nerve terminals (blue triangles in figure 2) associated with the electrocytes' caudal (tailward) surface. The released acetylcholine binds to the electrocytes, opening a chemically gated channel; this results in an initial influx of positive ions. The resulting depolarization causes voltage-sensitive sodium channels to open, and the subsequent influx of Na$^+$ ions briefly reverses the cells' internal potential, making it approximately 50 mV positive. (Recall that the potential inside the resting electrocyte is about 90 mV negative.) An inactivation process inherent in the channel mechanism stops the sodium influx, allowing the electrocytes to repolarize to their resting potential.

A single electrocyte's discharge, diagrammed in figure 2, lasts 2–3 milliseconds. Because voltage-sensitive sodium channels are present only on the cells' caudal surface, the sodium flux is unidirectional in the caudal-to-rostral direction, as indicated by the arrows. Insulating tissue surrounding the organ reduces current flow in local circuits, so when the approximately 6000 serially arranged electrocytes are synchronously activated, a head-positive discharge in excess of 600 volts results.[10] The more complex discharge waveforms seen in many species of South American and African weakly electric fish arise as a result of further specialization of the electrocytes or more complex activation patterns of subdivisions of the electric organ.[10,11]

## Electroreceptor organs

We now turn from organs that produce electricity to organs that detect it. The initial stage in processing received electrosensory information involves transforming the stimulus, a change in potential across the skin, into changes in the pattern of nerve impulses transmitted to the brain. This is accomplished by electroreceptor cells (related to auditory hair cells) contained in electroreceptor organs within the animal's skin.

Electroreceptor organs are commonly divided into two categories based on their anatomy and their sensitivity to electric signals.[12] Low-frequency electrorecep-

**Mechanism** by which the electric eel, *Electrophorus electricus*, generates an electric organ discharge. The plot shows the discharge waveform produced by a single electrocyte. **Figure 2**

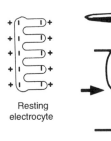

Resting electrocyte

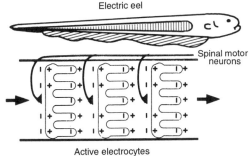

Electric eel

Spinal motor neurons

Active electrocytes

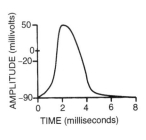

**Electroreceptor organs.** Equivalent circuits and illustrations of receptor cell currents are shown for the ampullae of Lorenzini, low-frequency marine receptors (**a**), and the tuberous, or high-frequency, receptors of weakly electric freshwater fish (**b**). Small x's near the sensory neurons represent neurotransmitter released by the receptor cells; "cc" stands for the covering cells. Other terms are described in the text. (Adapted from ref. 15.) **Figure 3**

tors include the ampullae of Lorenzini of marine sharks and rays and the ampullary receptors of freshwater fish. These are most sensitive to frequencies below 50 Hz, and the minimum voltage gradient, or threshold stimulus, capable of generating responses can be as low as 50 microvolts per centimeter in freshwater species and 1 $\mu$V/cm in marine organisms. The South American and African weakly electric fish possess high-frequency receptors, or tuberous receptors, in addition to low-frequency receptors. These are less sensitive to voltage gradients, having thresholds ranging from tens to hundreds of microvolts per centimeter, and are "tuned" to the major frequency components of the electric organ discharges of the respective species.[13,14]

Figure 3a summarizes the operation of a marine ampullary receptor. Hundreds of individual receptor cells (red) are grouped together at the base of an epidermal pit, which communicates to the surface of the skin via a canal roughly 1 mm in diameter and up to 20 cm in length. The canal is filled with a jelly-like substance having a resistivity approximating that of seawater, while the tissue lining the canal has a higher resistance. Because the resistance along the canal (the luminal resistance $R_L$) is much lower than the resistance $R_W$ across the wall, the canal forms a very effective cable connecting the interior of the organ to the external environment. The wall capacitance $C_W$, attributable to the cell membranes lining the canal, provides a low-impedance pathway shunting high-frequency signals away from the receptor cells. This contributes to the organ's low-frequency tuning; however, mechanisms intrinsic to the receptor cells themselves also determine their frequency selectivity.[15]

The receptor cells lie embedded in the tissues below the ampullary floor, with only the small "apical" portion of their membrane protruding into the lumen, or interior, of the canal. The larger, "basal" portion of the cells resides below the ampullary lining and communicates with the electrosensory neurons. The apical membrane is coupled to the exterior of the animal via the low-resistance canal, and the basal region is in direct contact with the animal's internal tissues. Therefore the receptor cells effectively measure any voltages that develop across the skin resistance ($R_S$) and across the resistance $R_T$ of the internal tissues.

When the outside of the animal becomes negative relative to its interior, current flows through the receptor cells and into the lumen of the ampullae, as illustrated for the enlarged receptor cell by the black arrows. Current entering through the large-surface-area (and therefore low-resistance) basal portion of the receptor causes an insignificant voltage drop compared with that which develops across the higher-resistance apical membrane. Hence the inside of the receptor cell becomes less negative or depolarized. This initial depolarization opens a voltage-sensitive channel, allowing calcium ions to enter the cell. The calcium current $I_{Ca^{2+}}$ further depolarizes the cell and increases the rate at which the receptor cell releases neurotransmitter, increasing the frequency with which nerve impulses are sent to the brain. The depolarizing effect of the $Ca^{2+}$ influx is counterbalanced by an outward flow of potassium ions $I_{K^+}$, which repolarizes the cell after a short delay. The potassium channel is probably activated by the increased intracellular $Ca^{2+}$ ion concentration (a calcium-activated potassium channel).[16]

The opposite stimulus polarity, outside positive, increases the receptors' internal negativity, with the result that transmitter release and nerve impulse frequency are reduced.

The tuberous, or high-frequency, receptors (figure 3b) are restricted to the South American and African freshwater fish that generate electric organ discharges. There are two subtypes of these receptors. One is specialized to encode precisely the timing of the electric organ discharges, while the second encodes discharge amplitude. Several features of tuberous receptors relate to the freshwater habitat and to the receptors' frequency tuning; as a result, they contrast with the characteristics of marine ampullary receptors. The canals linking the receptors to the exterior are much shorter in freshwater animals. The skin of freshwater fish is of very high resistance compared with that of the internal tissues, and therefore the principal voltage drop occurs across the skin. Unlike in marine sharks and rays, the voltage drop across the relatively low-resistance internal tissue contributes little compared with that developed across the skin, so there is no advantage to placing the cells deep within the body. The lumen of the tuberous receptor canal is filled with a loose collection of epidermal cells (yellow in figure 3b), and a sheet of covering cells further protects the receptor cells from the dilute freshwater environment.[12]

The position of the receptor cells within the organ also differs from that in marine fish. The cells lie predominantly within the lumen of the organ, with only small basal portions of their membrane penetrating the floor. This arrangement results in reversed polarity sensitivity for freshwater electroreceptors compared with that of the marine ampullary receptors. Outside-positive stimuli depolarize these cells, because the predominant voltage drop occurs across the smaller, high-resistance basal region of the cell, as illustrated by black arrows for the enlarged tuberous receptor.

The tuberous electroreceptors act as bandpass filters tuned to the spectral characteristics of the fish's electric organ discharge. This tuning is due partly to the passive electrical properties of the organ itself and partly to the characteristics of the receptor cells' ion channels. The walls of tuberous organs are constructed in a manner that reduces wall capacitance $C_W$, minimizing the shunting of high frequencies to the surrounding tissues. The series capacitance of the covering cells' membrane, plus that of the large, convoluted apical surface of the receptors, summarized as $C_L$, acts as a blocking capacitor and contributes to the receptors' low-frequency insensitivity.[10] Outside-positive stimuli initially depolarize tuberous receptor cells and, as in marine ampullary receptors, probably activate an inward calcium current $I_{Ca^{2+}}$. The influx of $Ca^{2+}$ ions further depolarizes the cells and increases the rate at which neurotransmitter is liberated. An outward potassium ion current $I_{K^+}$, which is probably calcium activated, follows the depolarization.[15]

Brief stimuli cause these receptors to resonate, or "ring." The resonant frequency of these receptors, recorded as damped oscillations outside the receptor pore, typically matches the frequency to which the receptors are tuned. This electrical resonance underlies the cell's tuning and is thought to be due to cyclic activation of the inward calcium and outward potassium currents. Electrical resonance similar to that first observed for electroreceptors[10] was later found in hair cells in auditory systems and probably contributes to auditory frequency selectivity in some cases.[17] (See the article by A. J. Hudspeth and Vladislav S. Markin on page 22.)

## Electric communication

The unique characteristics of electric organ discharge waveforms (such as the pulse duration and number and the sequence of phases in pulse fish or the discharge frequency and harmonic content in wave fish) contain sufficient information to enable individuals to recognize one another as members of the same species. Additionally, in many species, discharge characteristics differ between males and females, facilitating sex recognition.

A South American wave fish, *Sternopygus*, was the first example found in which the electric organ discharges of males and females differ. Carl Hopkins of Cornell University, studying these fish in their natural habitat, found that mature males have electric organ discharge frequencies of about 60 Hz, while mature females have frequencies of about 120 Hz. During the breeding season, males produce stereotyped changes in their discharges when females swim by: transient frequency increases termed "rises" and brief pauses, or "interruptions." Hopkins used an electronic signal generator to mimic fish signals and showed that the males readily produced these electrical courtship displays in response to sinusoidal

signals as long as the signal frequency was typical of females. Signals mimicking the discharges of males or of other species failed to elicit courtship responses. These studies demonstrated that the fish use their ability to generate and receive electrical signals as a communication channel.[5]

Pulse fish also can identify members of the opposite sex on the basis of their electric organ discharges. In this case, however, time-domain rather than frequency-domain cues seem most important. The discharges of male and female pulse fish often differ in waveform duration, and males will respond with courtship displays to tape recordings of the discharges of females and to mimics as simple as square pulses, as long as the waveform duration is similar to that of a female's electric organ discharge pulse.[18]

The temporal cues resolved by the fish can be amazingly subtle; one species of African fish discriminates between pulses differing in duration by only 200 microseconds. This acuity relies on electroreceptors specialized to detect the precise timing of electrical events and requires that the signals themselves be minimally distorted by the aquatic environment. Unlike acoustic signals, which can be significantly degraded as they are transmitted through the environment, electric signals, owing to their nonpropagated nature, can maintain their temporal fine structure over the range of distances within which they are detectable.[18] The repetition rate of pulse fish discharges is also variable, and such fish use stereotyped sequences of pulse-rate modulations of the electric organ discharge in communication as well.[5,19]

## Passive electrolocation

The ability to locate objects in the environment using information acquired with the electrosensory system is termed electrolocation. Electrolocation is considered passive when the animal relies on electrical signals emanating from extrinsic sources. It is active when the information arises from the interaction of a target with an individual's electric organ discharge field or when the information results from the animal's own movements.

A shark's ability to discover fish buried in the sand by orienting to the potentials produced by the prey's gills is an example of passive electrolocation. Elegant experiments by A. J. Kalmijn of the Scripps Institution of Oceanography demonstrated that sharks will preferentially attack electrodes producing very weak electric fields even when sources of food odor are present.[4] The threshold voltage gradient capable of eliciting this feeding behavior is on the order of 5 nV/cm. This astounding sensitivity is one to two orders of magnitude lower than the measurable threshold sensitivity of individual electroreceptor neurons. Presumably, central nervous system processing that integrates inputs from populations of receptors enables the fish to resolve such weak signals.

The electrical sensitivity of sharks and rays is sufficient to allow these animals to respond to voltage gradients induced by the flow of ocean currents through Earth's magnetic field. Induced fields range from less than 5 to at least 500 nV/cm. It is likely that these electric fields provide important orientational cues or electrical landmarks that aid electroreceptive animals as they navigate. Kalmijn showed that free-swimming stingrays, in a locale where the strength and direction of the environmental electric fields were known, changed course in a predictable manner when the field direction was altered with an imposed field.[4] It is also possible

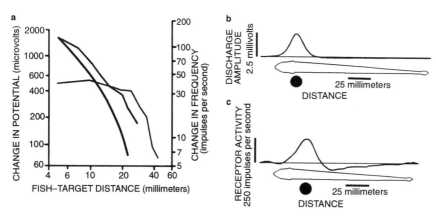

**Effect of distance** on active electrolocation. **a:** Changes in potential across the skin of *Apteronotus leptorhynchus* due to a 12-mm-diameter cylindrical metal object (black curve), and corresponding changes in electroreceptor and cerebellar nerve impulse frequencies (red and blue curves, respectively), as a function of lateral fish–target distance. **b,c:** Spatial profiles of changes in electric organ discharge amplitude and electroreceptor activity due to the presence of the 12-mm metal target (black circles). **Figure 4**

that sharks and rays respond to the voltage gradients induced as *they* swim through Earth's magnetic field—a type of active electrolocation—and use this information as the basis of a compass sense. Kalmijn trained stingrays to choose an enclosure based on its position relative to Earth's magnetic field—for example, to enter an enclosure in the magnetic east of a holding tank and to avoid enclosures in the west. Reversing the horizontal component of the magnetic field with Helmholtz coils reversed the animals' preferences, providing evidence that the animals can sense and orient to Earth-strength magnetic fields.[4]

## Active electrolocation

Weakly electric fish also locate and identify objects by analyzing the distortions of their electric organ discharge fields caused by those electrolocation targets. For an object to be detectable, its impedance must differ from that of the water; the fish can discriminate both resistive and capacitive characteristics.[20] The stimulus encoded by the electroreceptors during active electrolocation consists of amplitude and, in some cases, phase modulations of the electric organ discharge waveform. The range and resolution of active electrolocation are determined both by the characteristics of the distortion in the electric organ discharge due to the target and by the amplitude sensitivity and AM frequency response characteristics of the electroreceptors.

The distance between the fish and the target is the principal determinant of the distortion amplitude; as the black curve in figure 4a shows, voltage changes measured across the animal's skin decay rapidly as a function of fish–target distance. Larger objects will, of course, cause larger amplitude distortions. However, distortion gains resulting from increased object size are small relative to losses due to increased target distance: The diameter of cylindrical objects must be increased roughly fivefold to compensate for the amplitude reduction resulting from doubling the fish–target distance.[21,22] The spatial extent of a given object's effect, or "electrical image," is large relative to the actual target size, as shown by measurements of voltage changes across the skin (figure 4b). Because there is no focusing mechanism associated with the electric sense, changes in receptor activity (figure 4c)

closely parallel the spatial distribution of voltage changes, and "fuzzy images" are conveyed to the brain.

Motion of the fish relative to electrolocation targets imparts a temporal component to the electric organ discharge distortions, and the spectral characteristics of these amplitude modulations also influence an electrical target's detectability. Electroreceptors and many higher electrosensory neurons are most sensitive to relatively high AM frequencies, between 32 and 64 Hz, so shifting the frequency components of a given electric organ discharge distortion toward this range improves detectability. Thus the animals can enhance an object's detection simply by altering the speed at which they move past it.

Because the two parameters that most strongly influence the detectability of an electrolocation target—fish–target distance and velocity—are under the animal's control, it can use exploratory behavior patterns to optimize the perception of a target. Additionally, although the amplitude of the electric organ's output is normally constant, the geometry of the electric field changes as the animal changes posture. By bending its trunk and tail into an arc, an animal can increase the field strength on the side of the body toward which the tail is displaced. As a fish explores a novel electrical target, it continuously sweeps its tail to and fro, effectively "painting" the target with fluctuating field intensities. Simulations indicate that these active alterations in field geometry not only enhance the magnitude of electrical images but also increase contrast, facilitating the separation of images when multiple targets are present.[22]

The range of active electrolocation is limited by the rapid decay in the amplitude of the electrical image as the target distance increases, as shown in figure 4a for a 12-mm-diameter cylindrical metal object. A nonlinear relationship exists between changes in voltage across the skin and receptor responses, with the result that the latter decay somewhat more slowly (red curve). When the object is further than about 30 mm lateral to the fish, however, changes in a single electroreceptor's activity are not discernible from spontaneous fluctuations (noise). Electrosensory neurons in higher brain regions show about a 30% improvement in range, responding to targets at least 40 mm away. The ability of cells at higher levels within the brain to respond to such weak stimuli presumably results from noise reduction strategies based on averaging information collected from large populations of electroreceptors. Behavioral experiments confirm the physiological results that indicate that active electrolocation is a very short-range system.[6,21,22]

## Electrical noise and jamming avoidance

Unwanted signals, or noise, can seriously degrade the operation of any sensory system, and electrosensory organisms must deal with interference from both animate and inanimate sources. The major nonbiological source of interference is lightning. Because the electromagnetic waves resulting from lightning flashes propagate very effectively over long distances, electrosensory organisms can be faced with a nearly continuous barrage of electrical events.[18] Other potential nonbiological noise sources include magnetic storms and electrical events associated with seismic activity.[13] The strange behavior of catfish documented to occur prior to earthquakes is thought to be due to their perception of changes in the electrical environment. Man-made sources also probably interfere with electrosensory systems, but the effects of these have yet to be studied.

Weakly electric fish are themselves the major biological source of interfering signals for other electric fish, and several species have developed specific behaviors—jamming-avoidance responses—for preserving their ability to electrolocate in the face of the deleterious effects of their neighbors' discharges. When two fish approach to within about 1 meter, each senses their summed discharges, which in the case of wave fish result in a beat waveform like that shown in figure 5a. If the difference in the animals' discharge frequencies, or beat frequency, is less than about 15 Hz, electrolocation ability deteriorates, because the amplitude modulations of the beats are similar to those resulting from electrolocation targets.[6,22]

The jamming-avoidance response of the South American weakly electric fish *Eigenmannia* is now perhaps the most thoroughly understood vertebrate behavior. Walter Heiligenberg of the Scripps Institution of Oceanography and his colleagues have unraveled the algorithms used by the brain to produce this behavior and have described the neuronal hardware implementing these computations.

Upon sensing a beat pattern such as that diagrammed in figure 5a, each *Eigenmannia* alters its discharge frequency. The animal discharging at the higher frequency increases its frequency, while the lower-frequency animal reduces its discharge frequency. This maneuver increases the beat frequency to higher values that can be distinguished from the lower-frequency amplitude modulations due to most electrolocation targets, and electrolocation performance improves.

The animals determine the optimum direction in which to shift their respective frequencies virtually immediately and without error.[23] The decision to increase or decrease the electric organ discharge frequency is based on each individual's analysis of the amplitude and phase modulations of the beat pattern that it perceives. The time course of the amplitude modulation sensed by either fish, illustrated in figure 5b, is independent of whether the interfering discharge frequency is higher or lower than the individual's own. That is, the AM portion of the beat cannot provide the information needed to decide whether to shift the electric organ discharge frequency upward or downward.

The phase of the beat waveform, however, measured relative to the animal's "uncontaminated" electric organ discharge, does contain information about whether the interfering signal is of higher or lower frequency. If the interfering signal is of higher frequency, as perceived by fish 1 in figure 5, the phase of individual cycles within the beat will lag behind the uncontaminated electric organ discharge as the beat amplitude rises and will lead it as the amplitude falls, as the solid line in figure 5c shows when compared to the curve in figure 5b. If the interfering electric organ discharge is of lower frequency, as perceived by fish 2, then the reverse sequence of phase lead and lag occurs (dashed line). However, a fish cannot unambiguously interpret phase without referring to beat amplitude as well. It isn't possible to determine whether the interfering signal is higher or lower in frequency without knowing where in the beat cycle the phase lead or lag occurs. The animal can obtain unambiguous information by simultaneously evaluating amplitude and phase. One can conveniently represent the modulation of amplitude and phase by a circular graph, or Lissajous figure, as shown in figure 5d. The point representing the instantaneous values of amplitude and phase will rotate counterclockwise when a weaker interfering electric organ discharge has a higher frequency and clockwise if a weaker interfering signal is of a lower frequency.[24]

The amplitude of the interfering electric organ discharge is encoded by amplitude-sensitive electroreceptors. Other electroreceptors encode the electric organ discharge timing with high precision, and cells higher within the nervous system determine phase by computing the timing differences between the electric organ discharge waveforms sensed at different sites on the body. The phase information is then integrated with amplitude modulation data.

Within the highest centers of the processing hierarchy are found neurons that are active only when an interfering electric organ discharge is of higher frequency. Other cells within the same structure are active only when the interfering signal is of lower frequency. These neurons make up a population of specific feature detectors that provide input to the brain centers that ultimately control the animal's electric organ discharge frequency. The neural circuitry controlling the jamming-avoidance response can be thought of as reading the direction of rotation of plots such as the one in figure 5d.[24]

The fish are very sensitive to amplitude and phase modulations: They can resolve changes in electric organ discharge amplitude of less than 0.05% and can resolve phase changes on the basis of timing differences of less than 400 nanoseconds. Heiligenberg has recently summarized the studies of the jamming-avoidance response of *Eigenmannia*, providing the most complete description to date of how a vertebrate brain integrates complex sensory inputs to produce a specific behavior.[24]

The electric sense is perhaps the most recently discovered sensory modality. Since its initial description, less than 35 years ago, enormous progress has been made in defining the biological and physical properties of the relevant signals, of the detectors and of the brain mechanisms involved in integrating electrosensory information. The intense interest in organisms possessing this sense is partly motivated by the desire to understand creatures who view their world so differently than we view ours. More importantly, despite tremendous differences in the nature of the stimuli that organisms exploit, the brain

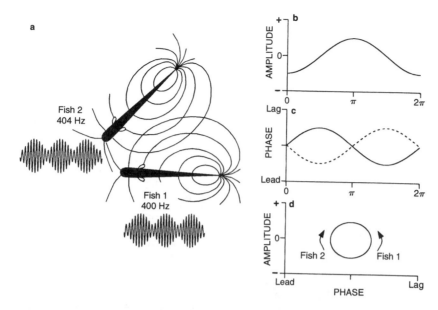

**Interference** between the discharges of wave-type weakly electric fish.
**a:** Superimposed electric organ discharge fields and the beat pattern
perceived by two fish in close proximity. **b:** The time course of the
modulation in electric organ discharge amplitude sensed by either fish,
plotted over one beat cycle. **c:** The time courses of the phase changes
perceived by the lower-frequency fish (solid line) and higher-frequency fish
(dashed line) as a function of time within the beat cycle. **d:** Beat amplitude
as a function of beat phase. Fish 1 will perceive a counterclockwise rotation
of the amplitude–phase relationship; fish 2, a clockwise rotation. **Figure 5**

mechanisms involved in processing that information are
amazingly similar. An understanding of the simpler
nervous systems of animals like the weakly electric fish
provides important clues as to how more complex organisms process information.

Additionally, species such as weakly electric fish are
in a sense overspecialized, relying heavily on just one
sensory modality. Such animals are particularly useful
as model systems, because it is often easier to identify
in such animals the critical stimulus features that must
be evaluated, and the information that must be extracted,
for a given behavior's initiation and control. Studies of
"specialists" such as electric fish will continue to provide
insight fundamental to understanding the more complex
nervous systems of higher animals.

## References

1. T. H. Bullock, Annu. Rev. Neurosci. **5**, 121 (1982).
2. H. Scheich, G. Langner, C. Tidemann, R. B. Coles, Nature **319**, 401 (1986).
3. E. Gould, W. McShea, T. Grand, J. Mammology **74**, 108 (1993).
4. A. J. Kalmijn, in *Sensory Biology of Aquatic Animals*, J. Atema, R. R. Fay, A. N. Popper, W. N. Tavolga, eds., Springer-Verlag, New York (1988), ch. 6.
5. C. D. Hopkins, Annu. Rev. Neurosci. **11**, 497 (1988).
6. J. Bastian, in *Comparative Perception, Vol. 2: Complex Signals*, W. C. Stebbins, M. A. Berkley, eds., Wiley, New York (1989), ch. 2.
7. B. Kramer, F. Kirschbaum, H. Markel, in *Sensory Physiology of Aquatic Lower Vertebrates* (Advances in Physiological Sciences, vol. 31), T. Szabo, G. Czeh, eds., Pergamon, New York, and Akademiai Kiado, Budapest (1981), p. 195.
8. E. I. Knudsen, J. Comp. Physiol. **99**, 103 (1975).
9. B. Rasnow, C. Assad, J. M. Bower, J. Comp. Physiol. **172**, 481 (1993).
10. M. V. L. Bennett, in *Fish Physiology*, vol. V, W. S. Hoar, D. J. Randall, eds., Academic, New York (1971), chs. 10 and 11.
11. A. H. Bass, in *Electroreception*, T. H. Bullock, W. Heiligenberg, eds., Wiley, New York (1986), ch. 2.
12. T. Szabo, in *Electroreceptors and Other Specialized Receptors in Lower Vertebrates* (Handbook of Sensory Physiology, vol. III/3), A. Fessard, ed., Springer-Verlag, New York (1974), ch. 2.
13. A. J. Kalmijn, in *Electroreceptors and Other Specialized Receptors in Lower Vertebrates* (Handbook of Sensory Physiology, vol. III/3), A. Fessard, ed., Springer-Verlag, New York (1974), ch. 5.
14. H. H. Zakon, in *Electroreception*, T. H. Bullock, W. Heiligenberg, eds., Wiley, New York (1986), ch. 4.
15. H. H. Zakon, in *Sensory Biology of Aquatic Animals*, J. Atema, R. R. Fay, A. N. Popper, W. N. Tavolga, eds., Springer-Verlag, New York (1988), ch. 32.
16. M. V. L. Bennett, S. Obara, in *Electroreception*, T. H. Bullock, W. Heiligenberg, eds., Wiley, New York (1986), ch. 5.
17. A. C. Crawford, R. Fettiplace, J. Physiol. (London) **312**, 377 (1981).
18. C. D. Hopkins, in *Sensory Biology of Aquatic Animals*, J. Atema, R. R. Fay, A.N. Popper, W. N. Tavolga, eds., Springer-Verlag, New York (1988), ch. 9.
19. B. Kramer, *Electrocommunication in Teleost Fishes: Behavior and Experiments* (Zoophysiology, vol. 29), Springer-Verlag, New York (1990).
20. G. von der Emde, T. Ringer, Ethology **91**, 326 (1992).
21. J. Bastian, in *Electroreception*, T. H. Bullock, W. Heiligenberg, eds., Wiley, New York (1986), ch. 19.
22. W. Heiligenberg, *Studies of Brain Function, Vol. 1: Principles of Electrolocation and Jamming Avoidance*, Springer-Verlag, New York (1977).
23. T. H. Bullock, R. H. Hamstra, H. Scheich, J. Comp. Physiol. **77**, 1 (1972).
24. W. Heiligenberg, *Neural Nets in Electric Fish*, MIT P., Cambridge, Mass. (1991). ∎

Reprinted with permission from *Nature* 375, 230-232 (1995). Copyright 1995 Macmillan Magazines Limited.

# Interactions in the flexible orientation system of a migratory bird

**Kenneth P. Able & Mary A. Able**

Department of Biological Sciences, State University of New York, Albany, New York 12222, USA

MIGRATING birds rely on interacting compass senses: magnetic, star, polarized light and perhaps Sun compasses[1,2]. During the development of orientation mechanisms, celestial rotation of stars at night[3] and of polarized skylight patterns during the day time[4] provide information about true compass directions that calibrates the direction of migration selected using the magnetic compass[3-11]. It might often be advantageous to adjust the magnetic preference by a geographic reference, especially at high northern latitudes where magnetic declination is large. Paradoxically, a magnetic preference so calibrated will be reliable only within a region of similar declination unless magnetic orientation remains open to calibration in older birds, something that earlier studies suggested was not the case[1,2]. We report here that in the Savannah sparrow (*Passerculus sandwichensis*) the same sort of calibration of magnetic orientation found in very young birds also occurs in older individuals exposed during the migration period to clear day and night skies within a shifted magnetic field.

The Savannah sparrow is a medium-distance nocturnal migrant that nests in grassland, meadow and tundra across North America from the northern United States northwards to 60–70° N. It migrates to the southern United States southward to northern Central America in winter. Adult Savannah sparrows possess magnetic[12,13] and star compasses[8], and use visual cues associated with clear sunset skies (including skylight polarization patterns)[2,14,15] for orientation. We captured Savannah sparrows in local breeding fields in early September, 1994, before autumn migration. Of the 39 birds used in the experiment, 11 were adults (older than 1 year) and 28 were born during the 1994 nesting season (immature) (age determined by degree of skull ossification). Except during experimental and control treatments, the birds were housed in individual cages in a normal

| | | Order of tests | | Dates of exposure (1994) | |
|---|---|---|---|---|---|
| | Group | | Field shift | C | S |
| (1) | 4 adults, 6 immatures | C, S | 90° CCW | 9 Oct.–13 Oct. | 18 Oct.–27 Oct. |
| (2) | 3 adults, 6 immatures | S, C | 90° CCW | 27 Oct.–31 Oct. | 13 Oct.–18 Oct. |
| (3) | 4 adults, 6 immatures | C, S | 90° CW | 13 Oct.–18 Oct. | 3 Nov.–15 Nov. |
| (4) | 10 immatures | S, C | 90° CW | 15 Nov.–24 Nov. | 27 Oct.–31 Oct. |

TABLE 1 Experimental treatments

C, Outdoor exposure in unshifted magnetic field (control condition); S, outdoor exposure in shifted magnetic field (shifted field condition); CCW, counterclockwise; CW, clockwise.

magnetic field and under ambient photoperiod, but had no exposure to the outdoors or sky. Groups of 10 birds were placed in a single cage centred within a large (2.7 m) Rubens coil[16] that was used to shift the magnetic field direction. The birds remained in the cage day and night until the group had experienced four clear days and four clear nights. They were then returned to individual cages and their magnetic orientation recorded in covered Emlen funnel orientation cages[17] during tests conducted indoors. Each group of birds was exposed to the day and night sky within coils under two conditions: (1) in an unshifted magnetic field ($5.5 \times 10^4$ nT; inclination, 70°; declination, 13° W) (control condition); and (2) in a magnetic field ($5.6 \times 10^4$ nT; inclination, 64°) shifted either 90° clockwise or 90° anticlockwise (shift condition). Orientation was recorded from each individual following each type of exposure (see Table 1 for details).

Savannah sparrows typically show axially bimodal magnetic migration orientation when tested over several nights[8,10,13]. Individual birds usually orient in a unimodal direction in each test, but often switch to more or less opposite directions on subsequent nights. This is true of hand-raised birds as well as wild-caught immatures and adults. Tested immediately after outdoor exposure in the control condition, both adults and immatures exhibited NNW–SSE magnetic orientation (Fig. 1a), typical of Savannah sparrows that have been raised outdoors in situations where magnetic and geographic directions were roughly coincident[4,8,10,13]. After exposure under the shifted field condi-

**230**

FIG. 1 Magnetic orientation of the birds tested indoors in orientation cages covered with white translucent plastic sheets. a, Orientation of the birds after exposure to the clear daytime and night sky for four days in an unshifted magnetic field. These birds showed NNW–SSE magnetic orientation ($r=0.519$, modes $=160°$ and $340°$, $P<0.001$, Rayleigh test, $n=37$ birds). b, Orientation of birds after exposure to the clear daytime and night sky for four days in a magnetic field shifted 90° clockwise (magnetic N equals geographic E) or 90° anticlockwise (magnetic N equals geographic W). These birds showed NE–SW magnetic orientation ($r=0.416$, modes $=61°$ and $241°$, $P<0.001$, Rayleigh test, $n=38$ birds). Unfilled points represent the orientation of adult birds, solid points represent immatures. Points with a slash mark indicate hopping activity of birds that showed statistically bimodal orientation[18]. The broken and solid inner circles represent, respectively, the 5% and 1% significance levels for the Rayleigh test. mN, Magnetic north.

a  Control tests
mN

b  Post-shift tests
mN

METHODS. Orientation tests were done in a wooden frame garage with an ambient magnetic field of total intensity of $5.4 \times 10^4$ nT, inclination 70°. Birds were prevented from seeing outside the test cages by the translucent covers. A dim incandescent light, passing through two diffusers and the translucent cage cover, provided a light of 0.2–0.4 lux within the cages. This variation in light intensity occurred across the array of test cages. Light intensity within each cage was uniform. Tests began within 1 h of lights-off and lasted for 3 h. Each point represents the mean of the modal orientation directions of each bird (each bird tested 3–5 times). The orientation records were analysed blind with respect to treatment[28].

tion, the same birds oriented magnetic NE-SW (Fig. 1b). The distributions of orientation directions under the two test conditions were significantly different ($P<0.001$, Watson's $U^2$ test; no difference in dispersion, non-parametric test for dispersion[18]), and the difference in direction under the two test conditions (81° or 99°, depending upon sense of the shift) is very close to the 90° predicted by the hypothesis that magnetic orientation remains open to calibration by visual cues throughout life (predicted direction fell within 95% confidence intervals around the mean orientation direction).

Both adult (70%) and immature (54%) birds responded to the experimental treatment by shifting orientation direction and the proportion showing the predicted shifts in orientation did not differ between the two age classes. Tested after exposure in the shifted magnetic field, adult birds ($n=10$ individuals with orientation data under both conditions) exhibited a mean shift of 91° ($r=0.807$, $P<0.001$, Rayleigh test) relative to their individual means when tested after exposure under the control condition; immatures ($n=26$ individuals with orientation data under both conditions) exhibited a mean shift of 101° ($r=0.710$, $P<0.001$, Rayleigh test). Clockwise and anticlockwise field shifts produced similar changes in orientation (mean shift for clockwise groups was 89°, $r=0.798$, $P<0.001$; mean shift for anticlockwise groups was 110°, $r=0.687$, $P<0.001$, Rayleigh tests).

These results suggest that the interactions and relationships among orientation mechanisms are similar in young birds and older individuals. Exposure to large declination for several days can produce calibration of magnetic orientation in young birds before the first migration, in immatures during the first migration season, and in adults that have completed at least one round-trip migration. The importance of geographic compass directions in calibrating other orientation systems does not end before the first migration. The conventional view has developed that the hierarchical relationship among orientation cues changes as young birds reach the age of first migration[1,2,5]. Whereas celestial rotation assessed by visual cues seemed to be of overriding importance during early development, cue-conflict experiments during migration suggested precedence of other cues. Our results reported here indicate that no real difference exists in the relationships of orientation mechanisms in younger versus older birds. The fact that in cue-conflict experiments of short duration

or involving stationary star patterns, the magnetic field took precedence over and could even assign directionality to stars[19-23] is not necessarily inconsistent with calibration of magnetic orientation by several days of exposure to visual cues. The apparent differences may have resulted from the ways in which the experiments were done. Most cue-conflict experiments with birds of migratory age have lasted for only a few hours or at most a whole night, whereas in the ontogeny experiments birds were exposed to the cue conflict for many days. The design of the experiments may have precluded access by the birds to any information that could have revealed the axis of celestial rotation. It is therefore not surprising that magnetic orientation seemed stable and closed to modification in older birds.

The potential for repeated recalibration that we have described enables migratory birds to respond to spatial and temporal variability in the quality or availability of orientation information. Birds may encounter considerable variation in magnetic declination as they migrate and unfamiliar star patterns will be met as a first-time migrant moves southward. In the vicinity of the magnetic equator the inclination magnetic compass will face difficulties because field lines are horizontal, and birds that cross the magnetic equator must reverse their directional response to the field in order to continue southward[24,25]. Visual orientation cues may be obscured by cloud cover and some, such as sunset position, will change direction over the migration season. This latter cue has been shown to be calibrated by polarized skylight patterns in adult birds[26]. Contrary to the general consensus in the field[5], plasticity in the migratory orientation system is not confined to a sensitive period in the early life of the animal. Only the initial calibration of star patterns by stellar rotation seems to be irreversible once the bird reaches migratory age[27]. This is not surprising because under natural conditions the star compass should not require recalibration. □

Received 9 January; accepted 22 March 1995.

1. Wiltschko, W. & Wiltschko, R. in Orientation in Birds (ed. Berthold, P.) 16–37 (Birkhauser, Basel, 1991).
2. Able, K. P. Trends Ecol. Evol. 8, 367–371 (1993).
3. Able, K. P. & Able, M. A. Nature 347, 378–380 (1990).
4. Able, K. P. & Able, M. A. Nature 364, 523–252 (1993).
5. Able, K. P. in Orientation in Birds (ed. Berthold, P.) 166–179 (Birkhauser, Basel, 1991).

6. Able, K. P. & Able, M. A. *J. comp. Physiol. A* (in the press).
7. Wiltschko, W., Daum, P., Fergenbauer-Kimmel, A. & Wiltschko, R. *Ethology* **74,** 285–292 (1987).
8. Bingman, V. P. *Behaviour* **87,** 43–53 (1983).
9. Bingman, V. P., Beck, W. & Wiltschko, W. in *Migration: Mechanisms and Adaptive Significance* (ed. Rankin, M. A.) 544–552 (Marine Sci. Inst., Univ. Texas, Port Aransas, 1985).
10. Able, K. P. & Able, M. A. *Anim. Behav.* **39,** 905–913 (1990).
11. Prinz, K. & Wiltschko, W. *Anim. Behav.* **44,** 539–545 (1992).
12. Bingman, V. P. *Anim. Behav.* **29,** 962–963 (1981).
13. Able, K. P. & Able, M. A. *Ethology* **93,** 337–343 (1993).
14. Moore, F. R. *Anim. Behav.* **28,** 684–704 (1980).
15. Moore, F. R. *Anim. Behav.* **33,** 657–663 (1985).
16. Kirschvink, J. L. *Bioelectromagnetics* **13,** 401–411 (1992).
17. Emlen, S. T. & Emlen, J. T. *Auk* **83,** 361–367 (1966).
18. Batschelet, E. *Circular Statistics in Biology* (Academic, New York, 1981).
19. Wiltschko, W. & Wiltschko, R. *J. comp. Physiol. A* **109,** 91–99 (1976).
20. Wiltschko, W. & Wiltschko, R. *Zeits. f. Tierpsychol.* **37,** 337–355 (1975).
21. Wiltschko, W. & Wiltschko, R. *Zeits. f. Tierpsychol.* **39,** 265–282 (1975).
22. Bingman, V. P. *Auk* **104,** 523–525 (1987).
23. Beason, R. C. *J. Ornithol.* **128,** 317–324 (1987).
24. Wiltschko, W. & Wiltschko, R. *Ethology* **91,** 70–74 (1992).
25. Beason, R. C. *Ethology* **91,** 75–80 (1992).
26. Phillips, J. B. & Moore, F. R. *Behav. Ecol. Sociobiol.* **31,** 189–193 (1992).
27. Emlen, S. T. in *Animal Orientation and Navigation* (eds Galler, S. R., Schmidt-Koenig, K., Jacobs, G. J. & Belleville, R. E.) 191–210 (NASA, Washington DC, 1972).
28. Cherry, J. D. & Able, K. P. *Auk* **103,** 225–227 (1986).

ACKNOWLEDGEMENTS. We thank C. Walcott for use of the magnetometer, V. P. Bingman for comments, and the NSF for support of this work.

Reprinted with permission. Copyright 1994 by Biophysical Society.

Biophysical Journal   Volume 67   October 1994   1525–1533

# Interaction of Apical and Basal Membrane Ion Channels Underlies Electroreception in Ampullary Epithelia of Skates

Jin Lu and Harvey M. Fishman

Department of Physiology and Biophysics, University of Texas Medical Branch, Galveston, Texas 77555-0641 USA

ABSTRACT   The exquisite sensitivity of elasmobranch fishes to electric fields is thought to reside in electroreceptive organs called ampullae of Lorenzini. We measured the stimulus-response behavior of ampullary organs excised from skates. Under open-circuit conditions, the ampullary organ showed three distinct response states: spontaneous repetitive spikes, evoked spikes, and small, damped oscillatory responses. Under short-circuit conditions, the amplitude range for a linear current response to a sinusoidal (0.5 Hz) voltage clamp of an organ (assessed by spectral analysis of the harmonics generated) was 7–200 $\mu V$ rms. Changes in the spike firing rate of the afferent nerve innervating the organ were evident for voltage clamps of the ampullary epithelium of 3 $\mu V$ and the spike rate saturated for clamp steps exceeding 100 $\mu V$. Thus, the linear response range of the ampullary epithelium exceeded the range in spike firing rate of the afferent nerve. The steady-state transorgan electrical properties under voltage clamp conditions were obtained by analysis of complex admittance determinations in the frequency range 0.05–20 Hz for perturbations (<100 $\mu V$ rms) in the linear range. Admittance functions were distinctly related to the preparation states observed under open-circuit conditions. A negative real part in the organ admittance (i.e., a steady-state negative conductance generated by the preparation) was a common characteristic of the two (open-circuit) excitable states. The negative conductance was also confirmed by the direction of current flow through the ampullary epithelium in response to step voltage clamps. We conclude that the steady state-negative conductance is an essential property of the ampullary epithelium, and we suggest that the interplay of negative and positive conductances generated by ion channels in apical and basal membranes of receptor cells results in signal amplification that may contribute significantly to the electric field sensitivity of ampullary organs.

## INTRODUCTION

The macroscopic electrophysiology of the ampullary organ in elasmobranch fishes was characterized more than 15 years ago after establishment of its primary role in electroreception (Waltman, 1966; Murray, 1962, 1967; Obara and Bennett, 1972; Clusin and Bennett 1977a, b, 1979; Kalmijn, 1982). After a series of studies, Bennett and Clusin (1978) proposed a hypothesis of electroreceptor function in which oscillations and spike activity in the apical membrane of ampullary receptor cells play a crucial role. The oscillations are thought to synchronize individual electroreceptor cells in response to stimuli, and spike activity is thought to reflect the maintenance of a threshold membrane potential at which sensitivity is maximized.

A second hypothesis by Broun and Govardovskii (1983a, b, 1984) prompted a different interpretation. They showed how an assumed N-shaped current-voltage I(V) characteristic in the apical membrane of receptor cells could explain ampullary responses to stimuli. Although Bennett and Clusin reported that the receptor epithelium operated in a negative slope region of the I(V) curve, this observation did not have a significant role in their hypothesis. Broun and Govardovskii attributed the high sensitivity of ampullae to special properties of the synapses at the basal membranes of receptor

cells. Further, according to Broun and Govardovskii, the spikes observed by Clusin and Bennett (1977a) were the result of stimulation amplitudes (>50 nA), well beyond the operational range of ampullae. Consequently, these two groups placed different emphasis on the properties of an ampulla that are prerequisite for understanding ampullary function.

The present study was initiated to provide the information from which a resolution of apparent differences between the two groups could be made. We used harmonic analysis to determine the amplitude range over which the current through an ampullary organ responds linearly to voltage clamp stimuli. Then we determined the organ transfer characteristic, i.e., the dependence of afferent nerve output (spike frequency) on transampullary voltage. Finally, we examined the ampullary organ electrical properties by measurement and analysis of driving-point functions in the frequency domain (complex impedance or admittance; Fishman, 1992). Based on our experimental results, the essential property of the ampullary epithelium is the generation of a steady-state negative conductance, which Bennett and Clusin also reported and Broun and Govardovskii had assumed. From our measurements, we infer that the steady-state negative conductance is generated by ion channels in apical membranes of receptor cells and a steady-state positive conductance is characteristic of basal membrane ion conduction. Further, we show how the interplay between the negative and positive conductances can provide amplification of stimuli in the first stage of signal processing. We conclude then that the ampullary epithelium functions as a linear amplifier within its operational range ($\leq 100$ $\mu V$).

*Received for publication 27 April 1994 and in final form 19 July 1994.*

Address reprint requests to Dr. Harvey M. Fishman, Department of Physiology and Biophysics, University of Texas Medical Branch, Galveston, TX 77555-0641. Tel.: 409-772-1826; Fax: 409-772-3381.

© 1994 by the Biophysical Society

0006-3495/94/10/1525/09   $2.00

## MATERIALS AND METHODS

### Preparation and solutions

A preparation consisted of an isolated whole organ: a 3-cm length of canal with ampulla that was innervated by a 5-mm length of afferent nerve. Organs were excised from live, anesthetized skates (*Raja erinacea, Raja ocellata*) at the Marine Biological Laboratory in Woods Hole, MA. Several organs were removed simultaneously as a group, from one side of an animal. Solutions were prepared, and experiments were carried out at room temperature (20–22°C). The group of organs was placed in Elasmobranch saline (in mM: 415 urea, 340 NaCl, 6 KCl, 1.8 CaCl$_2$, 2.5 MgCl$_2$, 2.5 NaHCO$_3$, and 5 HEPES buffer, pH adjusted to 7.4) in a covered petri dish on a cold plate. Individual organs were dissected, as required, without noticeable deterioration of the group over the course of 4–6 h. Preparation cooling before usage did not affect the results.

Two solution-filled chambers, similar to that described previously (Clusin and Bennett, 1977a), separated by an air gap were used for stimulating and recording transorgan responses (Fig. 1). The portion of canal between the two chambers was suspended in air and was washed initially with deionized 0.8 M sucrose solution. The ampulla with attached nerve was placed in one chamber and bathed in Elasmobranch saline. The other cut end of the canal was placed in the second chamber, which was filled with artificial sea water (ASW in mM: 428 NaCl, 13 KCl, 10 CaCl$_2$, 50 MgCl$_2$, 75 urea, 5 HEPES, pH adjusted to 8.1). Afferent nerve responses were recorded by a saline-filled glass pipette with inserted Ag-AgCl electrode after sucking the nerve bundle (5–7 units) of an ampulla into the pipette and lifting the nerve into air.

### Electrodes and voltage clamp

A pair of chlorided-silver pellet electrodes (each having an impedance of 400 Ω or less over the frequency range of measurements) in each chamber was used to apply current or voltage stimuli to the organ. These electrodes were also used to record the corresponding transorgan voltage or current response without significant effects caused by current electrode polarization (see Fig. 1). Constant current stimuli were delivered by a Howland current pump. Voltage control of the organ was attained by use of an epithelial voltage clamp system (Fishman and Macey, 1969) connected to the chlorided-silver pellet electrodes. Voltage clamp of the ampullary epithelium was implemented by substitution of the measured transampullary voltage for the transorgan voltage in the clamp system. The transampullary voltage was obtained from a long, tapered electrolyte-filled pipette by placement of its tip near the lumenal surface of the ampulla.

### Conventional use of "depolarization" and "hyperpolarization"

The terms "depolarization" and "hyperpolarization" are defined as polarizations across the ampullary epithelium (basal side as the reference) that result in an increase (excitatory) and a decrease (inhibitory), respectively, in the spike firing rate of the afferent nerve innervating the ampulla. An applied current directed out of a canal (i.e., flowing across the ampullary epithelium from basal to lumenal surfaces) produces excitatory discharges in the afferent nerve and a negative lumenal potential. Thus, stimuli that make the lumen more negative are designated depolarizing, and stimuli that make the lumen more positive are designated hyperpolarizing.

### Assessment of the linearity of the transorgan response by harmonic analysis

The response of a linear system to a sinusoidal stimulus of a particular frequency is another sinusoid of the same frequency differing only in amplitude and phase. When the total harmonic content of the response (used as a measure of the degree of nonlinearity) was <1% of the fundamental, we considered the system to be linear (Moore et al., 1980). Under voltage clamp conditions, the fundamental and harmonic components of the current in response to a 0.5 Hz sinusoidal voltage stimulus of various amplitudes applied across the organ were determined by spectral analysis (Rockland Instruments, Model 512/s FFT Analyzer).

### Driving-point function determinations

To characterize the transorgan conduction properties, we used complex admittance spectroscopy (Fishman, 1992). The time course of the current, $I_{TO}(t)$, through an organ measured in response to a small amplitude, synthesized waveform (<100 μV rms), consisting of the sum of 400 sinusoids from 0.05 to 20 Hz, applied as a repetitive (waveform period of 20 s) transorgan voltage, $V_{TO}(t)$. Data were acquired in a steady state (after one or more cycles of the synthesized signal had occurred). The total experimental time to acquire a single response took about 2 min. The complex admittance, $Y_{TO}(jf)$, of the organ was computed as

$$Y_{TO}(jf) = \frac{\mathscr{F}[I_{TO}(t)]}{\mathscr{F}[V_{TO}(t)]} = \frac{I_{TO}(jf)}{V_{TO}(jf)} = G(f) + jB(f), \quad (1)$$

where $\mathscr{F}$ denotes a fast Fourier transform of the sampled functions of time $I_{TO}(t)$ and $V_{TO}(t)$, and $I_{TO}(jf)$ and $V_{TO}(jf)$ are the transformed functions of complex ($j = (-1)^{1/2}$) frequency ($f$). In Eq. 1, $G(f)$ is the *real part* and $B(f)$ is the *imaginary part* of $Y_{TO}(jf)$. Admittance data are presented as plots of *imaginary part* versus *real part*.

### Admittance modeling

Admittance data were fitted by a model based on the linearized Hodgkin-Huxley equations (Cole, 1968; Mauro et al., 1970) and generalized to the ampullary organ. The admittance model is

$$\frac{1}{Y_{TO}(jf)} = \frac{1}{g_c} + \frac{1}{Y(jf)}. \quad (2)$$

$g_c$ is the canal conductance dominated by the conducting jelly that fills the canal, which consists of relatively nonconducting epithelium (Waltman, 1966), and $Y(jf)$ is the ampullary (transepithelial) admittance given by

$$Y(jf) = j2\pi fC + g + Y_1(jf) \quad (3)$$

$$Y_1(jf) = \frac{g_1}{1 + j2\pi f\tau_1}; \qquad L = \frac{\tau_1}{g_1}, \quad (4)$$

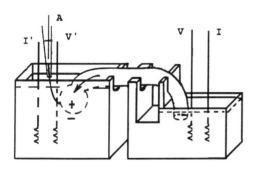

**Ampullary  Organ  Stimulus/Response  Measurement**

FIGURE 1    Diagram of an isolated organ preparation with electrodes for stimulus/response measurements. $I'$ is a virtual ground point used to measure currents through an ampullary organ; $V$–$V'$ are used to measure transorgan potentials; $I$ is a current-passing electrode for current-clamping the preparation from a constant current source or in voltage clamp mode is connected to the output of the control amplifier. See text for description of transampullary voltage clamp. Label $A$ is afferent nerve fiber potential, measured with respect to ground. Current flow in the direction of the arrow is a lumenal positive stimulus that inhibits nerve activity.

where $C$ is the transampullary capacitance, $g$ is the transampullary "infinite-frequency" conductance, and $g_1$ is a transampullary conductance that relaxes with characteristic time $\tau_1$ in response to voltage changes across the ampulla. By analogy to an electrical inductance, $L$ reflects an inductive-like susceptance associated with the relaxation kinetics of the transampullary conductance. Curve fits of the model were made by use of software described previously (Fishman and Lipicky, 1991), in which the mean square error between *real* and *imaginary* parts of the model and data at all frequencies was minimized to obtain model parameter estimates for the best fit. The mean square error is $\langle (G(f) - G_M(f)) \rangle^2 + \langle (B(f) - B_M(f)) \rangle^2$, where $G(f)$ and $B(f)$ are data obtained by use of Eq. 1, and $G_M(f)$ and $B_M(f)$ are the *real* and *imaginary* parts of the model admittance (Eq. 2), respectively.

## Transfer characteristic determinations

To obtain the relationship between a voltage-clamped ampulla at the $\mu$V level and its afferent nerve firing rate, we took advantage of the short-term (min) DC stability of electrodes and used short duration (0.5 s) pulses. The pulse duration of 0.5 s was chosen to avoid postsynaptic adaptation, which reduces firing rate to one-half its initial value in 3–5 s (Murray, 1974). The short-term (min) DC stability of all electrodes used for these experiments was measured to be no worse than 4 $\mu$V in a 5-min interval. To further minimize effects caused by electrode drift, the resting (reference) firing rate was determined in the 0.5-s interval immediately before application of each pulse. The relative firing rate was then computed as the ratio of the rate during the pulse to the rate before the pulse. Under these conditions, the relative firing rate was found to be reproducible for the same amplitude (3 $\mu$V or more) pulse applied at different times.

## RESULTS

### Open-circuit ampullary states

Under the conditions depicted in Fig. 1, the transorgan resting potential of the isolated ampulla ranged between $-0.1$ and $-4.0$ mV (basal side reference). Based on our measurements of the transorgan voltage, $V_{TO}$ (voltage between $V$ and $V'$), under current clamp conditions in more than 100 preparations, ampullae exhibited one of three response states. In State I, spontaneous repetitive spikes occurred (Fig. 2 A). In this state, $V_{TO}$ showed spontaneous, repetitive spikes (20–40 mV) at frequencies between 0.5 and 0.75 Hz. In State II, generation of all-or-nothing spikes (up to 80 mV amplitude) required a lumen negative (depolarizing) current stimulus $\geq 0.6$ nA (Fig. 2 B). In the third state (III), a small (<1 mV) oscillatory response (damped ringing) was seen in $V_{TO}$ when a stimulus was applied to the preparation (Fig. 2 C). Spikes in $V_{TO}$ could not be evoked in this state for stimulating currents up to 150 nA.

The total resistance of the preparation was also indicative of the state of the preparation. We used relatively large current pulses (5–10 nA) to assess the preparation resistance that yielded values for the ampullary organ resistance that ranged from 80 k$\Omega$ to 5 M$\Omega$. The mean resistance of the ampullary organ in State I was always highest (977 $\pm$ 346 k$\Omega$; SEM), ranging from 400 k$\Omega$ to 5 M$\Omega$. The resistance in this state (determined in six preparations) was the most variable (Table 1). The mean resistance of an ampullary organ in State II was high (322 $\pm$ 72 k$\Omega$; SEM), but always less than that found in State I. The mean resistance of State III was invariably the lowest (162 $\pm$ 28 k$\Omega$; SEM). High resistance usually is in-

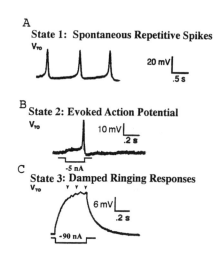

FIGURE 2   Three distinct open-circuit response states in isolated organ preparations. Trans-organ voltage, $V_{TO}$ (voltage between $V$ and $V'$) is as in Fig. 1. Downward current pulse indicates negative polarization of lumenal potential. (*A*) State I: Spontaneous repetitive spikes. (*B*) State II: Evoked spikes. (*C*) State III: Damped ringing responses.

**TABLE 1   Resistance Measurement ($n = 6$)**

| State I (k$\Omega$) | State II (k$\Omega$) | State III (k$\Omega$) |
|---|---|---|
| 977 $\pm$ 346 | 322 $\pm$ 72 | 162 $\pm$ 28 |

Note: Values are mean $\pm$ SEM.

dicative of a physiologically relevant condition of a preparation. Furthermore, freshly dissected ampullary organs from healthy, live animals usually existed in State I or State II (95/110 preparations). State III most often occurred at the end of experiments. Freshly dissected preparations were found in State III only when the organ was damaged. Therefore, we concluded that State III was indicative of a deteriorating preparation.

All states were stable lasting from minutes to hours. Transitions between states (I and II) occurred often but spontaneously rather than regularly. Fig. 4 C shows an example of such a transition of transorgan potential from State I to State II. An ampulla could also be forced to make a transition from State II to State I by application of current stimuli >5 nA. Once a preparation entered State III, it did not recover to State I or II. In a few rare cases, the ampulla initially exhibited State III behavior, but then made a transition to State I or II, indicating some recovery from trauma.

We also studied transorgan responses to current stimuli while the preparation was in State I. Repetitive spike discharges in the ampullary epithelium decreased as holding current hyperpolarized the preparation. Thus, the spike firing rate of the ampullary epithelium could be tuned by varying the amplitude of the holding current (Fig. 3 A). The steady-state firing rate of three preparations from different skates is shown in Fig. 3 B. These ampullary epithelial phenomena were also reflected in afferent nerve activity (see next section).

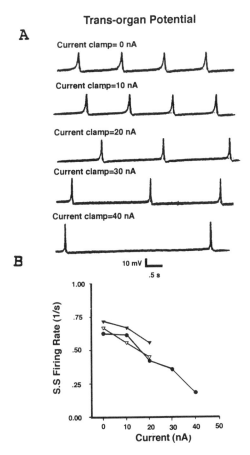

FIGURE 3   (A) Alteration of transorgan (ampullary epithelium) spike firing rate with applied constant current. (B) Plot of steady-state firing rate versus constant current level.

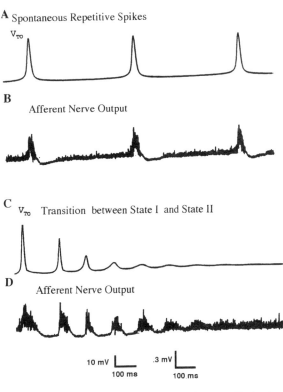

FIGURE 4   The relationship between transorgan (transampullary) voltage and afferent nerve activity under current clamp condition with no stimulus applied. (A) $V_{TO}$ in State I. (B) Afferent nerve output showing postsynaptic potentials and tonic activity reflecting the pattern of transorgan potential. (C) $V_{TO}$ reflecting the transition between State I and State II. (D) Afferent nerve activity corresponding to the transition between states shown in C.

## Transfer characteristic of ampullary epithelium to afferent nerve

We found that activity in the nerve innervating the basal membrane of receptor cells of the ampullary epithelium reflected transorgan potential changes directly. Without an applied stimulus to the ampullary epithelium, afferent nerve activity was tonic at about 30–40 spikes/s. This resting spike rate is in the range of single unit recordings from afferent nerve in situ on skates (Murray, 1962). However, Murray dissected the nerve to obtain only a few active units. The similarity between our resting spike rates and those of Murray suggests that our recordings were also from a few units. Fig. 4 A shows that postsynaptic potentials (PSPs) recorded from isolated, whole afferent nerve were synchronous with the occurrence of spikes during spontaneous repetitive activity in $V_{TO}$. In addition, resting, tonic spike-firing rate accelerated in nerve during the rising phase of spikes in $V_{TO}$ and decelerated during the falling phase in $V_{TO}$ until nerve spike discharge came to a complete halt at the "foot" of each ampullary spike. As $V_{TO}$ stabilized during the next 100 ms, nerve spike activity continued to be inhibited. Subsequently and before the occurrence of the next spike in $V_{TO}$, resting tonic

nerve discharge returned. Transitions between States I and II were also reflected directly in afferent nerve PSPs and spike discharge rate (Fig. 4, C and D). Therefore, the afferent nerve fibers indeed convey information about the transampullary epithelial voltage to the central nervous system by means of the afferent spike discharge rate.

The signal transfer characteristic from ampullary epithelium to afferent nerve was also determined (Fig. 5). During voltage clamps of receptor epithelium, the ampullary firing rate of the nerve showed inhibitory and excitatory responses to positive and negative lumen potentials ($\geq 3$ $\mu$V, $n = 3$), respectively. The sensitivity of an ampulla to electrical fields also was reflected in the very high slope of the transfer curve (3.7% of nerve firing rate at rest/$\mu$V). The nerve impulse generation rate saturated for stimuli above 100 $\mu$V ($n = 3$), which is indicative of the upper limit of the operational range of the afferent nerve.

## Short-circuit of ampullary organ

Under voltage clamp conditions, the steady-state current through an ampullary organ was in the opposite direction to that expected for a positive conductance in response to a small step voltage stimulus. Fig. 6 A shows that ampullary

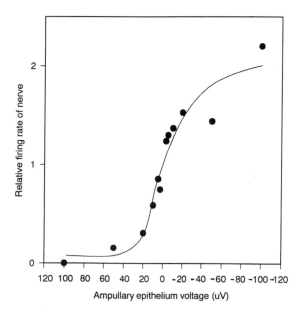

FIGURE 5   Transfer characteristic curve of an ampullary organ. Data were obtained by determining the firing rate of the afferent nerve relative to the resting firing rate in response to transepithelial voltage clamps from 0 mV holding potential. Solid line is a curve fit of a logistic function to the data. The slope of the curve at 0 mV is 1.05 Hz/$\mu$V. Note that ampullary epithelium voltage <0 (i.e., lumen negative) increases afferent nerve activity and, therefore, is excitatory.

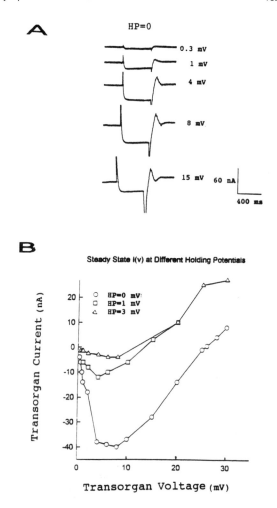

FIGURE 6   Step voltage clamp data from an ampullary organ. (A) The indicate voltages beside each trace are lumen-positive clamp steps from a transorgan holding potential (HP) of 0 mV relative to the basal side of receptor cells. A Downward (negative) deflection represents current directed from basal to lumenal membrane. (B) The preparation steady current response to voltage clamp steps from the different HPs. The current direction defined in A also applies to B.

currents were directed from basal to apical membrane of receptor cells (a downward deflection) in response to small pulses (lumenal positive) applied to the voltage-clamped ampullary organ. The amplitude of the current reached a steady-state level immediately after an early capacitive current transient. This steady current, directed out of the open end of the canal of the preparation, showed no obvious inactivation and was quite stable. With increasing voltage stimuli, the current responses first increased and then gradually decreased (see the responses of stimuli for 8 and 15 mV). The "tail current" response after the return of the clamp voltage to the holding potential showed overshoot and ringing for progressively larger clamp pulses. This ringing in the "tail current" response suggests that strong stimuli (mV) can drive the preparation from State I or II into State III.

Fig. 6 B shows that under different holding potentials (HP), the preparation exhibited more or less steady-state negative slopes in response to voltage pulses less than 4 mV. Preparations responded with increased negative current to increasingly negative lumenal holding potentials. The largest current often occurred in response to a 4–8 mV voltage stimulus. For voltage steps exceeding 8 mV, the preparation current showed a steady-state positive slope relationship.

## Linearity in harmonic measurements under voltage clamp conditions

Use of complex admittance determinations to describe preparation behavior requires that responses to changes in driving-function amplitude be proportionate (linear). The linear response range of a preparation is also an important attribute of preparation behavior. Harmonic generation is one of the simplest ways to determine the linear range of ampullary responses. For 0.5 Hz sinusoidal voltage stimuli, preparations gave linear responses (the rms value of all harmonics was <1% of the rms value of the fundamental) in the range of 7–200 $\mu$V rms (see Fig. 7 for data from 1 of 9 preparations used for harmonic analysis). Significant nonlinearity (harmonic content of 10% or more) was observed for stimuli in excess of 500 $\mu$V rms. In summary, within the voltage range (<200 $\mu$V) of ampullae, we found that the ampullary organ not only operates on the negative slope of its I(V) curve, but also operates linearly. Considering the operational range of the afferent nerve (Fig. 5) and the ampullary epithelium, an isolated ampullary organ functions at stimulus voltages below 100 $\mu$V.

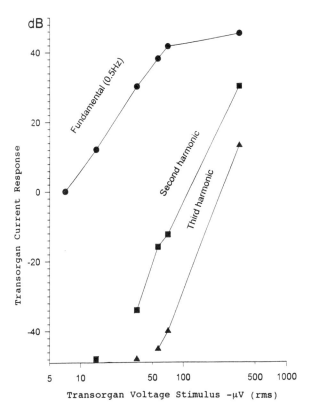

FIGURE 7   Harmonics generated by a voltage-clamped ampullary organ at a holding potential of 0 mV. Transorgan current was recorded in response to various amplitudes of 0.5 Hz sinusoidal voltage superposed on the holding potential. The generation of significant harmonics (2nd and 3rd) relative to the amplitude of the fundamental (0.5 Hz) is indicative of nonlinearity, which became significant (10% of fundamental) above 500 $\mu$V. The total harmonic content for this organ was <1% for stimuli <100 $\mu$V rms.

## Three distinct admittance functions correspond to the three states observed in current clamp

In the current clamp (open-circuit) condition, we found that the transorgan potential existed in one of three states (spontaneous repetitive spikes, all-or-nothing evoked spikes, and damped oscillations). Under voltage clamp (short-circuit) of the whole ampullary organ, we also observed three distinct characteristics of the ampullary organ in admittance measurements, which corresponded to the three response states observed under open-circuit conditions. Fig. 8 shows the locus of 400 data points (*dots*) plotted in the complex plane [($B(f)$ vs. $G(f)$], in the frequency range from 0.05 to 20 Hz. The salient feature of the admittance of the preparation in Fig. 8 *A* is that the low frequency (<20 Hz) locus is in the left half plane. Thus, the *real part* of $Y_{TO}(jf)$ (Eq. 1) is negative, and the low frequency behavior of the preparation, in the steady state, is described by a negative conductance. Another significant feature of the admittance locus is that the low frequency data (<2 Hz) have a negative *imaginary part*. The locus also intercepts the *real* axis (i.e., the *imaginary part* is zero) at 2.1 Hz, and at this frequency the admittance reflects solely a negative conductance. These organ admittance characteristics correspond to State I, observed in current clamp mode, because they were present whenever we switched the preparation to voltage clamp mode after observing State I in current clamp mode and vice versa. The distinguishing character of the admittance locus of the preparation in Fig. 8 *B*, corresponding to State II, is that the *real part* of $Y_{TO}(jf)$ is negative but the *imaginary part* is positive at all frequencies in the band, i.e., the locus does not cross the *real* axis. The admittance of the preparation in this state could be driven to the admittance corresponding to State I by

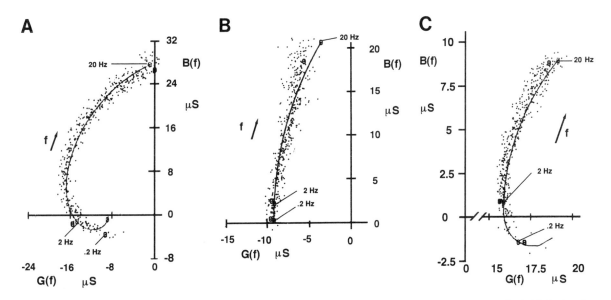

FIGURE 8   Complex admittance of an organ preparation under voltage clamp conditions. The dots are data; solid lines are best fits (minimization of mean square error) of the model in Fig. 9 to the data. *A* corresponds to open-circuit State I. *B* corresponds to open-circuit State II. *C* corresponds to open-circuit State III. In *A*, *B*, and *C*, voltage clamp of $V_{To}$ to 0 mV with superposed voltage stimulus (synthesized signal) of 16 $\mu$V ms for admittance determination.

increasing the stimulus amplitude. This observation in voltage clamp was similar to the one in current clamp in which the preparation could be driven from State II to I by increasing stimulus amplitude.

Fig. 8 C shows an example of the admittance corresponding to State III. The distinctive characteristic of this state in voltage clamp is that the *real part* of $Y_{TO}(jf)$ is positive, and the *imaginary part* of $Y_{TO}(jf)$ is negative at low frequencies.

## Model fitting

To obtain a quantitative description of the admittance at rest, Eqs. 4 and 5 were fitted to the data obtained at the various clamp voltages. The best fits of these equations allowing all quantities to be variable in the fitting process are shown in Fig. 8 (*solid curves*). A circuit realization of the model is shown in Fig. 9. The model parameter estimates obtained from the best fits of admittance data corresponding to each state are listed in Table 2. The conductance $g$ in the model (Eq. 3) was assumed to consist of the sum of a positive ($g_+$) and a negative ($g_-$) conductance as defined below.

$$g = g_- + g_+ \qquad (5)$$

$R_E$ and $R_{net}$ are zero-frequency resistances of the ampullary epithelium [$R_E = 1/(g_1 + g)$] and of the organ [$R_{net} = (1/g_c) + R_E$], respectively. Other parameters are defined in the admittance modeling section of Materials and Methods. Based on best fits of admittance measurements of nine different preparations, membrane capacitance was relatively constant in all states. Canal resistance estimates were also nearly invariant. $R_E$ in State I, II, and III was $-137$, $-124$, and $29$ k$\Omega$, respectively. The major difference between State I and II is that State I has an inductive-like susceptance with time constant of 114 ms and State II showed drastically reduced inductive-like susceptance with a time constant of 4 ms (see Eq. 4). The salient property of the preparation in State III was its net positive conductance character. The circuit in Fig. 9 is thus the simplest representation of the transorgan

admittance that can fit the admittance data obtained in these experiments.

## DISCUSSION

### Ampulla transepithelial response characteristics

The main observations in our open-circuit and short-circuit preparation experiments are summarized as follows:

1. State I (Fig. 2 A) was characterized by a regularly occurring stable behavior in over 60 isolated preparations which remained active from minutes to hours. Preparations made irregular transitions between State I and State II and back again for several hours. The preparation had the highest resistance while in State I, and this state may be physiologically relevant.

2. State II behavior was similar to that reported by Clusin and Bennett (1977a). We also observed this state frequently. However, Bennett and Clusin (1978) found that currents of 50–100 nA were required to elicit ampullary spikes, whereas we could elicit spikes with current pulses (0.6–10 nA) more than 10-fold less (Fig. 2 B). The lower current threshold may be because of the difference in observed resting transampullary potential. Bennett and Clusin (1978) reported resting potentials of 20–30 mV. However, we observed resting potentials no larger than 4 mV, which is closer to 2 mV or less observed by Broun and Govaerdovskii (1983a) in *Raja clavata*. A preparation resting, offset voltage of 16 mV or more, for whatever reason, could require substantially more current to reach threshold.

3. State III was marked by oscillatory and damped ringing responses. Our finding that this type of behavior only occurred after States I or II or in damaged preparations with the lowest resistances suggests that this state is characteristic of a deteriorating preparation.

4. The transampullary response was quite linear for low level voltage clamp stimuli (7–200 $\mu$V rms). In this range, the resistance of the preparation was negative. During open-circuit conditions (current clamp), the preparation showed positive resistances for hyperpolarizing stimuli (up to 150 nA), which is also reflected in Fig. 6 B (positive slope region of the curve). Because of the shunting effect on each organ of the relatively low resistance pathway through the sea water and the skin of elasmobranchs (Murray, 1967) to the capsule within which ampullae are contained, isolated ampullary organ responses under current clamp conditions (open-circuit) may not reflect the functional behavior of organs in intact animals in sea water.

5. Under short-circuit conditions, the transorgan admittance showed three distinct characteristics that correspond to the three states in current clamp conditions. Admittances corresponding to States I and II showed a steady-state negative conductance, but State I showed inductive-like susceptance, whereas State II did not. State III showed only a positive conductance and negative susceptance, indicative of a

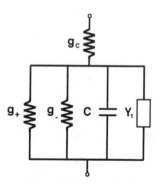

FIGURE 9   A circuit representation of trans-organ conductance model. $g_c$ stands for canal conductance, $g_+$ and $g_-$ are ampullary positive and negative conductances, respectively, $C$ is epithelial capacitance, and $Y_1(jf)$ branch stands for the relaxing conductance in the ampullary epithelium.

1532                                    Biophysical Journal                Volume 67   October 1994

TABLE 2   Parameter estimates from curve fits of admittance in the three states

| State | $C$ | $R_c$ | $R$ | $R_1$ | $R_z$ | $R_{net}$ | $\tau_1$ |
|-------|-----|-------|-----|-------|-------|-----------|----------|
|       | ($\mu$F) | (k$\Omega$) | (k$\Omega$) | (k$\Omega$) | (k$\Omega$) | (k$\Omega$) | (ms) |
| I   | 0.15 | 23 | −78 | 181 | −137 | −114 | 114 |
| II  | 0.14 | 16 | −91 | 342 | −124 | −108 | 4 |
| III | 0.20 | 23 | 40 | 101 | 29 | 52 | 1500 |

damped resonant circuit that would give ringing responses for current clamps.

## Ampullary organ transfer characteristics

Previous measurements of the minimum detectable change in afferent nerve activity in response to electric fields (1 $\mu$V/cm) applied to *intact animals* showed responses corresponding to $\mu$V changes in transampullary voltage (Murray, 1962, 1974). Although this response level of the organ is still a little more than an order of magnitude greater than that obtained from behavioral responses (Kalmijn, 1966, 1982) (10 nV/cm over a 10 cm length canal yields an epithelial voltage drop of 0.1 $\mu$V), it nevertheless is several orders more sensitive than most other synapses. Our data now indicate that $\mu$V sensitivity is a property of an *isolated organ preparation*. Further, we find that the afferent nerve firing rate saturates for epithelial voltages that exceed 100 $\mu$V which, together with our harmonic analysis, suggests that the ampullary epithelium behaves as a linear transducer over the operating range of the afferent nerve.

## Negative conductance in ampullary organ admittance

The ampullary electrical behavior can be explained simply (illustrated in Fig. 9) as the interaction of a negative conductance ($g_- < 0$), a positive conductance ($g_+ > 0$), a capacitance (C), and a $Y_1(jf)$ branch. The total admittance is given in Eq. 2. Data were fitted by an admittance model (Eqs. 2–4) represented by the circuit in Fig. 9. $Y_{TO}(jf)$, corresponding to open-circuit State I showed negative *real* and *imaginary* parts at low frequencies. In this case, the negative conductance ($g_-$) and the inductive (L) part of $Y_1(jf)$ are dominant; the positive conductance ($g_+$) was comparatively negligible. Admittance loci, corresponding to open-circuit State II, indicated that the negative conductance ($g_-$) and capacitance (C) elements of the model are dominant and that the other elements are negligible. In loci, corresponding to open-circuit State III, the positive conductance ($g_+$) is dominant and the data points shifted to the right half plane. The admittance of this simple circuit adequately accounts for the three distinctive admittance characteristics of preparations under short-circuit conditions.

A negative conductance is generated by all excitable membranes and is usually caused by the presence of either or both Na and Ca channels. Ca channels in the apical membrane of receptor cells have been reported previously (Clusin and Bennett, 1977a). A negative conductance arises if the voltage

dependence of the open probability of the channels in the membrane (i.e., the voltage dependence of the ionic conductance) is such that the membrane conductance increases when the membrane voltage approaches the magnitude of and is of the same polarity as the Nernst potential for the permeant ion of the channel. Thus, for a negative conductance the current flows in the direction of potential rise instead of in the direction of the drop. Thus, ion channel production of a negative conductance in the ampullary epithelium is the type of mechanism that can satisfy Murray's (1974) assertion that "only in the ampullae does a cathode above the receptor epithelium excite, and this is the polarity which would, by itself, result in hyperpolarization of the membrane at the base of the receptor cells, so whatever mechanism accounts for the greater sensitivity should also account for this reversal."

## Amplification by the interplay of apical negative conductance and basal positive conductance

The circuit representation in Fig. 9 lumps the electrical properties of the entire ampullary epithelium into a parallel element circuit. To illustrate the amplification mechanism underlying these observations, we consider the membrane resistance portion of the circuit model (Fig. 10) to be composed of two resistances in series: $R_a$ (apical resistance) and $R_b$ (basal resistance). $V_b$ is the voltage across the basal membrane, $V_A$ is the transepithelial voltage and $V_c$ is the voltage across the ampullary

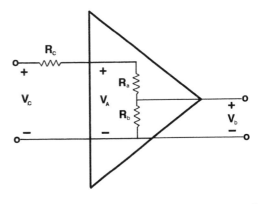

FIGURE 10   A circuit representation that accounts for separate membrane surfaces of receptor cells in the ampullary epithelium. $R_a$, $R_b$, and $R_c$ are apical, basal, and canal resistances, respectively. $V_c$, $V_A$, and $V_b$ are voltages across the ampullary organ, receptor, and the basal membrane, respectively. Input signal, $V_c$, can be amplified to produce an output, $V_b$, affecting neurotransmitter release to the postsynaptic afferent nerve because $R_a < 0$ and $R_b > 0$ (see Eq. 6).

organ. Then $V_b$ is

$$V_b = V_{c^*} \frac{R_b}{R_a + R_b + R_c}.$$  (6)

Our data show that a preparation in steady state has a net negative conductance under voltage clamp conditions (Figs. 6 and 8). The canal resistance $R_c$ (Fig. 10), dominated by the conducting jelly, is a positive conductance. Thus, the negative conductance must be generated by the ampullary epithelium. Because a lumenal negative stimulus ($V_c < 0$) causes excitation of the afferent nerve (Fig. 5), the basal membrane must be depolarized (for neurotransmitter release) and $V_b$ is positive. According to Eq. 6, to satisfy all these facts ($V_c < 0$, $V_b > 0$, $R_a + R_b + R_c < 0$), $R_b$ must be positive. The same logic applies for a lumenal positive stimulus, but the result is inhibition of nerve activity. Hence, $V_b < 0$ and, to satisfy all the conditions, our conclusion again is that $R_b$ must be positive. Furthermore, $R_a$ must be negative because our admittance data and step clamp data from a short-circuit organ showed that the total resistance ($R_a + R_b + R_c$) of an organ is negative.

The incremental voltage that is developed across the basal membrane of ampullary receptor cells by virtue of its effect on neurotransmitter release becomes the input to the afferent nerve. The interplay between the negative resistance of $R_a$ (presumably generated by ion channels in the apical membrane) and the positive resistance of $R_b$ (because of ion channels in the basal membrane) can result in high gain because of a reduction in the denominator in Eq. 6 as $R_a$ neutralizes ($R_b + R_c$). The amplification role of the ampullary receptors also explains the requirement of two functional voltage-sensitive membranes (apical and basal membranes) in series instead of a single conducting membrane. Based on Figs. 5–7, an ampullary organ is linear in its operational range ($\leq 100\ \mu V$). Apparently, the ampulla operates in this range as a linear amplifier (Fig. 10) with gain (gain factor is $R_b/(R_a + R_b + R_c)$). Further, if the amplification occurs with low background noise in this primary stage of signal processing, enhanced sensitivity could be achieved.

We thank Dr. A. J. Kalmijn for discussions and Drs. Richard Murphey, Todd L. Krause, and Harold Zakon for comments on the manuscript. We thank the Director of the Marine Biological Laboratory for the use of facilities.
This work was supported by Office of Naval Rererach grant N00014-90-J-1137 (H. M. Fishman).

## REFERENCES

Bennett, M. V. L., and W. T. Clusin. 1978. Physiology of the ampulla of Lorenzini, the electroreceptor of the elasmobranchs. In Sensor Biology of Sharks, Skates, and Rays. E. S. Hodgson and R. F. Mathewson, editors. U. S. Government Printing Office. 483–505.

Broun, G. R., and V. I. Govardovskii. 1983a. Electroreceptor mechanisms of the ampullae of Lorenzini in skates. Neirofiziologiya. 15:178–185.

Broun, G. R., and V. I. Govardovskii. 1983b. Electrical model of the electroreceptor of the ampulla of Lorenzini. Neirofiziologiya. 15:235–241.

Broun, G. R., V. I. Govardovskii, and V. L. Cherepnov. 1984. Effects of calcium, and potassium channel blockers on changes in transepithelial potential, and spike responses in Lorenzini ampullary electroreceptors in Raja clavata. Neirofiziologiya. 17:652–659.

Clusin, W. T., and M. V. L. Bennett. 1977a. Calcium-activated conductance in skate electroreceptors. Current clamp experiments. J. Gen. Physiol. 69:121.

Clusin, W. T., and M. V. L. Bennett. 1977b. Calcium-activated conductance in skate electroreceptors. Voltage clamp experiments. J. Gen. Physiol. 69:145.

Clusin, W. T., and M. V. L. Bennett. 1979. The oscillatory responses of skate electroreceptors to small voltage stimuli. J. Gen. Physiol. 73:685.

Cole, K. S. 1968. Test of the Hodgkin-Huxley axon. In Membranes, Ions and Impulses. K. S. Cole, editor. University of California Press, Berkeley, CA. 292–362.

Fishman, H. M. 1992. Assessment of conduction properties and thermal noise in cell membranes by admittance spectroscopy. Bioelectromagnetics Suppl. 1:87–100.

Fishman, H. M., and R. J. Lipicky. 1991. Determination of K+-channel relaxation times in squid axon membrane by Hodgkin-Huxley and by direct linear analysis. Biophys. Chem. 39:177–190.

Fishman, H. M., and R. I. Macey. 1969. The N-shaped current-potential characteristic in frog skin. Biophys. J. 9:127–139.

Kalmijn, A. J. 1966. Electroreception in sharks and rays. Nature. 212:1232–1233.

Kalmijn, A. J. 1982. Electric and magnetic field detection in elasmobranch fishes. Science. 218:916–918.

Mauro, A., F. Conti, F. Dodge, and R. Schor. 1970. Subthreshold behavior and phenomenological impedance of the squid giant axon. J. Gen. Physiol. 55:497–523.

Moore, L. E., H. M. Fishman, and D. J. M. Poussart. 1980. Small- signal analysis of K+ conduction in squid axons. J. Membr. Biol. 54:157–164.

Murray, R. W. 1962. The response of the ampullae of Lorenzini of elasmobranches to electrical stimulation. J. Exp. Biol. 39:119.

Murray, R. W. 1967. The function of the ampullae of lorenzini of Elasmobranchs. In Lateral Line Detectors. P. Cahn, editor. Indiana University Press. 277–293.

Murray, R. W. 1974. The ampullae of Lorenzini. In Handbook of Sensory Physiology. Vol. 3. A. Fessard, editor. Springer-Verlag, Berlin. 125–145.

Obara, S., and M. V. L. Bennett. 1972. Mode of operation of ampullae of Lorenzini of the skate, Raja. J. Gen. Physiol. 60:534.

Waltman, B. 1966. Electrical properties and fine structure of the ampullary canals of Lorenzini. Acta Physiol. Scand. Suppl. 264:1–60.

"Designing EMF Experiments: What is Required to Characterize Exposure?," P.A. Valberg, *Bioelectromagnetics* **16**, 396-401 (1995). Copyright © 1995 John Wiley & Sons, Inc. Reprinted with permission of Wiley-Liss, Inc., a division of John Wiley & Sons, Inc.

Bioelectromagnetics 16:396–401 (1995)

# Designing EMF Experiments:
## What Is Required to Characterize "Exposure"?

### Peter A. Valberg

*Gradient Corporation, Cambridge, Massachusetts, and Department of Environmental Health, Harvard School of Public Health, Boston*

Anyone who has attempted to organize and synthesize the results of research on biological effects of electric and magnetic fields (EMF) has experienced frustration when trying to evaluate the comparability of EMF exposures among separate studies. Reporting of exposure characteristics is often incomplete, and some investigators focus on particular nuances of exposure, which in other laboratories go unrecorded because they are not regarded as important. The obstacles encountered when comparing studies, when designing replication studies, and when evaluating research proposals could be reduced were a more standardized approach taken in describing "EMF exposure." To this end, a numerical listing of 18 separate parameters important to EMF exposure characterization is proposed. Although the goal of this list is primarily to expedite the description of EMF exposure, references are provided to examples of EMF exposures and to detailed discussions of EMF exposure systems. ©1995 Wiley-Liss, Inc.

Key words: electric fields, magnetic fields, power lines, ELF electromagnetic fields, EMF metrics, descriptive parameters, exposure indices, replication

## INTRODUCTION

When designing or interpreting biological experiments, investigators are accustomed to considering choices about chemical dose, numbers of animals, animal species and sex, cell lines to use, endpoints to evaluate, chemical coexposures, preexisting susceptibilities, background levels of pathology, and so forth. Electric and magnetic field (EMF) exposure presents a new challenge. Defining the exposure of a biological system to EMF (sometimes called the "EMF metric") requires a markedly greater number of decisions than in the case of a chemical exposure. Moreover, effective planning, reporting, and evaluation of EMF results depend critically on documenting the exposure conditions.

Both in an analysis of the EMF literature and during an initial review group (IRG) evaluation of grant proposals submitted to the National Institutes of Health, I found that many investigators were giving incomplete characterizations of their EMF exposure protocols. This not only makes it difficult for other investigators to replicate the findings but also poses a problem when interpreting results and in planning future studies. Although numerous articles have described EMF exposure both generally [Tenforde and Kaune, 1987] and in the in vivo context [Bracken, 1992] or from in vitro experiments [Misakian et al., 1993], a brief, succinct list of EMF exposure parameters has not been published. The goal of this article is to provide a numbered list by which applicable exposure parameters can be checked off and assigned values. Even though not all parameters will be relevant to every experiment, it is important to consider carefully the full spectrum of EMF exposure conditions and to document thoroughly those of primary interest. The rationale behind the choices should also be presented whenever possible.

## METRICS OF EMF EXPOSURE

EMF exposure attributes fall into five major categories, with a total of 18 separate parameters of the electric and magnetic field environment that should be considered. The five major categories are: A) exposure intensity and timing, B) frequency-domain characteristics,

---

Received for review July 14, 1994; revision received November 21, 1994.

Address reprint requests to Peter A. Valberg, Gradient Corporation, 44 Brattle Street, Cambridge, MA 02138-3753.

© 1995 Wiley-Liss, Inc.

C) spatial (geometric) descriptors, D) combined EMF exposure, and E) characteristics of the exposed system.

These five categories encompass 18 EMF exposure parameters, which are listed below. Each of these quantitative parameters must either be assigned a value or consciously determined to be not applicable. A review of articles on EMF bioeffects quickly reveals that this type of systematic characterization of the EMF exposure conditions is rare in spite of the fact that the reported bioeffect is meaningless in the absence of complete and quantitative EMF exposure information. In contrast, experiments on chemical exposures require only about three or four decisions regarding administration of the chemical, and adequate documentation of these choices is a more familiar process.

The following list was developed to help investigators organize their thinking about defining the EMF exposure protocol; the focus is primarily on extremely-low-frequency (ELF) magnetic field exposure. The first five parameters are the ones most often reported, but exposure characterization will not be complete unless many of the remaining (and perhaps additional) parameters have been addressed. EMF exposure characterization is necessary for both in vivo and in vitro experiments and is separate from the question of design and construction of exposure systems for in vivo [Baum et al., 1991; Stuchly et al., 1991] and in vitro [Jones and Sheppard, 1992; Mullins et al., 1993] experiments. The first four problems posed by EMF exposure are analogous to specifying, for a chemical exposure, the chemical concentration, the duration of chemical exposure, the repetition of chemical administration (chronic or acute), and the time of day for dose delivery.

## Exposure Intensity and Timing

**Intensity of the magnetic field.** Magnetic-field magnitude is often given as a single number, e.g., "1 µT (=10 mG)," but, even so, we need to state whether the field magnitude is "peak," "peak-to-peak," or "rms." For sinusoidal waveforms:

$$\text{rms} = \text{root mean square amplitude} = (\text{Avg}\{[B(t)]^2\})^{1/2}$$
$$= 0.707\ B_{Peak.}$$

The range of magnetic field intensities for which biological effects have been reported in the literature is vast, covering a range of more than 1,000,000, from less than 1 mG [Blackman et al., 1988, 1991], to hundreds of Gauss [Liburdy, 1992; Lorimore et al., 1990; Mevissen et al., 1993], to thousands of Gauss [Aarholt et al., 1980; Ripamonti et al., 1979]. The rationale for using a particular level of field intensity is often not given.

Frequently, AC current for driving 60 Hz (or 50 Hz) magnetic-field-exposure coils is taken directly from the utility mains. Although this may have the advantage of verisimilitude with "real world" currents, it should be recognized that power line AC is subject to transients, nonsinusoidal waveforms, and voltage fluctuations, all of which will appear in the magnetic field exposure. Any EMF exposure system should be monitored for power outages, surges, and brownouts.

**Timing and duration of each EMF exposure.** The most complete description here involves three components: a) age of the animal at initiation of EMF exposure or, for tissue culture, the time between the last disturbance of the cells (feeding, splitting, etc.) and the initiation of EMF exposure; b) duration of the exposure (the reported lengths of individual EMF exposures have ranged from minutes to hours to days); and c) time between the end of EMF exposure and assessment of biological outcome or endpoint (the postexposure interval).

**Repetition of exposure periods.** Some experiments are acute and involve a single exposure, whereas others are chronic and involve multiple separate exposures or continuous exposure. Some are for a very small fraction of the animal's lifetime [Yellon, 1994], whereas others may begin prenatally and extend over the entire life of the animal [Mandeville et al., 1993].

**Circadian time of exposure.** The sensitivity of the biological system can vary by time of day according to where the animal is in its wake-sleep cycle. Often EMF exposures are synchronized to a particular time of day and require that the animal's daily light-dark cycle be strictly controlled [Yellon, 1994].

The remaining 14 exposure questions deal with EMF parameters that have no corresponding analogue in chemical exposures. Among the most important are those that describe how the EMFs vary in time and the actual waveform used.

## Frequency-Domain Characteristics

**Frequency of field oscillation.** The basic periodicity of the applied EMF must be specified. Typically, field oscillation frequency is 60 Hz, although 50 Hz is used in European studies; also, other frequencies may be chosen (DC, 10 Hz, 24 Hz. 120 Hz . . .).

**Harmonic content.** A pure sinusoidal time variation requires the absence of harmonics, but even if this is the goal it is helpful to specify the measured harmonic content. Nonsinusoidal EMFs are common and can be described by wave shape or by frequency spectra. Extreme examples include pulses [Gailey and Easterly, 1994], square waves, and triangle waveforms, all of which have high harmonic content. Real-world exposures, such as electrified transportation systems ("Maglev") [Dietrich et al., 1993], have a very complex frequency spectrum. Likewise, video display terminals

(VDTs) produce electric and magnetic fields of varying frequencies [Haes and Fitzgerald, 1995].

**Intermittency.** How stable is the magnetic field intensity? Most experimenters strive for constancy of the amplitude of the AC magnetic field (and/or electric field) during the exposure period. However, other experimenters believe that variable intensity has more of a biological effect. For example, in experiments on human exposure to magnetic fields, subjects were exposed for 8 h during the night, every other hour, but, even during the hours when the magnetic field exposure occurred, it was turned on-off-on-off-on-off, etc., every 15 s [Graham et al., 1994].

**Turn-on and turn-off transients.** There are several ways in which magnetic fields can be turned on and off. The simplest is with a mechanical switch or relay, but this can result in rapid magnetic field changes called spikes. Several available methods reduce or eliminate transients. One is slowly to ramp up (i.e., increase) the field using a variable transformer and then to ramp it down at the end of exposure. Another way is to use a "zero-crossing" switch, which electronically senses the point in the sinusoidal cycle where the current passes through zero and turns the coils on or off at that point [Cohen et al., 1992]. Finally, the coils can be left on continuously and the biological system moved in and out of the coils. The characteristics of the method used should be specified.

**Coherence in time.** Some experimenters [e.g., Litovitz et al., 1991, 1993, 1994] believe that the phase stability of 60 Hz magnetic fields is important to their biological effect. That is, even though the average frequency remains solidly at 60 Hz, any second-by-second variations above and below this frequency are relevant. With standard systems, temporal stability is usually quite good, and, if frequency variations or added "noise" are desired as an experimental parameter, they would have to be introduced specifically.

## Spatial (Geometric) Characteristics

**Circular and linear polarization.** The magnetic (or electric) field is a vector, and its change in time can be envisioned as a change in length (i.e., magnitude) or a change in direction. An oscillation in length only (with a reversal in direction) is called linear polarization, whereas a fixed-magnitude vector with a change only in direction (a rotating vector) is called circular polarization. Two sets of coils with axes at right angles are required for circular polarization, and the phase (i.e., the time pattern) of the current in the two coils must be 90° (i.e., one-fourth of a cycle) out of step. However, some experiments use orthogonal coils with currents that are not exactly 90° out of step [Livingston et al., 1991], in which case we have a mixture of linear and circular

polarization called elliptic polarization. Electric and magnetic fields in the vicinity of three-phase transmission lines are typically elliptically polarized.

**Relative orientation and magnitude of AC and DC magnetic fields.** Ion "parametric" or "cyclotron" resonance models require *parallel* AC and DC magnetic fields [Blanchard and Blackman, 1994; Durney et al., 1988; Galt et al., 1993; Lednev, 1991; Liboff et al., 1990], whereas "biological magnetite" models respond to *perpendicular* AC and DC magnetic fields [Adair, 1993, 1994; Kirschvink et al., 1992; Polk, 1994]. Thus, experimenters must specify the relative orientation of the AC and DC magnetic fields as well as the specific relationship between AC and DC field magnitudes. In resonance models, the exact AC frequencies of interest are related to the magnitude of the DC field and the type of ions under study.

**Spatial homogeneity.** Most investigators try to use exposure systems (e.g., Helmholtz coils, Merritt coils [Merritt et al., 1983], long solenoids) in which the magnetic field magnitude varies little over the exposure region (e.g., ±5% or less). The actual degree of magnetic-field homogeneity achieved should be specified, preferably with measurements, because nearby ferrous and conducting structures can destroy the homogeneity calculated for coils in isolation. If magnetic-field gradients and nonhomogeneities are specifically part of the EMF exposure metric, they must be mapped out carefully.

## Exposure to Combined EMFs

**Superimposed electric fields.** Some experiments combine both electric and magnetic fields to approximate more closely the transmission-line environment. It is important to specify the relative orientations of the electric and magnetic fields. In general, this entire list of 18 exposure considerations would apply separately to the electric field exposure environment. In contrast to magnetic fields, electric fields are dramatically attenuated by body surfaces or upon crossing from air into conducting aqueous solutions. Hence, in tissue culture experiments, it is of utmost importance to specify whether the electric field is being set up in the air surrounding the culture dish or by way of electrodes inserted into the dish or tissue via a salt bridge. AC magnetic fields can also be used to induce AC electric fields in tissue culture solutions [McLeod et al; 1983; Bassen et al., 1992].

**Static (earth's) magnetic fields.** Static fields (DC fields) do not vary in time as do fields produced by alternating currents (AC fields). The magnitude of the geomagnetic or other static magnetic field should be specified along with its orientation relative to exposure region. The magnitude and orientation of the geomagnetic field vary according to location on the globe and are modified by the proximity of structural steel. Some experimenters null out the earth's field with shielding or with coils that produce an opposing DC field. Sometimes, reversal of the earth's magnetic field is part of the experimental protocol [Lerchl et al., 1991]. The operation of AC coils may also modify the remanent magnetization of nearby ferrous structures, so the DC field is best measured with the AC coils energized at their expected current levels. In summary, the exposed system reacts to the instant-by-instant vector sum of all field sources and not to the sources separately.

**Incidental, unplanned EMF exposure.** What measures are used to limit background and stray field exposure for experimental and for control (i.e., sham-exposed) animals or cells? Cell incubators can be a source of stray fields. Laboratory background fields of ~0.1 µT (=1 mG) are commonly tolerated, but fields greater than this are generally to be avoided. What steps are taken to ensure that neither control nor experimental animals and cells are accidentally exposed to EMF from laboratory equipment during transport and during nonexposure periods of storage or observation? For example, placing cells in a centrifuge or transporting animals on elevators may expose them to unanticipated, strong EMFs. If such exposure is likely or unavoidable, it may be desirable to have a "travel group" as one the control groups.

Some investigators use "mu-metal" shielding to control stray magnetic fields. Mu-metal has a high magnetic permeability, and magnetic field lines will travel in the mu-metal rather than in air. A mu-metal enclosure will shunt a significant fraction of both AC and DC magnetic field lines around the experimental region. Coils can be placed inside such mu-metal enclosures, but consideration should be given to possible heat buildup, distortion of the magnetic fields generated by the coils, vibration of the mu-metal due to AC magnetic field forces, and eddy currents induced in the mu-metal.

Even after the above-mentioned parameters of the system producing the exposure are specified, there is a third set of conditions dealing with additional features of the laboratory setup that may have to be considered before the results of EMF exposure can be considered as fully characterized within the system of interest. Again, there are no parallels with experiments on chemical toxicity for the following parameters.

## Characteristics of the Laboratory System

**Geometry of the cell culture system.** For cells placed within a magnetic field exposure system, the size, shape, and position of the cell culture vessel can influence the level of electric fields induced by AC magnetic fields [Hart et al., 1993; Misakian et al., 1993]. Cells in suspension will have an exposure history different from that of adherent cells. For both adherent cells and cells in suspension, the local currents induced are modified by the number density of the cells. Cells that establish gap junctions will likely experience induced currents different from those experienced by cells growing in isolation.

**Size, number, and movement of exposed animals.** For electric-field exposure, the fields produced within the body depend on animal size, proximity of other animals and cage boundaries, and animal orientation relative to the external electric field [Bracken, 1992]. Electric fields induced by AC magnetic field exposure likewise depend on animal size and orientation. Movement of the animals will cause static fields to appear as time-varying fields within the body. Currents may flow into the animals via watering spouts, indwelling catheters, or telemetry equipment. Thus, comparability of applied EMFs does not always guarantee comparability of internal EMF exposure or internal EMF candidate "dose."

**Accessory non-EMF exposure.** Magnetic field exposure systems are susceptible to producing audible hum, detectable vibration, detectable radiant heat, and perceptible temperature rise. Large electric fields can produce piloerection, hiss, corona, electrostatic precipitation, and ozone; both electric and magnetic field generation systems may produce out-gassing of the exposure equipment, particularly in new installations. What measures are taken to control for accessory exposure?

To control for non-EMF differences between exposure and sham exposure, it is desirable to use two identical EMF exposure systems in which magnetic fields are produced with double-wound coils (coils with two sets of turns in parallel, sometimes called bifilar coils). This allows an "active-sham" exposure system, with current levels identical to those of the experimental exposure system and with similar hum, vibration, and temperature rise. The active-sham system has no magnetic field owing to cancellation by operation in the opposed-current mode [Kirschvink, 1992]. Since vibration and hum are due to forces exerted on current-carrying wires by the magnetic field produced by the whole system, the zero-field sham exposure system will be less prone to vibration. But, even with double-wound coils, firm anchoring of the coil turns is required to minimize differences in vibration and audible noise.

The need for double-wound coils is minimized if vibration is eliminated by mechanical decoupling, if heating is negligible due to low current or short exposure, and if noise levels are similar in sham-exposed and exposed systems. However, control of differences in temperature between sham-exposed and exposed cells has been shown to be particularly important for in vitro cell experiments.

An important benefit of using an active-sham exposure system is that the implementation of double-blind protocols is easier. "Double-blind" refers to an experimental protocol in which the potential for unintentional bias is minimized. Neither the system under study (human subjects, animals, or cells) nor the investigators performing the work have available any cues that differentiate exposed from control status (other than the invisible exposure itself). This protocol requires concurrent processing of sham-exposed and exposed groups, with identification of exposed or control status only after outcomes have been analyzed and recorded. The utilization of simultaneous exposures and double-blind protocols has been proved very effective in differentiating real results from artifactual results due to subtle, unconscious bias.

One additional consideration regarding EMF exposure metrics relates to the possible presence of magnetic particles in the biological experimental system. Ferromagnetic particles have been proposed as a mechanism by which ELF magnetic fields may interact with living organisms [Adair, 1994; Kirschvink et al., 1992; Polk, 1994], and inadvertent contamination of tissue culture fluid with microscopic magnetite particles [Walker et al., 1985] should be considered [Kobayashi et al., 1995]. Magnetite particles ingested by or adherent to cells may modify the response to EMF exposure. Investigators should be alert to this possibility and might consider magnetic-cleaning techniques whereby confounding effects of ferromagnetic contamination can be minimized.

Confidence in the true EMF exposure can be achieved only after investigators have convinced themselves that questions on any of these 18 points can be answered when reporting their EMF experimental data. Without such confidence, research proposals, data reports, and analyses of experimental results will be far from satisfactory. The ultimate interpretation of EMF biological effects is likewise compromised when exposure information is incomplete.

## CONCLUSIONS

Many investigators approach experiments on the biological effects of EMF from a history of experience with the biological effects of chemicals or ionizing radiation, for which exposure can be characterized with just a few numbers. However, adequate description of the EMF exposure environment requires a considerably larger set of parameters, as summarized in the 18 points described herein. The complex nature of EMF exposure is often unappreciated, and the result is a brief and incomplete characterization that is of little value to subsequent investigators.

Omission of many EMF exposure parameters causes considerable difficulty in interpreting, extrapolating, and replicating EMF experiments: 1) Interpreting reported EMF bioeffects requires an accurate understanding of the EMF "dose," which can be derived only from a complete description of "exposure." 2) Extrapolation of results from one experimental system to another is rendered impossible when EMF experimental reports are inconsistent and fragmentary in terms of values given for the 18 parameters described above. 3) Investigators planning to replicate data face the task of duplicating the previous EMF exposure with regard to these 18 points (in addition to selecting and preparing the biological test system in a manner identical to that used in the initial investigation). If the report on which the planned replication is based is deficient, the ability to verify or to refute the validity of the original results is undermined.

Exposure characterization for EMF experiments can benefit greatly from a close collaboration between knowledgeable biological and physical scientists, beginning with the design phase, carrying through the performance phase, and including the reporting and analysis phase. Building an integrated picture of EMF bioeffects will require that experimental EMF exposure be more thoroughly described than has heretofore been the case, and the categorical list given above may help in that endeavor.

## ACKNOWLEDGMENTS

The author recognizes and appreciates the encouragement and support of Drs. Paul K. Strudler (NIH/DRG) and Michael J. Galvin (NIEHS/EHRB) and the editorial contributions of Dr. Martin Misakian (NIST/EEEL) and anonymous reviewers.

## REFERENCES

Aarholt EA, Flinn A, Smith C (1980): Biological effects of extremely-low-frequency nonionizing radiation. In: "Proceedings of the URSI Conference on Electromagnetic Waves and Biology." Paris: International Union of Radio Science, pp 153–156.

Adair RK (1993): Effects of ELF magnetic fields on biological magnetite. Bioelectromagnetics 14:1–4.

Adair RK (1994): Constraints of thermal noise on the effects of weak 60-Hz magnetic fields acting on biological magnetite. Proc Natl Acad Sci USA 91:2925–2929.

Bassen H, Litovitz T, Penafiel M, Meister R (1992): ELF in vitro exposure systems for inducing uniform electric and magnetic fields in cell culture media. Bioelectromagnetics 13:183–198.

Baum JW, Kuehner AV, Benz RD, Carsten AL (1991): A system for simultaneous exposure of small animals to 60-Hz electric and magnetic fields. Bioelectromagnetics 12:85–89.

Blackman CF, Benane SG, Elliott DJ, House DE, Pollock MM (1988): Influence of electromagnetic fields on the efflux of calcium ions from brain tissue in vitro. Bioelectromagnetics 9:215–228.

Blackman CF, Benane SG, House DE (1991): The influence of temperature during electric- and magnetic-field-induced alteration of calcium-ion release from in vitro brain tissue. Bioelectromagnetics 12:173–182.

Blanchard JP, Blackman CF (1994): Clarification and application of an ion parametric resonance model for magnetic field interactions with biological systems. Bioelectromagnetics 15:217–238.

Bracken TD (1992): Experimental macroscopic dosimetry for extremely-low-frequency electric and magnetic fields. Bioelectromagnetics 13(Suppl 1):15–26.

Cohen HD, Graham C, Cook MR, Phelps JW (1992): ELF exposure facility for human testing. Bioelectromagnetics 13:169–182.

Dietrich FM, Feero WE, Jacobs WL (1993): Safety of high speed guided ground transportation systems: Comparison of magnetic and electric fields of conventional and advanced electrified transportation systems. Washington, DC: Office of Research and Development, U.S. Department of Transportation Report DPT/FRA/ORD-93-07.

Durney CH, Rushforth CK, Anderson AA (1988): Resonant AC-DC magnetic fields: Calculated response. Bioelectromagnetics 9:315–336.

Gailey PC, Easterly CE (1994): Cell membrane potentials induced during exposure to EMP fields. Elec Magnetobiol 13:159–165.

Galt S, Sandblom J, Hamnerius Y, Hojevik P, Saalman E, Norden B (1993): Experimental search for combined AC and DC magnetic field effects on ion channels. Bioelectromagnetics 14:315–327.

Graham C, Cook MR, Cohen HD, Gerkovich MM (1994): A dose response study of human exposure to 60 Hz electric and magnetic fields. Bioelectromagnetics 15:447–463.

Haes DL, Fitzgerald MR (1995): Video display terminal very low frequency measurements: The need for protocols in assessing VDT user "dose." Health Phys 68:572–578.

Hart FX, Evely K, Finch CD (1993): Use of a spreadsheet program to calculate the electric field/current density distributions induced in irregularly shaped, inhomogeneous biological structures by low-frequency magnetic fields. Bioelectromagnetics 14:161–172.

Jones RA, Sheppard AR (1992): An integrated ELF magnetic field generator and incubator for long-term in vitro studies. Bioelectromagnetics 13:199–207.

Kirschvink JL (1992): Uniform magnetic fields and double-wrapped coil systems: Improved techniques for the design of bioelectromagnetic experiments. Bioelectromagnetics 13:401–411.

Kirschvink JL, Kobayashi-Kirschvink A, Woodford BJ (1992): Magnetite biomineralization in the human brain. Proc Natl Acad Sci USA 89:7683–7687.

Kobayashi AK, Kircshvink JL, Nassin MH (1995): Ferromagnetism and EMFs. Nature 374:123.

Lednev W (1991): Possible mechanism for the influence of weak magnetic fields on biological systems. Bioelectromagnetics 12:71–75.

Lerchl A, Nonaka KO, Reiter RJ (1991): Pineal gland "magnetosensitivity" to static magnetic fields is a consequence of induced electric currents (eddy currents). J Pineal Res 10:109–116.

Liboff AR, McLeod BR, Smith SD (1990): Ion cyclotron resonance effects of ELF fields in biological systems. In Wilson BW, Stevens RG, Anderson LE (eds): "Extremely Low Frequency Electromagnetic Fields: The Question of Cancer." Richland, WA: Battelle Press, pp 251–289.

Liburdy RP (1992): Calcium signaling in lymphocytes and ELF fields. FEBS Lett 301:53–39.

Litovitz TA, Krause D, Penafiel M, Elson EC, Mullins JM (1993): The role of coherence time in the effect of microwaves on ornithine decarboxylase activity. Bioelectromagnetics 14:395–404.

Litovitz TA, Montrose CJ, Doinov P, Brown KM, Barber M (1994): Superimposing spatially coherent electromagnetic noise inhibits field-induced abnormalities in developing chick embryos. Bioelectromagnetics 15:105–113.

Litovitz TA, Mullins JM, Krause D (1991): Effect of coherence time of the applied magnetic field on ornithine decarboxylase activity. Biochem Biophys Res Commun 178:862–865.

Livingston GK, Witt KL, Gandhi OP, Chatterjee I, Roti-Roti JL (1991): Reproductive integrity of mammalian cells exposed to power frequency electromagnetic fields. Environ Mol Mutagen 17:49–58.

Lorimore SA, Kowalczuk CI, Saunders RD, Wright EG (1990): Lack of acute effects of 20 mT, 50 Hz magnetic fields on murine haemopoiesis. Int J Radiat Biol 58:713–723.

Mandeville R, Mercier G, Oth D, Descoteaux JP, Lis M, Franco E, Houde M, Tremblay L (1993): IAF chronic carcinogenicity evaluation of 60 Hz linear sinusoidal continuous-wave magnetic fields in rats: Protocol outline and quality assurance program development. In Blank M (ed): "Electricity and Magnetism in Biology and Medicine." San Francisco: San Francisco Press, pp 419–422.

McLeod BR, Pilla AA, Sampsel MW (1983): Electromagnetic field induced by helmholtz aiding coils inside saline-filled boundaries. Bioelectromagnetics 4:357–370.

Merritt R, Purcell C, Stroink G (1983): Uniform magnetic fields produced by three, four, and five square coils. Rev Sci Instrument 54:879–882.

Mevissen M, Stamm A, Buntenkotter S, Zingelberg R, Wahnschaffe U, Loscher W (1993): Effects of magnetic fields on mammary tumor development induced by 7,12-dimethylbenz(a)anthracene in rats. Bioelectromagnetics 14:131–143.

Misakian M, Sheppard AR, Krause D, Frazier ME, Miller DL (1993): Biological, physical, and electrical parameters for in vitro studies with ELF magnetic and electric fields: A primer. Bioelectromagnetics 14(Suppl 2):1–73.

Mullins RD, Sisken JE, Hejase HN, Sisken B (1993): Design and characterization of a system for exposure of cultured cells to extremely low-frequency electric and magnetic fields over a wide range of field strengths. Bioelectromagnetics 14:173–186.

Polk C (1994): Effects of extremely-low-frequency magnetic fields on biological magnetite. Bioelectromagnetics 15:261–270.

Ripamonti AE, Ettienne M, Frankel RB (1979): Effect of homogeneous magnetic fields on responses to toxic stimulation in *Spriostomum ambiguum*. Bioelectromagnetics 2:187–198.

Stuchly MA, Lewyer DW, McLean J (1991): Cancer promotion in a mouse-skin model by a 60-Hz magnetic field. I. Experimental design and exposure system. Bioelectromagnetics 12:261–271.

Tenforde TS, Kaune WT (1987): Interaction of extremely-low-frequency electric and magnetic fields with humans. Health Phys 53:585–606.

Walker MM, Kirschvink JL, Perry A, Dizon AE (1985): Detection, extraction, and characterization of biogenic magnetite. In Kirschvink JL, Jones DS, MacFadden BJ (eds): "Magnetite Biomineralization and Magnetoreception in Organisms: A New Biomagnetism." New York: Plenum Press, pp 155–166.

Yellon SM (1994): Acute 60 Hz magnetic field exposure effects on the melatonin rhythm in the pineal gland and circulation of the adult Djungarian hamster. J Pineal Res 16:136–144.

Reprinted with permission from "Residential Exposure to Magnetic Fields and Acute Lymphoblastic Leukemia in Children," M.Linet, et al, *New England J. Medicine* **337**, 1-8. Copyright © 1997 Massachusetts Medical Society. All rights reserved.

# The New England
# Journal of Medicine

© Copyright, 1997, by the Massachusetts Medical Society

| VOLUME 337 | JULY 3, 1997 | NUMBER 1 |

# RESIDENTIAL EXPOSURE TO MAGNETIC FIELDS AND ACUTE LYMPHOBLASTIC
# LEUKEMIA IN CHILDREN

Martha S. Linet, M.D., Elizabeth E. Hatch, Ph.D., Ruth A. Kleinerman, M.P.H., Leslie L. Robison, Ph.D.,
William T. Kaune, Ph.D., Dana R. Friedman, Ph.D., Richard K. Severson, Ph.D., Carol M. Haines, M.P.H.,
Charleen T. Hartsock, B.S., Shelley Niwa, M.A., Sholom Wacholder, Ph.D.,
and Robert E. Tarone, Ph.D.

## ABSTRACT

*Background* Previous studies found associations between childhood leukemia and surrogate indicators of exposure to magnetic fields (the power-line classification scheme known as "wire coding"), but not between childhood leukemia and measurements of 60-Hz residential magnetic fields.

*Methods* We enrolled 638 children with acute lymphoblastic leukemia (ALL) who were under 15 years of age and were registered with the Children's Cancer Group and 620 controls in a study of residential exposure to magnetic fields generated by nearby power lines. In the subjects' current and former homes, data collectors blinded to the subjects' health status measured magnetic fields for 24 hours in each child's bedroom and for 30 seconds in three or four other rooms and outside the front door. A computer algorithm assigned wire-code categories, based on the distance and configuration of nearby power lines, to the subjects' main residences (for 416 case patients and 416 controls) and to those where the family had lived during the mother's pregnancy with the subject (for 230 case patients and 230 controls).

*Results* The risk of childhood ALL was not linked to summary time-weighted average residential magnetic-field levels, categorized according to a priori criteria. The odds ratio for ALL was 1.24 (95 percent confidence interval, 0.86 to 1.79) at exposures of 0.200 $\mu$T or greater as compared with less than 0.065 $\mu$T. The risk of ALL was not increased among children whose main residences were in the highest wire-code category (odds ratio as compared with the lowest category, 0.88; 95 percent confidence interval, 0.48 to 1.63). Furthermore, the risk was not significantly associated with either residential magnetic-field levels or the wire codes of the homes mothers resided in when pregnant with the subjects.

*Conclusions* Our results provide little evidence that living in homes characterized by high measured time-weighted average magnetic-field levels or by the highest wire-code category increases the risk of ALL in children. (N Engl J Med 1997;337:1-7.)

©1997, Massachusetts Medical Society.

RESULTS of investigations of a possible link between childhood leukemia and residential exposures to magnetic fields at a frequency of 50 to 60 Hz from nearby power lines have been inconsistent.[1-9] In a recent comprehensive report,[10] consistent two- to threefold excesses of leukemia among U.S. children were associated with surrogate indicators of residential magnetic-field exposure,[1,3,5] such as the Wertheimer–Leeper power-line classification scheme,[1,3,11] hereafter designated "wire coding." These surrogate indicators use visual assessments of power lines near homes to estimate magnetic-field measurements within the homes. Wire coding includes characteristics of power lines such as distance from the home and physical configuration. An excess incidence of leukemia in Swedish children was linked to estimated electrical current flow, derived from historical records of power companies and the configuration of high-voltage power lines close to homes where the children lived at the time of diagnosis.[6] However, the risk of childhood leukemia has not been correlated with residential measurements of magnetic fields made shortly after the time of diagnosis.[3-6]

The shortcomings of earlier epidemiologic studies have been extensively reviewed.[10,12-15] Inconsistent

From the Division of Cancer Epidemiology and Genetics, National Cancer Institute, Bethesda, Md. (M.S.L., E.E.H., R.A.K., D.R.F., S.W., R.E.T.); the Children's Cancer Group, Arcadia, Calif. (L.L.R., R.K.S.); the Division of Pediatric Epidemiology and Clinical Research, University of Minnesota School of Medicine, Minneapolis (L.L.R., R.K.S.); EM Factors, Richland, Wash. (W.T.K.); Westat, Inc., Rockville, Md. (C.M.H., S.N.); and Information Management Services, Rockville, Md. (C.T.H.). Address reprint requests to Dr. Linet at the Division of Cancer Epidemiology and Genetics, National Cancer Institute, Executive Plaza North, Suite 408, Bethesda, MD 20892-7362.

Investigators and institutions participating in the Children's Cancer Group are listed in the Appendix.

findings, discrepancies between results based on proxy estimates and those based on direct magnetic-field measurements, and the absence of supportive laboratory evidence or a plausible biologic mechanism of disease causation[10,16] have resulted in uncertainties about the relation, if any, between childhood leukemia and exposure to magnetic fields. Widespread concern and the limitations of previous studies led us to evaluate residential exposure to magnetic fields in a comprehensive case–control study of acute lymphoblastic leukemia (ALL) in childhood, conducted by the Children's Cancer Group.

## METHODS

### Subjects

The methods of this study are described in detail elsewhere.[17] Briefly, a group of the 1914 children with ALL and the 1987 controls participating in a nationwide telephone-interview study conducted by the Children's Cancer Group was eligible for the assessment of residential exposure to magnetic fields. Eligible case children received a diagnosis of ALL before the age of 15 years, between 1989 and 1994, and were registered with the Children's Cancer Group. Eligible controls were selected by random-digit telephone dialing[18] and were individually matched to the children with ALL according to the first eight digits of the telephone number, age, and race. Eligibility for the assessment of magnetic-field exposure was restricted to the 851 case patients and the 825 controls who participated in the initial telephone interview (representing 96 percent and 75 percent, respectively, of those who were eligible) and who resided in one of nine states (Illinois, Indiana, Iowa, Michigan, Minnesota, New Jersey, Ohio, Pennsylvania, and Wisconsin) on the reference date, defined as the date of diagnosis of ALL for each case patient. The same date was assigned to the case patient's matched control for the purpose of determining which children's residences would have magnetic-field assessments. Mothers of 98 percent of the children with ALL (832 case patients) and 97 percent of the controls (n = 801) who responded to the telephone interview also provided lifetime residential histories for the subjects. Because we did not evaluate 65 of these case patients and 76 of the controls further, once the sample-size goals had been achieved, 767 case patients and 725 controls were eligible for measurements of residential magnetic fields.[17]

For each child under the age of five years, we attempted to measure magnetic fields in all the homes the subject had lived in for at least six months and required that at least 70 percent of the child's life have been spent in the measured homes. For each child over the age of five, we measured one or two homes, provided that the child had lived in them for at least 70 percent of the five years immediately preceding the reference date. We chose the five-year reference period closest to the date of diagnosis because of hypothesized cancer-promoter effects, since no evidence exists that the low strength of residential magnetic fields can induce genotoxic effects.[10,16]

Overall, 78 percent of the eligible patients participated (83 percent participation among the 767 case patients eligible for residential measurements times 98 percent participation in the lifetime residential history times 96 percent participation in the initial telephone interview), as did 63 percent of the controls (86 percent participation among the 725 eligible controls times 97 percent and 75 percent, respectively), resulting in a final study population of 638 case patients and 620 controls. Reasons for nonparticipation included refusal by the child's parents, inability to locate the child or too many changes of residence, lack of approval by the hospital institutional review board for the magnetic-field measurements, and refusal by the child's physician (this was a factor only for the children with cancer). Some subjects could not be included because the current occupants of subjects' former homes denied permission for the magnetic-field measurements.

We ascertained the residential wire-code category for a subgroup of the pairs of children with ALL and their controls who were eligible for magnetic-field measurements. We restricted assessment of wire codes to pairs in which both the case patient and the matched control had "residential stability" — that is, both paired members had lived in one home for at least 70 percent of the reference period (this residence is hereafter designated the "main residence"). Among the 428 such residentially stable pairs identified, 12 pairs were excluded because the technician could not locate the home or accurately diagram nearby power lines at one of the residences. Technicians assessed most homes eligible for wire-code classification even if they could not obtain permission to measure magnetic fields, since access to the residence or the surrounding property was not necessary for wire coding. To evaluate the risk of ALL associated with the subject's residential wire code during the mother's pregnancy with the subject, technicians evaluated residences in which the subject's family had resided for at least five months during the index pregnancy ("residence during pregnancy") for all subjects under the age of three years (151 matched case–control pairs) and for those whose homes were assessed as part of the wire coding of the main residence, for a total of 230 case–control pairs.

### Measurement Protocol

#### Magnetic-Field Measurements

Technicians blinded to the subjects' case or control status used an Emdex-C meter (Electric Field Measurements, West Stockbridge, Mass.), which measures extremely-low-frequency magnetic fields (40 to 300 Hz, a range that includes 50-Hz and 60-Hz levels, frequencies evaluated in prior epidemiologic studies) with a three-axis induction-coil sensor.[17] Derived from two personal-exposure studies,[19,20] the standardized measurement protocol included a 24-hour measurement in the child's bedroom (with the meter placed under or adjacent to the bed); 30-second measurements in the center of the child's bedroom, the family room, the kitchen, and the room in which the mother slept during the index pregnancy; and a 30-second outdoor measurement made within 0.9 m (3 ft) of the front door.[17]

#### Wire Coding

Technicians (who were unaware of whether a case patient or a control currently or formerly lived in each residence evaluated) drew diagrams and recorded systematically the distance from the home of any overhead power lines within 46 m (150 ft) of the residence, including transmission lines, thick and thin three-phase primary-distribution lines (which carry electric power from substations to surrounding neighborhoods), any open (with separated wires) or spun (with wires bound together) secondary distribution lines, and first-span secondary distribution lines.[17] On the basis of the diagrams, a computer algorithm assigned a wire code to each residence according to the five-category Wertheimer–Leeper classification[1,3,11] and the modified three-category Kaune–Savitz scheme.[21] As in earlier studies,[3,5] we found that measured magnetic-field levels (i.e., the arithmetic means of 24-hour measurements from 858 residences) rose with increasing Wertheimer–Leeper[1,3,11] and Kaune–Savitz[21] wire-code categories (unpublished data).

### Statistical Analysis

#### Magnetic-Field Measurements

For each eligible residence, a summary magnetic-field level was calculated from a weighted average of the room measurements. The weights were derived from the personal-exposure study and based on the estimated time spent by children according to age.[17,19,20] If measurements were not obtained in all rooms, then the weighted average was based on a standardized hierarchy of measurements.[17] The primary measure of exposure for each subject was an average of the summary level for all the eligible measured homes, weighted according to the duration of residence. We used odds ratios and 95 percent confidence intervals to estimate the risk of ALL.[22] Before undertaking any case–control comparisons, we identified four exposure categories for residential magnetic-field levels (<0.065 $\mu$T [the reference group], 0.065 to 0.099 $\mu$T, 0.100 to 0.199 $\mu$T, and ≥0.200 $\mu$T), based on the distribution of measurements in the control homes. These categories were similar to those used in earlier investigations.[3,5,6] We calculated results using unmatched analysis as well as analysis of matched case–control pairs.[22]

We used stratified and logistic-regression analyses to explore the effects of age at the reference date, sex, race (though the very small number of nonwhites limited this evaluation), socioeconomic status (indicated by family income, the mother's and father's educational level and occupation, home ownership, and family size), temporal factors (year, season, and time of day when the measurements were made), demographic characteristics (degree of urbanization and type of residence), and dose–response relations using continuous measurements.[22] We also evaluated birth order, birth weight, the mother's age at the child's delivery, and medical x-ray studies during pregnancy as potential confounding factors. We excluded nine case patients and one control who had Down's syndrome, since this disorder has been linked to 10-to-40-fold increases in the risk of acute leukemia.[23] We included 629 case patients and 619 controls in the final unmatched analysis, and 463 case–control pairs in the matched analysis.

### Wire Coding

Because the relation between power-line configurations and magnetic-field strength may vary geographically,[5,24] we retained the matched design of the initial nationwide phase of the study for the wire coding of the main residence. The Wertheimer–Leeper wire-code categories used in the analysis include underground (buried) power lines plus very-low-current configuration (the reference group), ordinary low-current configuration, ordinary high-current configuration, and very-high-current configuration.[1,3,11] The modified Kaune–Savitz wire-code categories were as follows: low (the reference group), medium, and high.[21] We used matched-pairs analysis to evaluate the risk of ALL in relation to the wire-code category of the main residence (including 408 case–control pairs, after the exclusion of subjects with Down's syndrome) and the residence during pregnancy (a total of 225 pairs, including 149 pairs of subjects under the age of three, after the exclusion of subjects with Down's syndrome); conditional logistic regression was used to control for socioeconomic and demographic factors and other potential confounders.[22]

## RESULTS

### Characteristics of the Subjects

The controls were similar to the case patients (Table 1), except for their higher total family income (P<0.001). ALL was not associated with the mother's age at delivery of the subject, the number of children in the family, the birth order of the subject (data not shown), the type of residence, the degree of urbanization, home ownership, or the interval between the reference date and the date of the measurements (data not shown). All estimates of risk have been adjusted for the age of the subject at the reference date, the subject's sex, the mother's educational level, and family income.

### Summary Measures of Residential Magnetic-Field Exposures

Risk estimates based on the summary residential magnetic-field exposures for a priori measurement categories did not differ significantly from unity either for all the subjects (629 case patients and 619 controls) or for the 463 matched pairs (Table 2), nor did risk increase significantly with increasing summary magnetic-field levels (P for trend = 0.22 for the unmatched analyses and 0.12 for the matched analyses). Risk was higher with estimated summary exposures of 0.300 $\mu$T or more (odds ratio, 1.72; 95 percent confidence interval, 1.03 to 2.86; 45 case patients and 28 controls); however, risk did not increase significantly with increasing exposure when exposure was evaluated as a continuous variable (P for trend = 0.15 for the unmatched analysis and 0.09 for the matched analysis).

When the analysis was restricted to subjects who lived in a single home during the study period or to those who lived for the entire reference period in homes for which we obtained 24-hour bedroom measurements, the risks differed little from those shown in Table 2 (data not shown). The results were also virtually unchanged if a partial time-weighted average bedroom measurement for less than 24 hours (i.e., 4 p.m. to 6 a.m. or 10 p.m. to 6 a.m.) was substituted for the full 24-hour average to reflect more accurately the specific period of time subjects spent in their bedrooms. Also, risk estimates were similar after adjustment for differences between case patients and controls in the calendar year, season, or time of day of the measurements. We found no consistent pattern in the relation of summary residential magnetic-field levels to the risk of ALL according to family income, parental educational level or occupation, birth order, or other socioeconomic or residential characteristics.

### Main-Residence Wire-Code Patterns

For the main residence, we found no association between the risk of ALL and residence in a home classified in the highest wire-code category according to either wire-code classification (Table 3). There were no positive or statistically significant dose–response trends, and results were not materially changed when adjusted for potentially confounding variables.

### Magnetic-Field Levels and Wire Codes of Residences during Pregnancy

As regards the homes resided in during pregnancy by the mothers of 257 case patients and 239 controls, the odds ratio for ALL was 0.75 (95 percent confidence interval, 0.45 to 1.24) for a magnetic-field level of 0.065 to 0.099 $\mu$T, as compared with the reference category (<0.065 $\mu$T); 1.32 (95 percent confidence interval, 0.81 to 2.15) for a level of 0.100 to 0.199 $\mu$T; and 1.24 (95 percent confidence interval, 0.69 to 2.23) for a level of 0.200 $\mu$T or higher (P for trend = 0.25). Among the 225 matched pairs whose mothers' residences during pregnancy were wire-coded, the odds ratios for ALL were 1.20 (95 percent

**TABLE 1.** CHARACTERISTICS OF 629 CHILDREN WITH ACUTE LYMPHOBLASTIC LEUKEMIA (CASE PATIENTS) AND 619 CONTROLS WITH MEASUREMENTS OF 60-HZ RESIDENTIAL MAGNETIC-FIELD LEVELS AND 408 MATCHED CASE–CONTROL PAIRS OF CHILDREN WITH STABLE RESIDENCES AND WIRE-CODING DATA.

| CHARACTERISTIC | MAGNETIC-FIELD MEASUREMENTS* | | WIRE CODING† | |
| --- | --- | --- | --- | --- |
| | CASE PATIENTS (N=629) | CONTROLS (N=619) | CASE PATIENTS (N=408) | CONTROLS (N=408) |
| | number (percent) | | | |
| Age at diagnosis or reference date (yr)‡ | | | | |
| <2 | 65 (10.3) | 81 (13.1) | 52 (12.7) | 68 (16.7) |
| 2–4 | 304 (48.3) | 273 (44.1) | 184 (45.1) | 165 (40.4) |
| 5–9 | 169 (26.9) | 182 (29.4) | 110 (27.0) | 116 (28.4) |
| ≥10 | 91 (14.5) | 83 (13.4) | 62 (15.2) | 59 (14.5) |
| Sex | | | | |
| Male | 329 (52.3) | 323 (52.2) | 204 (50.0) | 218 (53.4) |
| Female | 300 (47.7) | 296 (47.8) | 204 (50.0) | 190 (46.6) |
| Mother's education | | | | |
| <12 yr | 43 (6.8) | 23 (3.7) | 32 (7.8) | 16 (3.9) |
| High-school graduate | 204 (32.4) | 218 (35.2) | 132 (32.4) | 164 (40.2) |
| Some college or post–high-school education | 215 (34.2) | 197 (31.8) | 133 (32.6) | 112 (27.5) |
| ≥College graduate | 167 (26.6) | 181 (29.2) | 111 (27.2) | 116 (28.4) |
| Annual family income ($) | | | | |
| <20,000 | 96 (15.4) | 71 (11.5) | 63 (15.6) | 42 (10.4) |
| 20,000–29,999 | 117 (18.8) | 83 (13.5) | 65 (16.0) | 51 (12.6) |
| 30,000–39,999 | 141 (22.6) | 105 (17.1) | 90 (22.2) | 75 (18.5) |
| 40,000–49,999 | 102 (16.3) | 111 (18.0) | 62 (15.3) | 75 (18.5) |
| ≥50,000 | 168 (26.9) | 245 (39.8) | 125 (30.9) | 162 (40.0) |
| Mother's age at birth of subject (yr) | | | | |
| <25 | 178 (28.3) | 154 (24.9) | 106 (26.0) | 102 (25.0) |
| 25–29 | 251 (39.9) | 257 (41.5) | 162 (39.7) | 165 (40.4) |
| ≥30 | 200 (31.8) | 208 (33.6) | 140 (34.3) | 141 (34.6) |
| No. of children in family | | | | |
| 1 | 90 (14.3) | 67 (10.8) | 56 (13.7) | 41 (10.0) |
| 2 | 280 (44.5) | 265 (42.8) | 190 (46.6) | 184 (45.1) |
| ≥3 | 259 (41.2) | 287 (46.4) | 162 (39.7) | 183 (44.9) |
| Type of residence | | | | |
| Single-family home | 509 (83.2) | 485 (81.8) | 326 (83.2) | 319 (82.2) |
| Apartment | 24 (3.9) | 25 (4.2) | 17 (4.3) | 16 (4.1) |
| Other | 79 (12.9) | 83 (14.0) | 49 (12.5) | 53 (13.7) |
| Home-ownership status | | | | |
| Owned home | 486 (80.2) | 499 (84.6) | 325 (83.5) | 335 (86.8) |
| Rented home | 101 (16.7) | 77 (13.0) | 58 (14.9) | 45 (11.7) |
| Other | 19 (3.1) | 14 (2.4) | 6 (1.5) | 6 (1.6) |
| Degree of urbanization | | | | |
| Urban | 152 (24.2) | 126 (20.4) | 117 (28.7) | 89 (21.9) |
| Suburban | 278 (44.2) | 289 (46.8) | 161 (39.5) | 192 (47.2) |
| Rural | 199 (31.6) | 203 (32.8) | 130 (31.9) | 126 (31.0) |

*Data were missing on income for 5 case patients and 4 controls, on type of residence for 17 case patients and 26 controls, on home ownership for 23 case patients and 29 controls, and on degree of urbanization for 1 control. Percentages are of subjects with data available. See the text for details of magnetic-field measurements.

†Data were missing on income for 3 case patients and 3 controls, on type of residence for 16 case patients and 20 controls, on home ownership for 19 case patients and 22 controls, and on degree of urbanization for 1 control. Percentages are of subjects with data available. See the text for details of wire coding.

‡The reference date for each control was defined as the date of diagnosis in the corresponding matched case patient.

confidence interval, 0.74 to 1.95) for the Wertheimer–Leeper code-configuration category of "ordinary low"; 1.07 (95 percent confidence interval, 0.61 to 1.86) for "ordinary high"; and 1.49 (95 percent confidence interval, 0.66 to 3.37) for "very high," as compared with the reference category of "underground plus very low" (P for trend=0.07). For children under the age of three whose mothers' homes during pregnancy were wire-coded (149 matched pairs), the odds ratios were not significantly elevated and the risks did not increase significantly with higher wire-code categories (P for trend=0.19).

**TABLE 2.** RISK OF CHILDHOOD ACUTE LYMPHOBLASTIC LEUKEMIA ACCORDING TO TIME-WEIGHTED AVERAGE SUMMARY LEVELS OF 60-Hz RESIDENTIAL MAGNETIC FIELDS IN THE UNMATCHED AND MATCHED ANALYSIS.*

| MAGNETIC-FIELD LEVEL ($\mu$T) | UNMATCHED ANALYSIS† | | | MATCHED ANALYSIS‡ | | |
|---|---|---|---|---|---|---|
| | NO. OF CASE PATIENTS | NO. OF CONTROLS | OR (95% CI)§¶ | NO. OF CASE PATIENTS | NO. OF CONTROLS | OR (95% CI)§‖ |
| <0.065 | 267 | 285 | 1.00 | 206 | 215 | 1.00 |
| 0.065–0.099 | 123 | 117 | 1.10 (0.81–1.50) | 92 | 98 | 0.96 (0.65–1.40) |
| 0.100–0.199 | 151 | 143 | 1.10 (0.83–1.48) | 107 | 106 | 1.15 (0.79–1.65) |
| ≥0.200 | 83** | 70** | 1.24 (0.86–1.79)†† | 58** | 44** | 1.53 (0.91–2.56)†† |
| 0.200–0.299 | 38 | 42 | 0.92 (0.57–1.48) | 29 | 26 | 1.31 (0.68–2.51) |
| 0.300–0.399 | 22 | 17 | 1.39 (0.72–2.72) | 14 | 11 | 1.46 (0.61–3.50) |
| 0.400–0.499 | 14 | 5 | 3.28 (1.15–9.39) | 10 | 2 | 6.41 (1.30–31.73) |
| ≥0.500 | 9 | 6 | 1.41 (0.49–4.09) | 5 | 5 | 1.01 (0.26–3.99) |

*The analysis used a measure for each subject that was based on the time-weighted average summary values for each eligible home (including measurements in the child's bedroom, family room, and kitchen or outside the front door, weighted according to the age of subject); these values were weighted according to the number of years the subject spent living in each residence.[16,19,20]

†Five case patients and four controls for whom information on confounders was missing are excluded.

‡The controls were matched to the case patients according to age at the reference date, race, and telephone number (first eight digits).

§OR denotes odds ratio, and CI confidence interval.

¶Odds ratios have been adjusted for age at the reference date, sex, mother's educational level, and family income.

‖Odds ratios have been adjusted for sex, mother's educational level, and family income.

**The numbers of case patients and controls are based on four exposure categories.

††The risk estimates are based on four exposure categories selected a priori.

## DISCUSSION

We found no significant excess risk of childhood ALL associated with time-weighted average summary residential magnetic-field levels of 0.200 $\mu$T or greater, nor did we observe any significant dose–response trends. There was a tendency for the risk to be higher among subjects with summary exposure levels of 0.300 $\mu$T or more, but the number of children with such high levels was small. The risk of childhood ALL was not associated with high wire codes for either the subject's main residence or the mother's residence during pregnancy. Adjustment for socioeconomic, demographic, or other potentially confounding variables had little effect on the risk.

In contrast to three earlier U.S. studies,[1,3,5] we found no association between the highest wire-code category and an elevated risk of childhood ALL. Our data demonstrated a significant correlation between measured magnetic fields and wire codes (unpublished data), as was found in previous studies.[24-26] The lack of association between childhood ALL and wire-code categories is particularly noteworthy since public concern[10] has been driven primarily by the excess risks linked with surrogate or historical estimates of residential magnetic-field exposure.[1,3,5,6]

**TABLE 3.** RISK OF CHILDHOOD ACUTE LYMPHOBLASTIC LEUKEMIA AMONG 408 MATCHED PAIRS OF CHILDREN WITH STABLE RESIDENCES, ACCORDING TO THE WERTHEIMER–LEEPER AND MODIFIED KAUNE–SAVITZ WIRE-CODE CLASSIFICATIONS OF THE MAIN RESIDENCE.*

| WIRE-CODE CATEGORY† | NO. OF CASE PATIENTS | NO. OF CONTROLS | OR (95% CI)‡ |
|---|---|---|---|
| Wertheimer–Leeper | | | |
| UG + VLCC | 175 | 175 | 1.00 |
| OLCC | 116 | 114 | 1.07 (0.74–1.54) |
| OHCC | 87 | 87 | 0.99 (0.67–1.48) |
| VHCC | 24 | 26 | 0.88 (0.48–1.63) |
| Kaune–Savitz | | | |
| LWC | 237 | 249 | 1.00 |
| MWC | 114 | 105 | 1.22 (0.85–1.75) |
| HWC | 51 | 48 | 1.04 (0.65–1.66) |

*Because of missing data for some variables, the numbers of subjects do not total 408 in each group.

†UG denotes underground or buried power lines, VLCC very-low-current configuration, OLCC ordinary low-current configuration, OHCC ordinary high-current configuration, VHCC very-high-current configuration, LWC low wire code, MWC medium wire code, and HWC high wire code.

‡OR denotes odds ratio, and CI confidence interval. These odds ratios have been adjusted for sex, mother's educational level, and family income.

---

The results of our measurements of magnetic-field levels, like those of four earlier investigations,[3-6] also show no significant increase in the risk of ALL among children whose residences had measured magnetic-field levels of 0.200 $\mu$T or higher, based on a priori categories. The small increase in risk at estimated exposures of 0.300 $\mu$T or more derived from a significant excess incidence of ALL at the intermediate level of 0.400 to 0.499 $\mu$T, but the odds ratios were close to unity for estimated exposure levels of 0.500 $\mu$T or greater, and the P value for trend was not significant. We cannot exclude the possibility of a small increase in risk among children in homes with very high magnetic-field levels, as suggested in studies using historical estimates of residential magnetic-field exposure.[4,6,7]

We designed our investigation to address the limitations of earlier studies, particularly the lengthy intervals (typically years or decades) between the diagnosis of ALL and measurements of magnetic fields. In our study magnetic fields were usually measured within 24 months after the date of diagnosis in the children with ALL.[17] Previous studies also included fewer cases of childhood leukemia, measured fields during a smaller proportion of the reference period or lacked a standardized reference interval for the evaluation of magnetic fields, and evaluated fewer potential confounding variables. Some of the earlier studies selected controls who moved less frequently than the case patients or failed to blind data collectors to the case or control status of the subjects living in each residence evaluated.[10,12-15] We measured residential magnetic-field levels for nearly four times the numbers of case patients and controls in the largest previous investigation.[5] An important strength of our study was that magnetic-field measurements covered more than 95 percent of the reference period for 77 percent of subjects and more than 90 percent of the reference period for 83 percent of subjects.[17]

We made a major effort to achieve a high rate of participation in the study, despite the substantial burden for families (an average of three hours for interviews and measurements). Overall, 78 percent of eligible case patients and 63 percent of eligible controls participated. Many of the reasons for not participating were unrelated to refusal by the subjects or their parents; they included refusals of permission for testing by current occupants of former residences or the failure of subjects to meet eligibility requirements (such as residential stability).

To address concern about possible response bias,[27-29] we instructed the technicians to diagram the homes of 119 children who were identified during random-digit dialing as potential controls but whose parents declined permission for participation; we found that the proportion of these homes assigned by the computer algorithm to the highest wire-code category was similar to that among the subjects in our study.[17] Moreover, the technicians diagrammed virtually all eligible residences of subjects whose families refused permission for magnetic-field measurements, since neither residential nor property access was necessary for assigning wire codes to residences. Residential mobility was similar for case patients and controls in this study, in contrast to an earlier investigation,[3] which has been criticized because the case patients changed residences considerably more often than the controls.[10,12-15] Additional strengths of our investigation included the collection of the exposure data on a blinded basis; the personal-exposure studies to develop[19] and evaluate[20] the measurement protocol; the routine calibration of all magnetic-field (Emdex) meters; the lengthy initial training, retraining, and site visits of measurement staff; the independent rediagramming of a substantial proportion of residences, which showed good concordance of assigned wire codes (unpublished data); and the regular review of all measurements, with detailed investigation of potential errors.[17]

A limitation of our investigation and all previous studies is the absence of measurements for individual residences in the years preceding the diagnosis of cancer. It is not known how well a single 24-hour measurement characterizes contemporary exposure, much less magnetic-field exposure years earlier. Very limited data suggest a moderate correlation between repeated spot measurements taken in the same residential location several years after the initial measurements.[30] To examine the reproducibility and seasonal variation of magnetic-field measurements, we initiated a detailed longitudinal study of 50 homes in Detroit and Minneapolis. The preliminary results suggest good reproducibility and relatively little seasonal variation over a one-year period (Banks R, et al.: unpublished data). Repeated measurements in a large sample of homes over a longer period would help to resolve this issue. The selection of controls by random-digit dialing has known weaknesses,[27] but the use of alternative control groups was not feasible.[17] The only major difference between the case patients and the controls — a higher family income among controls — was probably due to the use of controls obtained by random-digit dialing,[27] but this difference did not confound the relation between magnetic-field exposure and childhood ALL.

In summary, our comprehensive case–control investigation did not find significantly increased risks of ALL associated with time-weighted average summary residential magnetic-field measurements or with residence in homes characterized by a high wire-code category during the five years immediately preceding the diagnosis of ALL or during the index pregnancy. The finding of a tendency for risk to be higher at measured magnetic-field levels of 0.300 $\mu$T or greater was based on small numbers and was not characterized by a consistent pattern or a significant trend. Our results provide little support for the hypothesis that living in homes with high time-weighted average magnetic-field levels or in homes close to electrical transmission or distribution lines is related to the risk of childhood ALL.

Supported in part by a grant from the National Cancer Institute (RO1 CA48051) and by the University of Minnesota Children's Cancer Research Fund.

*We are indebted to the members of the Advisory Committee (including Dr. Lawrence Fischer, director of the Institute for Experimental Toxicology, Michigan State University [chairperson]; Dr. Ron Brookmeyer, Department of Biostatistics, Johns Hopkins University School of Hygiene and Public Health; Dr. Raymond Greenberg, vice-president for academic affairs and provost, Medical University of South Carolina; Dr. Martin Misakian, National Institute of Standards and Technology; and former member Dr. Howard Wachtel, Department of Electrical Engineering, University of Colorado) for their guidance and their numerous constructive suggestions on all aspects of the study. We are also indebted to Dr. John Boice, Jr., former chief of the Radiation Epidemiology Branch, National Cancer Institute, for his support in all phases of the study; to the staff of Westat, Inc., Rockville, Md. (including Beth Bridgeman, Kathy Deutchman, Susan Englehart, Susan Gardner, Vickie Griffis, Teferra Hailu, Barbara Hood, Nancy LaVerda, Pat Leonard, Judy Light, Bob McConnell, Pat Mueller, Arbarna Nathan, Margaret Pacious, Michelle Tanenbaum, Shirley Tipton, Susan Ditty Van-Till, and Freda Wentz), for data collection and data-management support; to the employees of Enertech, Campbell, Calif., for wire coding (Bob Workley and Esther Workley) and for programming meters (Richard Iriye); and to Mr. Jan Erik Deadman, School of Occupational Health, McGill University, Montreal, for advice on the assessment of magnetic-field exposure.*

## APPENDIX

The principal investigators and participating institutions in the Children's Cancer Group (with grants from the National Cancer Institute in parentheses) were as follows: W.A. Bleyer, A. Khayat, H. Sather, M. Krailo, J. Buckley, D. Stram, and R. Sposto, Group Operations Center, Arcadia, Calif. (CA13539); R. Hutchinson, University of Michigan Medical Center, Ann Arbor (CA02971); S. Shurin, Rainbow Babies and Children's Hospital, Cleveland (CA20320); E. Baum, Children's Memorial Hospital, Chicago (CA07431); F.L. Johnson, Wyler Children's Hospital, Chicago; F. Ruymann, Children's Hospital of Columbus, Columbus, Ohio (CA03750); J. Mirro, Children's Hospital, Pittsburgh (CA36015); W. Woods, University of Minnesota, Minneapolis (CA07306); A. Meadows, Children's Hospital, Philadelphia (CA11796); P. Brietfield, Riley Hospital for Children, Indianapolis (CA13809); R. Wells, Children's Hospital Medical Center, Cincinnati (CA26126); R. Tannous, University of Iowa Hospitals and Clinics, Iowa City (CA29314); G. Gilchrist, Mayo Clinic, Rochester, Minn. (CA28882); and M. Donaldson, University of Medicine and Dentistry of New Jersey, Camden.

## REFERENCES

1. Wertheimer N, Leeper E. Electrical wiring configurations and childhood cancer. Am J Epidemiol 1979;109:273-84.
2. Fulton JP, Cobb S, Preble L, Leone L, Forman E. Electrical wiring configurations and childhood leukemia in Rhode Island. Am J Epidemiol 1980;111:292-6.
3. Savitz DA, Wachtel H, Barnes FA, John EM, Tvrdik JG. Case-control study of childhood cancer and exposure to 60-Hz magnetic fields. Am J Epidemiol 1988;128:21-38.
4. Tomenius L. 50-Hz electromagnetic environment and the incidence of childhood tumors in Stockholm County. Bioelectromagnetics 1986;7:191-207.
5. London SJ, Thomas DC, Bowman JD, Sobel E, Cheng T-C, Peters JM. Exposure to residential electric and magnetic fields and risk of childhood leukemia. Am J Epidemiol 1991;134:923-37. [Erratum, Am J Epidemiol 1993;137:381.]
6. Feychting M, Ahlbom A. Magnetic fields and cancer in children residing near Swedish high-voltage power lines. Am J Epidemiol 1993;138:467-81.
7. Olsen JH, Nielsen A, Schulgen G. Residence near high voltage facilities and risk of cancer in children. BMJ 1993;307:891-5.
8. Verkasalo PK, Pukkala E, Hongisto MY, et al. Risk of cancer in Finnish children living close to power lines. BMJ 1993;307:895-9.
9. Tynes T, Haldorsen T. Electromagnetic fields and cancer in children residing near Norwegian high-voltage power lines. Am J Epidemiol 1997;145:219-26.
10. Committee on the Possible Effects of Electromagnetic Fields on Biologic Systems. Possible health effects of exposure to residential electric and magnetic fields. Washington, D.C.: National Academy Press, 1996:113-87.
11. Wertheimer N, Leeper E. Adult cancer related to electrical wires near the home. Int J Epidemiol 1982;11:345-55.
12. Savitz DA, Pearce NE, Poole C. Methodological issues in the epidemiology of electromagnetic fields and cancer. Epidemiol Rev 1989;11:59-78.
13. Poole C, Trichopoulos D. Extremely low-frequency electric and magnetic fields and cancer. Cancer Causes Control 1991;2:267-76.
14. Oak Ridge Associated Universities Panel. Health effects of low-frequency electric and magnetic fields. Washington, D.C.: Government Printing Office, 1992:V-1–V-18. (Publication no. 029-000-00443-9.)
15. Electromagnetic fields and the risk of cancer: report of an advisory group on non-ionising radiation. In: Documents of the NRPB. Vol. 3. No. 1. Didcot, United Kingdom: National Radiological Protection Board, 1992:54-80.
16. Tenforde TS. Interaction of ELF magnetic fields with living systems. In: Polk C, Postow E, eds. Handbook of biological effects of electromagnetic fields. 2nd ed. Boca Raton, Fla.: CRC Press, 1996:185-230.
17. Kleinerman RA, Linet MS, Hatch EE, et al. Magnetic field exposure assessment in a case-control study of childhood leukemia. Epidemiology (in press).
18. Robison LL, Daigle A. Control selection using random digit dialing for cases of childhood cancer. Am J Epidemiol 1984;120:164-6.
19. Kaune WT, Darby SD, Gardner SN, Hrubec Z, Iriye RN, Linet MS. Development of a protocol for assessing time-weighted-average exposures of young children to power-frequency magnetic fields. Bioelectromagnetics 1994;15:33-51.
20. Friedman DR, Hatch EE, Tarone R, et al. Childhood exposure to magnetic fields: residential area measurements compared to personal dosimetry. Epidemiology 1996;7:151-5.
21. Kaune WT, Savitz DA. Simplification of the Wertheimer-Leeper wire code. Bioelectromagnetics 1994;15:275-82.
22. Breslow NE, Day NE. Statistical methods in cancer research. Vol. I. The analysis of case-control studies. Lyon, France: International Agency for Research on Cancer, 1980:122-279. (IARC scientific publications no. 32.)
23. Robison LL, Neglia JP. Epidemiology of Down syndrome and childhood acute leukemia. In: McCoy EE, Epstein CJ, eds. Oncology and immunology of Down syndrome. Vol. 246 of Progress in clinical and biological research. New York: Alan R. Liss, 1987:19-32.
24. High Voltage Transmission Research Center. Survey of residential magnetic field sources. Vol. 1. Goals, results, and conclusions. Palo Alto, Calif.: Electric Power Research Institute, 1993:6-1–6-118.
25. Kaune WT, Stevens RG, Callahan NJ, Severson RK, Thomas DB. Residential magnetic and electric fields. Bioelectromagnetics 1987;8:315-35.
26. Barnes F, Wachtel H, Savitz D, Fuller J. Use of wiring configuration and wiring codes for estimating externally generated electric and magnetic fields. Bioelectromagnetics 1989;10:13-21.
27. Wacholder S, Silverman DT, McLaughlin JK, Mandel JS. Selection of controls in case-control studies. II. Types of controls. Am J Epidemiol 1992;135:1029-41.
28. Jones TL, Shih CH, Thurston DH, Ware BJ, Cole P. Selection bias from differential residential mobility as an explanation for associations of wire codes with childhood cancers. J Clin Epidemiol 1993;46:545-8.
29. Gurney JG, Davis S, Schwartz SM, Mueller BA, Kaune WT, Stevens RG. Childhood cancer occurrence in relation to power line configurations: a study of potential selection bias in case-control studies. Epidemiology 1995;6:31-5.
30. Dovan T, Kaune WT, Savitz DA. Repeatability of measurements of residential magnetic fields and wire codes. Bioelectromagnetics 1993;14:145-59.

Reprinted with permission from "Power Lines, Cancer and Fear," E. Campion, *New England J. Medicine* **337**, 44-46. Copyright © 1997 Massachusetts Medical Society. All rights reserved.

## POWER LINES, CANCER, AND FEAR

OVER the past 18 years, there has been considerable interest in the possible link between electromagnetic fields and cancer, especially leukemia. The story of this highly publicized research has been marked by mystery, contradiction, and confusion. When something as ubiquitous and misunderstood as extremely-low-frequency electromagnetic fields is accused of causing cancer in children, people's reactions may be driven more by passion than by reason.

Each year in this country about 2000 children are given a diagnosis of acute lymphoblastic leukemia (ALL), the most common childhood cancer. Despite the remarkable advances in treatment, ALL still carries a 30 percent mortality. Other than exposure to ionizing radiation, its cause remains a mystery. ALL is more common among whites and children of higher socioeconomic class, and for unclear reasons the incidence of ALL has increased by about 20 percent in the past two decades.[1,2] During the past 50 years, per capita use of electricity has increased more than 10 times. Some investigators have claimed that living close to major power lines causes cancer, particularly leukemia in children.

In this issue of the *Journal,* Linet et al.[3] report the results of a major study showing that the risk of ALL does not increase with increasing electromagnetic-field levels in children's homes. This study has several strengths. It was large, including 629 children with leukemia and 619 controls, and it included measurements of electromagnetic fields, made by technicians blinded to the case or control status of the subjects, both in the houses where the children had lived and, in 41 percent of cases, in the homes in which their mothers resided while pregnant. Linet et al. also found no relation between the risk of ALL and residential wire-code classifications, again determined by technicians blinded to the children's health status. The wire-code classifications are important, because several of the earlier positive studies relied on these proxy indicators rather than on actual measurements of electromagnetic fields.

This whole saga began when two Denver researchers, puzzled by small clusters of cancer in children, came to believe that living in close proximity to high-voltage power lines was a cause of leukemia.[4] The analysis they published in 1979 was crude and relied on distances from homes to power lines and on wiring configurations rather than on direct measures of exposure to electromagnetic fields. They found that the risk of childhood leukemia was more than doubled among children living near such power lines, a finding that led to more studies and more concern. Soon activists and the media began to spread the word that electromagnetic fields cause cancer.

The hypothesized cause was exposure to extremely-low-frequency magnetic fields generated by the electrical current in power lines. Physicists understand these invisible fields well, but most physicians, parents, and patients do not. The movement of any electrical charge creates a magnetic field that can be measured.[5] Even the 60-Hz residential electric current (50 Hz in Europe) creates a very weak oscillating field, which, like all magnetic fields, penetrates living tissue. These low-frequency electromagnetic fields are known as nonionizing radiation, since the amount of energy in them is far below that required to break molecular bonds such as those in DNA.

One ironic fact about low-frequency electromagnetic fields is that we live and worry about them within the Earth's static magnetic field of 50 $\mu$T, which is hundreds of times greater than the oscillating magnetic field produced by 110/220-V current in houses (0.01 to 0.05 $\mu$T).[5,6] Even directly under high-voltage transmission lines, the magnetic field is only about 3 to 10 $\mu$T, which is less than that in an electric railway car and much weaker than the magnetic field close to my head when I use an electric razor (about 60 $\mu$T).

Although most physicists find it inconceivable that power-line electromagnetic fields could pose a hazard to health, dozens of epidemiologic studies have reported weak positive associations between proximity to high-voltage power lines and the risk of cancer.[6,7] The negative or equivocal studies did not end the controversy. Fear of leukemia is a powerful force, and the media response amplified the perception of electromagnetic fields as a health hazard. In 1989 *The New Yorker* published three articles by journalist Paul Brodeur that described in mesmerizing detail how maverick researchers had discovered a cause of cancer that the establishment refused to accept.[8-10] Like many of the epidemiologic studies themselves, these widely quoted articles described biologic mechanisms of action for electromagnetic fields that were hypothetical, even fanciful. Brodeur went so far as to claim that the search for the truth about the hazards of electromagnetic fields was threatened most by the "obfuscation of industry, the mendacity of the military, and the corruption of ethics that industrial and military money could purchase from various members of the medical and scientific community."[8] Suspicion spread to many other wavelengths on the nonionizing electromagnetic spectrum, producing fears about occupational exposure to electricity as well as exposure to microwave appliances, radar, video-display terminals, and even cellular telephones. Dozens of studies looked for associations with brain cancer, miscarriages, fetal-growth retardation, lymphoma, breast cancer, breast cancer in men, lung cancer, all cancers, immunologic abnormalities, and even changes in the behavior of animals.

When people hear that a scientific study has implicated something new as a cause of cancer, they get worried. They get even more worried when the exposure is called radiation and comes from dangerous-looking high-voltage power lines controlled by government and industry, which some distrust deeply. Such exposure seems eerie when people hear that electromagnetic fields penetrate their homes, their bodies, their children. The worried citizens took action. Frightened people, including parents of children with leukemia, undertook their own epidemiologic studies and fought to get high-power transmission lines moved away from their children. Congress responded with large direct appropriations for wider research on the effects of electromagnetic fields. After a large apparently positive study in Sweden,[7] the Swedish government came close to mandating the relocation of schools to at least 1000 meters from large power lines. But cooler heads prevailed once it became clear that the absolute incremental risk was small at most, the conclusions were based on a tiny fraction of all Swedish children with leukemia, and the increase in risk was found only in relation to some estimates of magnetic fields, not to the actual fields measured in children's homes.

Serious limitations have been pointed out in nearly all the studies of power lines and cancer.[11,12] These limitations include unblinded assessment of exposure, difficulty in making direct measurements of the constantly varying electromagnetic fields, inconsistencies between the measured levels and the estimates of exposure based on wiring configurations, recall bias with respect to exposure, post hoc definitions of exposure categories, and huge numbers of comparisons with selective emphasis on those that were positive. Both study participation and residential wire-code categories may be confounded by socioeconomic factors. Often the number of cases of ALL in the high-exposure categories has been very small, and controls may not have been truly comparable. Moreover, all these epidemiologic studies have been conducted in pursuit of a cause of cancer for which there is no plausible biologic basis. There is no convincing evidence that exposure to electromagnetic fields causes cancer in animals,[6] and electromagnetic fields have no reproducible biologic effects at all, except at strengths that are far beyond those ever found in people's homes.

In recent years, several commissions and expert panels have concluded that there is no convincing evidence that high-voltage power lines are a health hazard or a cause of cancer.[6,13] And the weight of the better epidemiologic studies, including that by Linet et al., now supports the same conclusion. It is sad that hundreds of millions of dollars have gone into studies that never had much promise of finding a way to prevent the tragedy of cancer in children. The many inconclusive and inconsistent studies have generated worry and fear and have given peace of mind to no one. The 18 years of research have produced considerable paranoia, but little insight and no prevention. It is time to stop wasting our research resources. We should redirect them to research that will be able to discover the true biologic causes of the leukemic clones that threaten the lives of children.

EDWARD W. CAMPION, M.D.

## REFERENCES

**1.** Pui C-H. Childhood leukemias. N Engl J Med 1995;332:1618-30.
**2.** Ries LAG, Miller BA, Hankey BF, Kosary CL, Harras A, Edwards BK, eds. SEER cancer statistics review, 1973-1991: tables and graphs. Bethesda, Md.: National Cancer Institute, 1994. (NIH publication no. 94-2789.)
**3.** Linet MS, Hatch EE, Kleinerman RA, et al. Residential exposure to magnetic fields and acute lymphoblastic leukemia in children. N Engl J Med 1997;337:1-7.
**4.** Wertheimer N, Leeper E. Electrical wiring configurations and childhood cancer. Am J Epidemiol 1979;109:273-84.
**5.** Hitchcock RT, Patterson RM. Radio-frequency and ELF electromagnetic energies: a handbook for health professionals. New York: Van Nostrand Reinhold, 1995.
**6.** National Research Council. Possible health effects of exposure to residential electric and magnetic fields. Washington, D.C.: National Academy Press, 1997.
**7.** Feychting M, Ahlbom A. Magnetic fields and cancer in children residing near Swedish high-voltage power lines. Am J Epidemiol 1993;138:467-81.
**8.** Brodeur P. Annals of radiation: the hazards of electromagnetic fields. I. Power lines. The New Yorker. June 12, 1989:51-88.
**9.** *Idem.* Annals of radiation: the hazards of electromagnetic fields. II. Something is happening. The New Yorker. June 19, 1989:47-73.
**10.** *Idem.* Annals of radiation: the hazards of electromagnetic fields. III. Video-display terminals. The New Yorker. June 26, 1989:39-68.
**11.** Savitz DA, Pearce NE, Poole C. Methodological issues in the epidemiology of electromagnetic fields and cancer. Epidemiol Rev 1989;11:59-78.
**12.** Poole C, Trichopoulos D. Extremely low-frequency electric and magnetic fields and cancer. Cancer Causes Control 1991;2:267-76.
**13.** Oak Ridge Associated Universities Panel. Health effects of low-frequency electric and magnetic fields. Washington, D.C.: Government Printing Office, 1992:V-1–V-18. (Publication no. 029-000-00443-9.)

©1997, Massachusetts Medical Society.

Reprinted with permission from "Magnetic Field Exposure in Relation to Leukemia and Brain Cancer Mortality Among Electrical Utility Workers," D.Savitz and D.Loomis, *Am. J. Epidemiology* **141**, 123-124 (1995).

American Journal of Epidemiology
Copyright © 1995 by The Johns Hopkins University School of Hygiene and Public Health
All rights reserved

Vol. 141, No. 2
*Printed in U.S.A.*

# Magnetic Field Exposure in Relation to Leukemia and Brain Cancer Mortality among Electric Utility Workers

David A. Savitz[1] and Dana P. Loomis[1]

Reports of leukemia and brain cancer among men in electrical occupations suggest a small increase in risk, but most previous studies have failed to classify magnetic field exposure accurately or to consider potential confounders. The authors conducted an historical cohort mortality study of 138,905 men employed at five large electric power companies in the United States between 1950 and 1986 with at least 6 months of work experience. Exposure was estimated by linking individual work histories to data from 2,842 workshift magnetic field measurements. Mortality follow-up identified 20,733 deaths based on 2,656,436 person-years of experience. Death rates were analyzed in relation to magnetic field exposure history with Poisson regression. Total mortality and cancer mortality rose slightly with increasing magnetic field exposure. Leukemia mortality, however, was not associated with indices of magnetic field exposure except for work as an electrician. Brain cancer mortality was modestly elevated in relation to duration of work in exposed jobs and much more strongly associated with magnetic field exposure indices. Brain cancer risk increased by an estimated factor of 1.94 per microtesla-year of magnetic field exposure in the previous 2–10 years, with a mortality rate ratio of 2.6 in the highest exposure category. In contrast to other studies, these data do not support an association between occupational magnetic field exposure and leukemia but do suggest a link to brain cancer. *Am J Epidemiol* 1995;141:123–34.

brain neoplasms; electromagnetic fields; leukemia

More than a decade ago, Milham's (1) analysis of mortality among men in the state of Washington suggested that electrical workers experience an increased risk of leukemia, possibly as a result of their workplace exposure to electric and magnetic fields. The underlying assumption of that study and dozens that have followed is that the occupation of "electrical worker," which includes such job titles as lineman, electrician, and electrical engineer, is indicative of elevated occupational exposure to electric and magnetic fields. Subsequent reports on both leukemia and brain cancer in diverse populations and across a range of workplaces have generally, but not always, found a small increase in risk associated with such job titles (2, 3). Nonetheless, the question of whether occupational exposure to electric and magnetic fields causes any type of cancer remains unanswered.

Exposure assessment surveys corroborate the assumption that men engaged in such jobs generally do have exposures to magnetic fields greater than background levels found in home or office environments (4, 5). Recent epidemiologic studies have incorporated magnetic field measurements to assign exposure (6–9), but the results continue to be inconsistent: Matanoski et al. (6) found leukemia to be associated with magnetic fields based on only some exposure indices; Floderus et al. (7) reported a strong association between jobs with elevated magnetic field exposure and chronic lymphocytic leukemia but not other types of leukemia or brain cancer; Sahl et al. (8) found no association with either leukemia or brain cancer among electric utility workers; and Thériault et al. (9) identified an increased risk for leukemia, primarily acute myeloid leukemia, but little association for brain cancer.

To extend and improve on this literature, we conducted a study of mortality among electric utility workers that included the use of more than 2,800 randomly sampled personal magnetic field measurements to estimate individual exposure. We also attempted to account for exposure to two classes of potentially carcinogenic workplace chemicals that are prevalent in the electric utility industry, polychlori-

Received for publication August 5, 1994, and in final form November 1, 1994.

CI, confidence interval; ICD-9, *International Classification of Diseases*, Ninth Revision; RR, rate ratio; SMR, standardized mortality ratio.

[1] Department of Epidemiology, School of Public Health, University of North Carolina, Chapel Hill, NC.

Reprint requests to Dr. David A. Savitz, Department of Epidemiology, Campus Box #7400, University of North Carolina, Chapel Hill, NC 27599.

nated biphenyls and solvents, as potential confounders of the association with magnetic fields. Finally, we were able to identify and study a sufficiently large cohort to obtain precise results even for causes of death as rare as leukemia subtypes. The study was focused on mortality from leukemia and brain cancer among electric utility workers in relation to their history of workplace exposure to magnetic fields.

## MATERIALS AND METHODS

### Cohort identification

A retrospective cohort mortality study was conducted on workers at five electric utility companies throughout the United States. Volunteers were sought among member companies of the Electric Power Research Institute who were willing to provide access to data, allow monitoring of workers, and give the necessary technical assistance. Given the practical advantage of enrolling fewer large companies to attain the needed study size, the study was conducted at Carolina Power and Light Company, Virginia Electric Power Company, PECO Energy Company (formerly Philadelphia Electric Company), Tennessee Valley Authority, and Pacific Gas and Electric Company. All men who had been employed full time any time between January 1, 1950, and December 31, 1986, and had accrued a total of at least 6 months of continuous employment were eligible for the study; however, unavailability of records led to start dates of September 1, 1954, and January 1, 1955, at two of the companies. Women were excluded because until recently they had rarely worked in jobs with elevated magnetic field exposure. Workers who spent their entire careers in the nuclear divisions of the companies were excluded, but we included men who had qualifying nonnuclear work experience regardless of nuclear division activity.

Personnel records served to identify the cohort. We collected information on date of birth, race, Social Security number (for mortality follow-up), and a complete history of employment at the company, with start dates for each new position held at the company. Workers who were missing date of birth ($n = 51$), had unknown start dates ($n = 30$), had major errors in job history data ($n = 7$), or had important inconsistencies between job history and mortality follow-up data ($n = 3$) were excluded. Data on workers who were employed at more than one of the participating companies ($n = 112$) were merged for analysis. Workers were classified as active (still employed), retired with pension, or terminated (quit or fired) as of December 31, 1988, the study cutoff date. A total of 138,905 eligible workers were included in the analysis.

## Mortality follow-up and classification of causes of death

All 76,934 retired and terminated workers were sought for vital status ascertainment through December 31, 1988. For men who were still employed on January 1, 1979, or later, we relied on the National Death Index, a comprehensive roster of US deaths. Given the completeness and quality of our data on date of birth and Social Security number, failure to match such men in a computerized search was accepted as an indication that they were still alive (10, 11).

Workers who had terminated employment prior to 1979 were followed using several data sources. We matched them against Social Security Administration Death Benefit records and Health Care Financing Administration files, which identify living beneficiaries and decedents. Drivers' license records were matched with the cohort rosters to identify men who were still alive based on license renewal. Men not located through those methods were traced through credit bureaus, and a man was identified as alive if his record indicated that he had completed a new credit application after 1979. Telephone tracing was the final step in seeking to identify living men, and information was obtained from voter registration records, post offices, and other sources that did not require direct contact with the men or their families. Finally, men who were likely to have died based on their calculated present age were sought in vital records offices of the states where they were last employed. Through this effort, 55,423 cohort members who were retired or terminated were classified as living at the study cutoff date, 20,733 were classified as deceased, and only 778 (0.6 percent of the total cohort, 1.0 percent of retired and terminated workers) were lost to follow-up. Men who were lost to follow-up were considered lost when they were last known to be alive, which is when they ceased employment.

Death certificates were sought from state vital records offices for all men identified as deceased, with 20,068 (96.8 percent) obtained. Certificates were coded by trained nosologists according to the *International Classification of Diseases*, Ninth Revision (ICD-9) (12), with the 665 certificates that were not found included only in analyses of total mortality. Underlying cause of death information provided the basis for assignment to the cause-of-death groups used in the National Institute for Occupational Safety and Health Life Table Analysis System (13). Cancers were also classified using all available death certificate information according to the *International Classification of Diseases for Oncology* (ICD-O) (14) from which we attempted to define subtypes of leukemia and brain cancer.

*Am J Epidemiol*   Vol. 141, No. 2, 1995

## Work history organization

Complete work histories of cohort members were abstracted and computerized. To assign exposures and conduct the analysis, it was necessary to collapse thousands of job titles held over several decades at the five companies into a smaller number of meaningful groups for analysis. Jobs of a similar nature based on general activity, level of responsibility, and, indirectly, exposure potential were grouped into a total of 28 occupational categories, as described in detail elsewhere (15). Some occupational categories were not represented at all five companies, so a total of 120 separate company-occupational category cells existed. Those entities define the rows of job-exposure matrices for assignment of magnetic field and chemical exposures.

## Magnetic field exposure assessment

We measured personal magnetic field exposures to estimate the average exposures for occupational categories since no historical monitoring data were available. As described in detail elsewhere (16), all current workers at each company were placed into occupational categories, and we randomly selected individuals within those company-occupational category cells for measurement. The desired number of measurements was based on two criteria: 1) the estimated distribution of person-years across companies, with larger companies allocated more measurements; and 2) the presumed magnetic field exposure in the occupational category, divided a priori into low, medium, and high, with a ratio relative to low of 3 : 1 and 5 : 1, respectively, for the medium and high categories.

A study coordinator from each of the five companies was provided with a list of randomly selected workers who were asked to wear an Average Magnetic EXposure (AMEX) meter (Enertech Consultants, Campbell, CA) (17) for that day's work shift. The AMEX meter is worn on a pouch around the waist and accrues an electrical charge in proportion to the cumulative magnetic field over the time it is worn, yielding a time-weighted average exposure. As each meter was returned, it was read and sent out to the next eligible worker. Assignment of measurement days was random, and workers who were unavailable on the chosen day were excluded. After every 6–10 measurements, the meter was returned for a calibration check.

Among the 4,094 attempted measurements, data were lost due to worker absence ($n = 446$), worker refusal ($n = 121$), procedural errors ($n = 346$), instrument failure ($n = 10$), failure to meet the calibration criteria ($n = 286$), and work shifts of <4 or >12 hours ($n = 43$), leaving 2,842 usable measurements. These data were used to derive a job-exposure matrix, as described in detail elsewhere (18). Individual work shift time-weighted averages were computed and the arithmetic means were calculated for each company-occupational category combination.

Because some cells had very few measurements, the individual company-occupational category cells were aggregated to optimize the balance between statistical precision and separation of groups with distinct exposure levels. An analysis of variance to compare within- and between-group variances under several different approaches to grouping allowed us to identify the optimal aggregation, as described in detail elsewhere (18). Collapsing the individual cells into five groups increased the precision of the estimates with negligible loss in the amount of between-group variability. Five groups were formed by rank ordering the cells and aggregating adjacent ones, with arithmetic mean values of 0.12, 0.21, 0.39, 0.62, and 1.27 $\mu$T. The lower three groups correspond to quartiles of the exposure distribution, while the upper quartile was divided to create the two highest exposure groups. The group average was assigned to all occupational categories that fell within the group. Exposure estimates for individual workers were derived from the occupational category; and the group average magnetic field score was assigned to it, summed over time as described below.

## Chemical exposure assessment

Potential exposure to polychlorinated biphenyls and solvents, judged to be the most widely used potentially carcinogenic chemicals in the electric utility industry, was assessed through a series of meetings with expert panels at each of the five participating companies. Employees familiar with the company operations over extended periods of time (e.g., industrial hygienists, department managers, long-term employees) were convened and asked to assess the potential for exposure to these agents for each of the occupational categories based on the presence or absence of the agent in the work environment with consideration of whether the category of worker had direct or indirect contact with the agent of interest. This information was supplemented by site visits by study staff and integrated into calendar time-specific estimated exposure potential for each company-occupational category combination. Workers were classified as unexposed to an agent up to the time when they entered a job with exposure potential, and they remained classified as exposed thereafter. Although we included workers who spent part of their career in the nuclear division, exposures to ionizing radiation were believed to be insufficient to produce confounding.

*Am J Epidemiol* Vol. 141, No. 2, 1995

## Data analysis

Mortality rates of the cohort of electric utility workers were compared first with the US population, with indirect adjustment for age and calendar year using the National Institute for Occupational Safety and Health Life Table Analysis System (13). This analysis generated standardized mortality ratios, presented with 95 percent confidence intervals (19).

The comparisons of primary interest are internal to the cohort, contrasting cancer mortality rates among the electric utility workers based on their history of exposure to magnetic fields. These contrasts were based on several indices of magnetic field exposure: 1) duration of employment in any of 18 occupational categories with greater than background exposure, including a number of jobs generally classified as "electrical workers" (linemen, electricians, power plant operators, etc.) as well as other workers in operating areas that had elevated magnetic field levels (technical workers, mechanics, boilermakers, etc.); 2) duration of employment as a lineman, electrician, and power plant operator, the three most common jobs with mean magnetic field exposures of 0.65, 1.11, and 0.79 $\mu$T, respectively; 3) cumulative magnetic field exposure based on measured magnetic fields associated with each occupational category and aggregated over time. In all instances, person-years (and deaths) were allocated to a given duration of employment or exposure stratum only until the cumulative score qualified them for allocation to the next higher stratum.

We examined cumulative exposure in four time intervals: from the start of employment until <2 years previously ("career exposure"), ≥2–<10 years previously, ≥10–<20 years previously, and >20 years previously. A minimum 2-year latency was imposed because we were studying deaths rather than incident cancers, and this interval allows for at least some of the unknown time between diagnosis and death. In addition to considering a possible latency of effect, in which adverse effects of exposure require some period of time to become manifest, it is possible that magnetic fields exert an influence for only a limited period of time after the cessation of exposure. These time windows were chosen to address possible latency and persistence of any adverse effects of magnetic field exposure.

For analysis of the duration of exposure in specific occupational categories, intervals of 0–<5 years (referent, including those with no work in that job), ≥5–<20 years, and >20 years were considered, with only two levels of <5 and >5 years analyzed for leukemia subtypes due to small numbers. For analyses involving cumulative exposure, we first assigned the measured time-weighted average to each job held using the

methods described above and then estimated the average exposure in each calendar year of work, averaging across jobs when more than one were held in a year. These were summed over calendar time and multiplied by the proportion of all hours spent at work, 0.23 (250 days × 8 hours per day divided by 365 days × 24 hours per day), to yield workday exposure expressed in microtesla-days and divided by 365 to yield microtesla-years of occupational exposure.

For each of the four time windows of exposure, we separately derived the dose estimate for all decedents at the time of their death. These scores were used to establish cutpoints for deciles of exposure in units of microtesla-days, ensuring an equitable distribution of deaths across groups. For career exposure, person-years below the 30th percentile of that distribution formed the referent category, with the other percentiles defined as 30–<50, ≥50–<70, ≥70–<90, and ≥90. For the other three time windows, 0 dose was chosen as the referent category (person-years of men who were not employed in the relevant window) and compared with person-years in percentiles of >0–<30, ≥30–<60, ≥60–<80, and ≥80. The numbers of intervals and cutpoints were chosen to provide an equitable distribution of deaths while allowing examination of risk in the upper end of the exposure distribution. Although the actual quantitative cutpoints differ across time windows, they were developed using a consistent rationale. In each case, the lowest exposure group served as the referent category with which the other four groups were compared. For leukemia subtypes, additional aggregation of the upper categories was sometimes necessary to achieve a minimum cell size of four cases in each stratum. We also conducted analyses eliminating men who had not worked in the specific time window, and the pattern of results remained the same.

We also estimated the relation between exposure and risk on a continuous scale by assigning the midpoints of the deciles as exposure scores and treating those scores as a continuous measure. The results were calculated as risk per microtesla-day but were converted to more interpretable units of risk per microtesla-year of occupational exposure. A difference of 1 $\mu$T-year of occupational exposure would be produced by working 5 years on a job with 0.9 $\mu$T, or 10 years on a job with 0.4 $\mu$T, for example. These analyses assume a log-linear relationship between exposure and mortality, estimating a common odds ratio across the range of exposure.

Adjusted mortality rate ratios and 95 percent confidence intervals were estimated by Poisson regression (20) using Generalised Linear Interactive Modeling (21), with routine adjustment for age, calendar time (in decades), race (white, nonwhite), social class, active versus inactive work status, potential exposure to polychlorinated biphenyls, and potential exposure to solvents. Age was treated as a continuous variable using the interval midpoints for each 5-year group, scaled to reflect the log-linear relation with total mortality and the power relation with cancers (log age related to log of risk). The definition of social class was based on the worker's job at hire, grouped as upper white collar, lower white collar, skilled blue collar, and unskilled blue collar. Work status was a time-dependent variable constructed to reflect whether the worker was or was not employed in a given year of observation, with a 2-year lag intended to control the healthy worker effect (22). Although little confounding by social class or chemical exposures was found, we included those variables in all Poisson regression analyses for consistency.

Mortality from all causes was obtained, but the principal outcomes of interest based on previous studies were leukemia, leukemia subtypes (chronic lymphocytic, acute myeloid), and brain cancer. Among all 164 leukemia deaths, 34 (21 percent) were classified as chronic lymphocytic leukemia (ICD-9 code 204.1), 49 (30 percent) were classified as acute myeloid leukemia (ICD-9 codes 205.0, 206.0, and 207.0), 24 (15 percent) were classified as acute lymphocytic or chronic myeloid leukemia (insufficient numbers for analysis), and 57 (35 percent) could not be classified into any of these groups. Among the 144 brain cancers, 102 (71 percent) were classified as gliomas (ICD-O morphology codes 9380–9489) (14). Results for total brain cancers and gliomas were similar so that only the former is presented.

## RESULTS

The distribution of the 2,656,436 person-years and 20,733 deaths in the cohort generally followed the patterns expected for an industrial workforce (table 1). Mortality from all causes was 23 percent less than that of the general population, consistent with the "healthy worker effect" in which selection for employment produces favorable mortality rates compared with the general population. The measure of social class based on first job held in the company identified a clear gradient of mortality that favored the most advantaged men. Age, calendar year, and time since hire showed the expected patterns of a movement toward the mortality of the general population with the passage of time.

More than 90 percent of the men in the cohort were white and most of them were blue collar workers. Person-time experience was concentrated in men younger than 50, in more recent calendar time periods,

TABLE 1. Person-years and deaths from all causes: US Utility Worker Mortality Study, 1950–1988

| | Deaths | Person-years | SMR* | 95% CI* |
|---|---|---|---|---|
| Total cohort | 20,733 | 2,656,436 | 0.77 | 0.76–0.78 |
| Race | | | | |
| White | 17,162 | 2,410,101 | 0.73 | 0.72–0.75 |
| Nonwhite | 3,571 | 246,335 | 1.05 | 1.01–1.08 |
| Social class | | | | |
| Upper white | 2,201 | 371,665 | 0.63 | 0.60–0.66 |
| Lower white | 2,895 | 408,497 | 0.74 | 0.71–0.77 |
| Skilled blue | 9,044 | 1,046,129 | 0.80 | 0.78–0.81 |
| Unskilled blue | 6,579 | 828,326 | 0.83 | 0.81–0.85 |
| Age (years) | | | | |
| <50 | 3,502 | 1,871,978 | 0.62 | 0.60–0.64 |
| 50–59 | 3,733 | 420,899 | 0.68 | 0.66–0.70 |
| 60–69 | 5,771 | 248,917 | 0.80 | 0.78–0.82 |
| ≥70 | 7,727 | 114,643 | 0.92 | 0.90–0.94 |
| Calendar year | | | | |
| 1950–1959 | 641 | 291,708 | 0.29 | 0.27–0.31 |
| 1960–1969 | 3,608 | 538,168 | 0.66 | 0.64–0.69 |
| 1970–1979 | 7,491 | 857,767 | 0.85 | 0.83–0.87 |
| 1980–1988 | 8,993 | 968,793 | 0.87 | 0.85–0.89 |
| Time since hire (years) | | | | |
| <5 | 614 | 538,702 | 0.37 | 0.34–0.40 |
| 5–19 | 5,428 | 1,359,515 | 0.68 | 0.66–0.70 |
| 20–29 | 5,674 | 458,940 | 0.82 | 0.80–0.84 |
| ≥30 | 9,017 | 299,278 | 0.88 | 0.86–0.90 |

\* CI, confidence interval; SMR, standardized mortality ratio.

and in the 5- to 20-year employment duration. The only anomalous result was the slightly elevated mortality rate for nonwhites, possibly because national data pertain to a spectrum of non-Caucasian groups whereas the nonwhite segment of our study population is believed to consist largely of African-Americans.

Mortality data from selected causes of death for the entire cohort are presented in table 2, with particular attention to cancers. The large cohort and long follow-up period generate notably precise estimates of standardized mortality ratios for nearly all causes of death. As would be expected, overall cancer mortality was lower than anticipated based on general population rates (standardized mortality ratio (SMR) = 0.86), but to a lesser extent than cardiovascular disease (SMR = 0.76) and nonmalignant respiratory disease (SMR = 0.69). No cause of death was notably elevated relative to the general population, with standardized mortality ratios of 0.95 or greater found only for skin cancer, brain and nervous system cancer, other lymphatic neoplasms, and neoplasms of unspecified malignancy of the brain and eye. Smoking-related causes of death do not suggest a pattern of increased tobacco use in this cohort (lung cancer SMR = 0.91, nonmalignant respiratory disease SMR = 0.69), nor

TABLE 2.    Standardized mortality ratios for selected causes of death: US Utility Worker Mortality Study, 1950–1988

| Cause of death (ICD-9-CM*, codes)† | Observed deaths | Expected deaths | SMR* | 95% CI* |
|---|---|---|---|---|
| All deaths | 20,733 | 26,779.5 | 0.77 | 0.76–0.78 |
| All cancers (140–239) | 4,833 | 5,615.1 | 0.86 | 0.84–0.89 |
| MN* of buccal cavity and pharynx (142–149) | 110 | 162.2 | 0.68 | 0.56–0.82 |
| MN of stomach (151) | 175 | 260.5 | 0.67 | 0.58–0.78 |
| MN of intestine excluding rectum (152–153) | 468 | 503.4 | 0.93 | 0.85–1.02 |
| MN of rectum (154) | 109 | 138.7 | 0.79 | 0.65–0.95 |
| MN of pancreas (157) | 243 | 289.2 | 0.84 | 0.74–0.95 |
| MN of trachea, bronchus, and lung (162) | 1,692 | 1,859.5 | 0.91 | 0.87–0.95 |
| MN of breast (174–175) | 6 | 7.5 | 0.80 | 0.29–1.74 |
| MN of prostate (185) | 387 | 432.7 | 0.89 | 0.81–0.99 |
| MN of kidney (189.0–189.2) | 101 | 132.5 | 0.76 | 0.62–0.93 |
| MN of urinary organs (188, 189.3–189.9) | 129 | 151.9 | 0.85 | 0.71–1.01 |
| MN of skin (172–173) | 116 | 111.9 | 1.04 | 0.86–1.24 |
| MN of brain and nervous system (191–192) | 151 | 158.4 | 0.95 | 0.81–1.12 |
| Neoplasms of lymphatic and hematopoietic tissue | 439 | 532.4 | 0.82 | 0.75–0.91 |
| Lymphosarcoma and reticulosarcoma (200) | 69 | 89.6 | 0.77 | 0.60–0.97 |
| Hodgkin's disease (201) | 30 | 55.9 | 0.54 | 0.36–0.77 |
| Leukemia and aleukemia (204–208) | 164 | 217.0 | 0.76 | 0.64–0.88 |
| Other lymphatic neoplasms (202–203) | 176 | 169.9 | 1.04 | 0.89–1.20 |
| Benign neoplasms of the eye and brain (224–225) | 6 | 10.9 | 0.55 | 0.20–1.20 |
| Neoplasms of unspecified nature of the eye and brain (237.5–238.9, 239.6–239.7) | 39 | 33.3 | 1.17 | 0.83–1.60 |
| Diabetes mellitus (250) | 219 | 389.2 | 0.56 | 0.49–0.64 |
| Diseases of the heart (390–429) | 7,768 | 10,209.1 | 0.76 | 0.74–0.78 |
| Cerebrovascular disease (430–438) | 1,244 | 1,695.1 | 0.73 | 0.69–0.78 |
| Diseases of the respiratory system (460–519) | 1,178 | 1,716.8 | 0.69 | 0.65–0.73 |
| Cirrhosis of the liver (571) | 410 | 648.4 | 0.63 | 0.57–0.70 |
| Transportation accidents (E800–848, E929.0–929.1) | 810 | 1,105.8 | 0.73 | 0.68–0.78 |
| Accidental falls (E880–888, E929.3) | 141 | 190.8 | 0.74 | 0.62–0.87 |
| Suicide (E950–959) | 536 | 661.3 | 0.81 | 0.74–0.88 |
| Homicide (E960–978) | 175 | 418.1 | 0.42 | 0.36–0.49 |

* CI, confidence interval; ICD-9-CM, *International Classification of Diseases*, Ninth Revision, Clinical Modification (12); MN, malignant neoplasm; SMR, standardized mortality ratio.
† Grouped according to the National Institute for Occupational Safety and Health (NIOSH) Life Table Analysis System (13).

does alcohol use appear to be excessive in the cohort (cirrhosis of the liver SMR = 0.63, transportation injuries SMR = 0.73).

Total mortality and cancers in the aggregate showed a small increase in risk of 5–20 percent in relation to duration of employment in exposed jobs (table 3). Leukemia showed no consistent elevations in mortality in relation to duration of work in exposed jobs except for work as an electrician, which was associated with a 2.5-fold elevation after 20 years of such work. Linemen actually showed modestly reduced leukemia mortality. Results for leukemia subtypes (not shown) were imprecise but yielded a similar pattern of somewhat reduced risks for work as a lineman, no association for power plant workers, and increased risk for work as an electrician (acute myeloid leukemia rate ratio (RR) = 2.0, 95 percent confidence interval (CI) 0.7–5.9; chronic lymphocytic leukemia RR = 1.9,

95 percent CI 0.5–6.5). Work for 5 or more years in any exposed occupation also yielded an increased risk of chronic lymphocytic leukemia (RR = 2.1, 95 percent CI 0.9–5.1).

Total mortality and total cancers again showed a small but statistically precise increase in risk (up to a mortality rate ratio of 1.2) with increasing cumulative magnetic field exposure (table 4), perhaps as a result of the diminution of the healthy worker effect. However, leukemia was not related to cumulative career magnetic field exposure or exposure in any of the other time windows. Acute myeloid and chronic lymphocytic leukemia showed a similar absence of association with the possible minor exceptions of an increased risk for acute myeloid leukemia in the greatest career exposure group and for chronic lymphocytic leukemia based on a continuous dose measure in the 2- to 10-year window (table 5).

**TABLE 3.  Mortality by duration of employment in selected occupations: US Utility Worker Mortality Study, 1950–1988**

| Duration of employment (years) | Exposed occupations* | | | Lineman | | | Electrician | | | Power plant operator | | |
|---|---|---|---|---|---|---|---|---|---|---|---|---|
| | No. of cases | RR† | 95% CI† | No. of cases | RR | 95% CI | No. of cases | RR | 95% CI | No. of cases | RR | 95% CI |
| **Total mortality** | | | | | | | | | | | | |
| 0–5 | 9,926 | 1.00 | | 18,414 | 1.00 | | 19,578 | 1.00 | | 19,205 | 1.00 | |
| 5–<20 | 6,252 | 1.09 | 1.05–1.13 | 1,534 | 1.16 | 1.10–1.22 | 744 | 1.01 | 0.94–1.09 | 1,000 | 1.04 | 0.98–1.11 |
| ≥20 | 4,555 | 1.13 | 1.09–1.18 | 785 | 1.12 | 1.04–1.21 | 411 | 1.17 | 1.06–1.29 | 528 | 1.11 | 1.02–1.21 |
| **Total cancers** | | | | | | | | | | | | |
| 0–5 | 2,151 | 1.00 | | 4,290 | 1.00 | | 4,558 | 1.00 | | 4,471 | 1.00 | |
| 5–<20 | 1,520 | 1.19 | 1.11–1.29 | 342 | 1.12 | 0.99–1.25 | 179 | 1.00 | 0.86–1.17 | 226 | 0.99 | 0.86–1.13 |
| ≥20 | 1,162 | 1.19 | 1.09–1.29 | 201 | 1.09 | 0.94–1.26 | 96 | 1.06 | 0.87–1.30 | 136 | 1.10 | 0.92–1.30 |
| **Leukemia** | | | | | | | | | | | | |
| <5 | 82 | 1.00 | | 154 | 1.00 | | 151 | 1.00 | | 152 | 1.00 | |
| 5–<20 | 54 | 1.31 | 0.87–1.97 | 6 | 0.53 | 0.23–1.23 | 7 | 1.35 | 0.62–2.94 | 12 | 1.10‡ | 0.92–1.30 |
| ≥20 | 28 | 1.00 | 0.60–1.65 | 4 | 0.68 | 0.25–1.86 | 6 | 2.50 | 1.08–5.76 | | | |
| **Brain cancer** | | | | | | | | | | | | |
| 0–<5 | 61 | 1.00 | | 123 | 1.00 | | 132 | 1.00 | | 133 | 1.00 | |
| 5–<20 | 56 | 1.87 | 1.20–2.92 | 15 | 1.58 | 0.89–2.80 | 12 | 1.64 | 0.89–3.03 | 7 | 0.99 | 0.46–2.13 |
| ≥20 | 27 | 1.45 | 0.83–2.53 | 6 | 1.21 | 0.52–2.83 | | | | 4 | 1.28 | 0.48–3.47 |

\* Exposed occupations include technical workers, craft supervisors, service workers, mechanics, machinists, boilermakers, electricians, linemen, instrument and control technicians, relay technicians, telecommunication technicians, cable splicers, power plant operators, substation operators, riggers, painters, pipe coverers, and welders.

† CI, confidence interval; RR, rate ratio (adjusted for age, calendar year, race, social class, work status (active/inactive), polychlorinated biphenyl exposure, and solvent exposure).

‡ Data were collapsed to obtain at least four cases in each stratum; rate ratio is defined for the interval plus all higher intervals.

Brain cancer was weakly associated with duration of work in exposed jobs in the aggregate and with the larger individual jobs (table 3), with rate ratios generally increased with longer duration of work. In contrast, the association between estimated magnetic field exposure and brain cancer was notably stronger. For career exposure, the categorical analysis yielded rate ratios of 1.5–1.7 in the middle three groups and a rate ratio of 2.3 in the highest interval, all of which were reasonably precise. The continuous measure predicted a more modest increase in risk of 5 percent per microtesla-year of exposure. Presumably, the absence of a gradient in the middle three groups (where 60 percent of the cases occurred) dampened the overall dose-response pattern. In the 2- to 10-year window, there was a monotonic dose-response gradient using a categorical measure, with an odds ratio of 2.6 in the highest interval, as well as a marked increase based on a continuous exposure measure. According to this model, brain cancer mortality increases by a factor of 1.94 for each microtesla-year of exposure accrued in the previous 2- to 10-year period. (Note that accrual of a microtesla-year requires much greater exposure differences within such narrow time windows.) Much smaller associations were found for a longer latency of 10–20 years or career exposure, with little indication of increased risk for exposures 20 or more years in the past.

## DISCUSSION

Mortality from most causes, including leukemia and brain cancer, was reduced in this cohort of electric utility workers relative to the US population. In comparisons among electric utility workers, leukemia mortality was somewhat increased among men who worked as electricians, but not among linemen, power plant operators, or exposed occupations in general. Quantitative indices of magnetic field exposure gave little indication of an increased risk with increasing exposure for leukemias in the aggregate, nor was there clear evidence of an increased risk with increasing exposure for acute myeloid or chronic lymphocytic leukemia.

Brain cancer, in contrast, was associated with increased mortality rate ratios with prolonged employment in exposed jobs. Notably larger rate ratios were found for the highest intervals of cumulative magnetic field exposure, peaking at 2.3 for career exposure and 2.6 for exposure 2–10 years previously. Risk per unit of exposure was markedly greater for exposure in the interval of 2–10 years previously (RR = 1.94 per microtesla-year) than for career exposures (RR = 1.07), suggesting a relatively short latency period for any adverse effect.

Previous studies of leukemia among electrical workers yielded relative risks generally in the range of 1.2 to 2.0 (2, 3, 23). The principal reason for a concern

**TABLE 4.** Mortality in relation to magnetic field exposure: US Utility Worker Mortality Study, 1950–1988

| Exposure level (µT-years) | Total mortality | | | Total cancer | | | Leukemia | | | Brain cancer | | |
|---|---|---|---|---|---|---|---|---|---|---|---|---|
| | No. of cases | RR* | 95% CI* | No. of cases | RR | 95% CI | No. of cases | RR | 95% CI | No. of cases | RR | 95% CI |
| **Total exposure** | | | | | | | | | | | | |
| 0–<0.6 | 6,314 | 1.00 | | 1,269 | 1.00 | | 54 | 1.00 | | 41 | 1.00 | |
| 0.6–<1.2 | 4,117 | 1.06 | 1.02–1.10 | 959 | 1.05 | 0.96–1.14 | 34 | 1.04 | 0.66–1.63 | 34 | 1.61 | 0.99–2.63 |
| 1.2–<2.0 | 4,118 | 1.04 | 1.00–1.09 | 1,055 | 1.10 | 1.01–1.20 | 35 | 1.13 | 0.70–1.82 | 26 | 1.47 | 0.84–2.56 |
| 2.0–<4.3 | 4,124 | 1.11 | 1.06–1.16 | 1,045 | 1.14 | 1.04–1.25 | 27 | 0.95 | 0.56–1.60 | 27 | 1.65 | 0.92–2.95 |
| ≥4.3 | 2,060 | 1.23 | 1.16–1.30 | 505 | 1.22 | 1.09–1.37 | 14 | 1.11 | 0.57–2.14 | 16 | 2.29 | 1.15–4.56 |
| RR per µT-year | 20,733 | 1.02 | 1.01–1.03 | 4,833 | 1.02 | 1.01–1.03 | 164 | 1.01 | 0.94–1.08 | 144 | 1.07 | 1.01–1.14 |
| **Past 2–10 years** | | | | | | | | | | | | |
| 0 | 8,388 | 1.00 | | 1,797 | 1.00 | | 65 | 1.00 | | 31 | 1.00 | |
| >0–<0.2 | 3,687 | 0.94 | 0.90–0.98 | 825 | 1.05 | 0.97–1.15 | 30 | 0.88 | 0.56–1.38 | 22 | 1.17 | 0.66–2.08 |
| 0.2–<0.4 | 3,070 | 0.96 | 0.91–1.00 | 752 | 1.05 | 0.95–1.16 | 25 | 0.87 | 0.51–1.49 | 26 | 1.39 | 0.75–2.58 |
| 0.4–<0.7 | 2,705 | 1.00 | 0.95–1.06 | 713 | 1.17 | 1.05–1.31 | 28 | 1.21 | 0.70–2.10 | 22 | 1.46 | 0.76–2.84 |
| ≥0.7 | 2,883 | 0.99 | 0.94–1.05 | 746 | 1.12 | 1.00–1.26 | 16 | 0.65 | 0.33–1.29 | 43 | 2.56 | 1.35–4.86 |
| RR per µT-year | 20,733 | 1.04 | 1.00–1.08 | 4,833 | 1.10 | 1.01–1.19 | 164 | 0.96 | 0.60–1.53 | 144 | 1.94 | 1.34–2.81 |
| **Past 10–20 years** | | | | | | | | | | | | |
| 0 | 4,127 | 1.00 | | 809 | 1.00 | | 40 | 1.00 | | 25 | 1.00 | |
| >0–<0.3 | 5,840 | 1.01 | 0.97–1.05 | 1,268 | 1.02 | 0.93–1.11 | 46 | 0.75 | 0.49–1.16 | 47 | 1.76 | 1.07–2.91 |
| 0.3–<0.5 | 4,113 | 1.04 | 1.00–1.09 | 1,033 | 1.12 | 1.02–1.23 | 33 | 0.80 | 0.50–1.29 | 23 | 1.26 | 0.69–2.29 |
| 0.5–<0.9 | 2,403 | 1.05 | 0.99–1.10 | 605 | 1.13 | 1.01–1.25 | 13 | 0.57 | 0.30–1.07 | 16 | 1.47 | 0.76–2.84 |
| ≥0.9 | 4,250 | 1.08 | 1.03–1.13 | 1,118 | 1.16 | 1.06–1.28 | 32 | 0.80 | 0.49–1.32 | 33 | 1.63 | 0.91–2.90 |
| RR per µT-year | 20,733 | 1.05 | 1.03–1.08 | 4,833 | 1.09 | 1.04–1.15 | 164 | 0.97 | 0.72–1.31 | 144 | 1.35 | 1.01–1.79 |
| **>20 years past** | | | | | | | | | | | | |
| 0 | 5,823 | 1.00 | | 1,142 | 1.00 | | 60 | 1.00 | | 63 | 1.00 | |
| >0–<0.4 | 4,508 | 1.08 | 1.04–1.13 | 1,095 | 1.11 | 1.01–1.21 | 34 | 0.65 | 0.41–1.03 | 24 | 0.76 | 0.45–1.27 |
| 0.4–<1.1 | 4,440 | 1.11 | 1.06–1.16 | 1,128 | 1.12 | 1.02–1.24 | 33 | 0.65 | 0.39–1.06 | 24 | 0.89 | 0.51–1.56 |
| 1.1–<2.0 | 2,980 | 1.13 | 1.-07–1.19 | 749 | 1.16 | 1.04–1.29 | 15 | 0.47 | 0.25–0.90 | 17 | 1.12 | 0.59–2.14 |
| ≥2.0 | 2,982 | 1.23 | 1.17–1.30 | 719 | 1.25 | 1.11–1.40 | 22 | 0.78 | 0.43–1.42 | 16 | 1.26 | 0.64–2.48 |
| RR per µT-year | 20,733 | 1.03 | 1.02–1.03 | 4,833 | 1.02 | 1.01–1.03 | 164 | 1.03 | 0.95–1.11 | 144 | 1.06 | 0.97–1.16 |

\* CI, confidence interval; RR, rate ratio (adjusted for age, calendar year, race, social class, work status (active/inactive), polychlorinated biphenyl exposure, and solvent exposure).

with excess risks of this magnitude has been the possibility that a much greater increase in risk among the subset of such workers with elevated magnetic field exposure has been diluted through exposure misclassification in studies using job titles alone. Outside the electric power industry, a study of telephone workers found imprecise indications of increased risk in relation to peak magnetic field exposures for leukemia subtypes other than chronic lymphocytic (6). A community-based study of diverse workplaces (7) did report a clear gradient of increasing risk with increasing magnetic field exposure exclusively for chronic lymphocytic leukemia, with relative risks increasing to 3.0 in the highest exposure quartile.

Two previous studies of electric power company workers yielded mixed results: Workers at Southern California Edison Company showed no evidence of increased leukemia mortality in relation to work in exposed occupations or estimated magnetic field exposure (8), but the study size was limited. The most methodologically sound study to date was recently reported concerning electric utility workers in Canada and France (9). This nested case-control study compared estimated occupational exposures, based on job titles and measurements, among men with cancer and controls from the same workforces. Among all 140 leukemia cases, a relative risk estimate of 1.5 was found for greater than median exposure, or 1.8 for exposures greater than the 90th percentile. Much stronger associations were found for acute myeloid leukemia (relative risk of 2.7 for greater than median exposure) and for chronic lymphocytic leukemia in the 20 years prior to diagnosis.

Our results for leukemia are most consistent with the Southern California Edison study (8) that reported an absence of association. The disparity with the Can-

*Am J Epidemiol* Vol. 141, No. 2, 1995

**TABLE 5.  Leukemia subtype risk by magnetic field exposure: US Utility Worker Mortality Study, 1950–1988**

| Exposure level (µT-years) | Acute myeloid leukemia | | | Chronic lymphocytic leukemia | | |
|---|---|---|---|---|---|---|
| | No. of cases | RR* | 95% CI* | No. of cases | RR | 95% CI |
| **Total exposure** | | | | | | |
| 0–<0.6 | 20 | 1.00 | | 8 | 1.00 | |
| 0.6–<1.2 | 12 | 1.28 | 0.59–2.77 | 8 | 1.33 | 0.49–3.63 |
| 1.2–<2.0 | 7 | 0.94 | 0.36–2.44 | 13 | 1.98 | 0.77–5.09 |
| 2.0–<4.3 | 5 | 0.72 | 0.24–2.18 | 5 | 0.55† | 0.17–1.82 |
| ≥4.3 | 5 | 1.62 | 0.51–5.12 | | | |
| RR per µT-year | 49 | 1.04 | 0.93–1.18 | 34 | 0.96 | 0.78–1.09 |
| **Past 2–10 years** | | | | | | |
| 0 | 17 | 1.00 | | 17 | 1.00 | |
| >0–<0.2 | 10 | 0.92 | 0.40–2.09 | 8 | 1.31 | 0.54–3.18 |
| 0.2–<0.4 | 9 | 0.98 | 0.37–2.58 | 9 | 1.08 | 0.38–3.07 |
| 0.4–<0.7 | 7 | 1.04 | 0.36–3.01 | | | |
| ≥0.7 | 6 | 0.82 | 0.25–2.68 | | | |
| RR per µT-year | 49 | 1.08 | 0.48–2.42 | 34 | 1.47 | 0.52–4.20 |
| **Past 10–20 years** | | | | | | |
| 0 | 17 | 1.00 | | 5 | 1.00 | |
| >0–<0.3 | 13 | 0.55 | 0.26–1.16 | 11 | 1.35 | 0.46–3.92 |
| 0.3–<0.5 | 8 | 0.59 | 0.24–1.41 | 10 | 1.82 | 0.61–5.41 |
| ≥0.5 | 11 | 0.54 | 0.23–1.24 | 8 | 1.02 | 0.32–3.25 |
| RR per µT-year | 49 | 0.94 | 0.53–1.69 | 34 | 0.87 | 0.44–1.74 |
| **>20 years past** | | | | | | |
| 0 | 22 | 1.00 | | 5 | 1.00 | |
| >0–<0.4 | 12 | 0.86 | 0.39–1.90 | 10 | 1.41 | 0.44–4.52 |
| 0.4–<1.1 | 6 | 0.54 | 0.19–1.52 | 11 | 1.27 | 0.38–4.24 |
| ≥1.1 | 9 | 0.75 | 0.27–2.04 | 8 | 0.66 | 0.18–2.45 |
| RR per µT-year | 49 | 0.96 | 0.79–1.17 | 34 | 0.92 | 0.75–1.12 |

\* CI, confidence interval; RR, rate ratio (adjusted for age, calendar year, race, social class, work status (active/inactive), polychlorinated biphenyl exposure, and solvent exposure).
†Data were collapsed to obtain at least four cases in each stratum; mortality rate ratio is defined for the interval plus all greater intervals.

ada-France study is notable (9), especially since their strongest associations were with acute myeloid leukemia for which our results were mostly negative except for work as an electrician and the highest career exposure interval. Relative to the large number of studies that yielded small increases in risk based on job titles alone, our failure to find an increasing risk with increasing exposure for total leukemia does not support the hypothesis that the modest risks reported in such studies reflect stronger associations among the men who were truly exposed to elevated magnetic fields. Although we acknowledge limitations in our ability to classify exposure (see below), our methods are clearly superior to a classification system based on job title from death certificates or cancer registry data. If there is a true causal association between some aspect of occupational magnetic field exposure and leukemia or leukemia subtypes, the occurrence or detection of it must be quite sensitive to study methods such as exposure or disease classification or other characteristics of the study population.

The literature regarding electromagnetic fields and brain cancer has included several reports of substantial elevations in risk (24–26), though in the aggregate the pattern of findings is similar to that for leukemia (2, 3): Most (but not all) studies that relied on job titles for exposure information showed a modest increase in risk for electrical workers in the range of 1.2 to 2.0.

The more recent studies that incorporated quantitative exposure measurements were not as supportive of an association with brain cancer as they were for an association with leukemia. The Southern California Edison cohort study (8) generated relative risk estimates very close to the null. The community study in Sweden (7) had relative risk estimates of 1.0, 1.4, and 1.5 across the upper three quartiles of exposure relative to the lowest quartile, providing limited evidence of an association. In the Canada-France study (9), the odds ratio between above-median exposure and brain cancer was 1.5 based on 108 cases, and somewhat larger but less precise for exposures 20 or more years in the past. Because they considered incident cases from cancer registries, they were able to examine histologic types in greater detail than was possible in our mortality study.

The present study identified increased brain cancer mortality risk with increased cumulative occupational magnetic field exposure. The reasons for this deviation from the previous studies are not apparent, though part of the contrast may be more subjective than real. Both the Swedish community study (7) and the Canada-France study (9) had stronger associations for leukemia than for brain cancer, diverting attention from the brain cancer results; and the authors downplayed the brain cancer associations for lack of statistical significance. Our risk estimates of 1.5–2.5 are not markedly discordant from their reported relative risks of approximately 1.5.

There is no obvious, coherent explanation for the discrepancies among the major studies of occupational magnetic fields in relation to leukemia and brain cancer. There are, however, several candidates for both real differences among populations and methodological errors in individual studies. Exposure and its assessment are the primary areas of concern. The assumption of equivalent magnetic field exposure across settings is tenuous, particularly comparing diverse workplaces (7) with the electric utility environment (8, 9). Identical average intensity or cumulative exposure may mask important differences in the temporal patterns of that exposure. Lacking a clear biologic rationale for selecting magnetic field indices or time windows of exposure, each set of investigators makes a series of informed but arbitrary choices. Furthermore, the approach to grouping workers, selecting individuals for exposure measurement (random in our study, nonrandom in others), the types of instruments used (time-integrating meter in our study, continuous field monitors in others), and use of the data to classify and analyze exposure (cumulative time-weighted average in our study, multiple indices in others) may all contribute to divergent results. Given the identical treatment of men who developed the cancers of interest and those who did not, in our study as well as the others, the exposure misclassification resulting from erroneous decisions is virtually certain to be nondifferential. Such decisions would very rarely produce or exaggerate associations (27–29).

Substantial heterogeneity in risk was identified across the three participating companies in the Canada-France study (9), with the strongest associations found at the utilities with greater exposures. Our study methods were identical across the five participating electric power companies so that fluctuations in risk across companies could reflect only random or otherwise inexplicable error. Furthermore, although the more urban electric utilities tended to have somewhat greater measured magnetic field exposures than less urban electric utilities, the major differences in exposure were within, rather than between, companies. Intercompany differences were incorporated into the exposure estimates for individual workers.

Relative to the Canada-France study (9) and the Southern California Edison study (8), our measured exposures by occupational group were somewhat lower, perhaps a result of our random sampling or a reflection of real differences. Nonetheless, the relative ranking across jobs was similar for the present study and the others (8, 9); and the absolute exposure scores were within the ranges observed in the Canada-France study. Incorporating information on duration of employment and considering the methods of calculating cumulative exposure, the median exposure for our study (5.2 $\mu$T-years based on the methods used in the Canada-France study) are quite compatible with theirs (6.3, 4.9, and 2.2 across the three participating companies). Thus, different ranges of exposure are unlikely to account for the discrepant results.

Our analyses (18) suggest substantial day-to-day variability for many of the categories of electric utility workers—as much as 69 percent of the total, with an additional 16 percent between workers within the occupational categories. In light of that heterogeneity for individuals over time, the sampling error and influence of nonrandom sampling may be substantial, perhaps accounting in part for inconsistent results across studies. In addition, all studies of this industry, including the present one, suffer from some degree of misclassification, although the estimation may be better for long-term averages than for any individual workday. A separate concern is with the applicability of these present-day measurements to the entire historical period of interest. Clearly, some additional loss of accuracy will be incurred, yet the consistency of the basic manner in which electricity has been generated and distributed over the past 50 years allows this extrapolation to be made with more confidence than for most industries. Changes due to shifting responsibilities and administrative changes in job titles are likely to be a more important source of error in the application of measurement data to the past.

Disease assessment and classification also differ across studies. Ours and the Southern California Edison study (8) are based on death certificate diagnoses, while the Swedish community study (7) and the Canada-France utility worker study (9) are based on cancer registry and medical record data for diagnostic information. The latter is undoubtedly superior, yet for the broad disease groups (i.e., leukemia and brain cancer), death certificates are generally accurate (30).

*Am J Epidemiol* Vol. 141, No. 2, 1995

For leukemia and brain tumor subtypes, however, misclassification across categories can be substantial from death certificate diagnoses (30), such that our results for leukemia subtypes should be interpreted with particular caution. Since associations with leukemia in the aggregate have been consistently modest or absent (7–9) whereas associations with specific histologic types have been notable (7, 9), this limitation in our study is a potentially important one. Death certificates were coded blindly in our study, ensuring that any misclassification would be independent of exposure history. For the cancers of interest, relative survival is low for brain cancer (approximately 15–25 percent relative 5-year survival over the period of the study) and somewhat higher for all leukemia (30–35 percent) (31), with very poor survival for acute myeloid leukemia (3 percent relative 5-year survival) and much higher survival for chronic lymphocytic leukemia (46 percent relative 5-year survival) (32). Differential survival in relation to exposure could distort mortality patterns relative to incidence patterns, but there are no relevant data to address that possibility.

Finally, the potential for confounding is present in varying degrees in all of these studies. Several of the recent studies including ours have considered and found no evidence of confounding (7, 9). Exposures to tobacco smoke (associated with leukemia (33)) and other behavioral factors such as diet and alcohol use were not incorporated in our study. Limited data on tobacco use at one of the companies in the Canada-France study (9) suggested no association with magnetic field exposure, consistent with the absence of elevations in mortality from smoking-related causes of death in the present study. It seems unlikely that confounding by unmeasured factors has occurred in a sufficient degree to create or mask sizable associations.

Firm conclusions regarding whether magnetic fields cause cancer, based on our study alone or on the entire literature, are not yet possible. Nonetheless, the methodological strengths of our study give our results sizable influence on the overall pattern. The general hypothesis that prolonged exposure to power frequency magnetic fields increases the risk of leukemia is not supported by our study. The same hypothesis applied to chronic lymphocytic leukemia is somewhat less clearly disputed. However, the hypothesis that prolonged exposure to power frequency magnetic fields increases the risk of brain cancer is rather strongly supported, with consistent evidence that more highly exposed jobs are associated with greater risk and an overall indication that greater exposure, particularly with a short latency period, is associated with an increased risk.

We could not test more specific and subtle hypotheses regarding other characteristics of exposure such as magnetic field peaks or transients or electric fields, nor could we address more refined disease categories such as astrocytoma. If disparate study results accurately reflect the consequences of electric or magnetic fields that differ in character across settings, then those subtle aspects of exposure need to be quantified and studied in relation to cancer. On the other hand, our markers of magnetic field exposure may be accurately identifying a real but very modest increase in risk, with variation in the prevalence of unidentified cofactors accounting for differences among populations. The populations studied in Sweden (7), Canada and France (9), and even southern California (8) may differ from our populations in ways that act in concert with magnetic field exposures to determine cancer risk.

Our study, in conjunction with the Canada-France study (9), has markedly improved exposure classification, has addressed occupational confounders, and has examined time windows of exposure without either refuting a positive association between exposure and the risk of brain cancer and leukemia or convincingly establishing its presence. Given the logistical challenge and expense of conducting large studies of these rare health outcomes, repetition of studies with only those virtues would be ill-advised. Future investigations of these diseases in relation to magnetic field exposure should be driven either by a unique opportunity to more accurately reconstruct historical exposure or by more specific, testable hypotheses regarding biologically relevant exposure metrics or markers of susceptibility to exposure that could test with more precision whether there is a causal link between exposure and disease.

## ACKNOWLEDGMENTS

This study was supported by contract RP-2964–05 from the Electric Power Research Institute (EPRI), Palo Alto, California.

We would like to acknowledge the following individuals' substantial contribution to the design, conduct, and analysis of this study: University of North Carolina colleagues Drs. Michael Flynn, Lawrence Kupper, Stephen Rappaport, and Lori Todd; Dr. Hans Kromhout of Wageningen Agricultural University in the Netherlands; research assistants Dr. Stephen Browning, Kevin Chen, Gary Mihlan, Dr. Lucy Peipins, and Sandy West; computer programmers Dr. Robert Kleckner, Richard Howard, Eileen Gregory, and Joy Wood; EPRI project officers Robert Black and Dr. Leeka Kheifets; EPRI scientific advisors Drs. A. A. Afifi, Patricia Buffler, and James Quackenboss; collaborating contractors

J. Michael Silva and Richard Iriye of Enertech Consultants; Dr. William Kaune of EM Factors; Dr. Margaret Pennybacker of Battelle–Survey Research Associates; Judy Rayner of Westat, Inc.; and William West. In addition, we are most appreciative of the large number of electric utility employees from Carolina Power and Light, Pacific Gas and Electric, PECO Energy Company (formerly Philadelphia Electric Company), Tennessee Valley Authority, and Virginia Electric Power Company who devoted a substantial amount of time assisting us with many aspects of the study.

## REFERENCES

1. Milham S. Mortality from leukemia in workers exposed to electrical and magnetic fields. (Letter). N Engl J Med 1982; 307:249.
2. Thériault GP. Health effects of electromagnetic radiation on workers: epidemiologic studies. In: Bierbaum PE, Peters JM, eds. Proceedings of the scientific workshop on the health effects of electric and magnetic fields on workers. Cincinnati, OH: National Institute for Occupational Safety and Health, 1991. (DHHS publication no. (NIOSH) 91–111).
3. Savitz DA, Ahlbom A. Epidemiologic evidence on cancer in relation to residential and occupational exposures. In Carpenter DO, Ayrapetyan S, eds. Biological effects of electric and magnetic fields, Vol II. San Diego: Academic Press, 1994: 233–61.
4. Deadman JE, Camus M, Armstrong BG, et al. Occupational and residential 60-Hz electromagnetic fields and high-frequency transients: exposure assessment using a new dosimeter. Am Ind Hyg Assoc J 1988;49:409–19.
5. Bowman JD, Garabrant DH, Sobel E, et al. Exposures to extremely low frequency (ELF) electromagnetic fields in occupations with elevated leukemia rates. Appl Ind Hyg 1988; 3:189–94.
6. Matanoski GM, Elliot EA, Breysse PN, et al. Leukemia in telephone linemen. Am J Epidemiol 1993;137:609–19.
7. Floderus B, Persson T, Stenlund C, et al. Occupational exposure to electromagnetic fields in relation to leukemia and brain tumors: a case-control study in Sweden. Cancer Causes Control 1993;4:465–76.
8. Sahl JD, Kelsh MA, Greenland S. Cohort and nested case-control studies of hematopoietic cancers and brain cancer among electric utility workers. Epidemiology 1993;4:104–14.
9. Thériault G, Goldberg M, Miller AB, et al. Cancer risks associated with occupational exposure to magnetic fields among electric utility workers in Ontario and Quebec, Canada, and France: 1970–1989. Am J Epidemiol 1994;139:550–72.
10. Acquavella JF, Donaleski D, Hanis NM. An analysis of mortality follow-up through the National Death Index for a cohort of refinery and petrochemical workers. Am J Ind Med 1986; 9:181–7.
11. Boyle CA, Decoufle P. National sources of vital status information: extent of coverage and possible selectivity in reporting. Am J Epidemiol 1990;131:160–8.
12. US Health Care Financing Administration. Commission on Professional and Hospital Activities. International Classification of Diseases. Ninth revision, clinical modification. 2nd ed. Washington, DC: US GPO, 1980. (DHHS publication no. (PHS) 80–1260).
13. Steenland K, Beaumont J, Spaeth S, et al. New developments in the Life Table Analysis System of the National Institute for Occupational Safety and Health. J Occup Med 1990;32: 1091–8.
14. Percy C, Van Holten V, Muir C, eds. International classification of diseases for oncology. 2nd ed. Geneva: World Health Organization, 1990.
15. Loomis DP, Peipins LA, Browning SR, et al. Organization and classification of work history data in industry-wide studies: an application to the electric power industry. Am J Industr Med 1994;26:413–25.
16. Loomis DP, Kromhout H, Peipins LA, et al. Sampling design and field methods of a large, randomized, multi-site survey of occupational magnetic field exposure. Appl Occup Environ Hyg 1994;9:49–52.
17. Kaune WT, Niple JC, Liu MJ, et al. Small integrating meter for assessing long-term exposure to magnetic fields. Bioelectromagnetics 1992;13:413–27.
18. Kromhout H, Loomis DP, Mihlan GJ, et al. Assessment and grouping of occupational magnetic field exposure in five electric utility companies. Scand J Work Environ Health (in press).
19. Bailar JC, Ederer F. Significance of variance to Poisson expectations. Biometrics 1964;20:639–43.
20. Frome EL, Checkoway H. Use of Poisson regression models in estimating incidence rates and ratios. Am J Epidemiol 1985;121:309–23.
21. Payne CD, ed. The GLIM System, release 3.77 manual. 2nd ed. Oxford, United Kingdom: Royal Statistical Society, 1987.
22. Steenland K, Stayner L. The importance of employment status in occupational cohort mortality studies. Epidemiology 1991; 2:418–23.
23. Savitz DA, Calle EE. Leukemia and occupational exposure to electromagnetic fields: review of epidemiological surveys. J Occup Med 1987;29:47–51.
24. Lin RS, Dischinger PC, Conde J, et al. Occupational exposure to electromagnetic fields and the occurrence of brain tumors. J Occup Med 1985;27:413–19.
25. Speers MA, Dobbins JG, Miller VS. Occupational exposures and brain cancer mortality: a preliminary study of east Texas residents. Am J Industr Med 1988;13:629–38.
26. Thomas TL, Stolley PD, Stemhagen A, et al. Brain tumor mortality risk among men with electrical and electronics jobs: a case-control study. J Natl Cancer Inst 1987;79:233–8.
27. Copeland KT, Checkoway H, McMichael AJ, et al. Bias due to misclassification in the estimation of relative risk. Am J Epidemiol 1977;105:488–95.
28. Dosemeci M, Wacholder S, Lubin JH. Does nondifferential misclassification of exposure always bias a true effect toward the null value? Am J Epidemiol 1990;132:746–8.
29. Brenner H, Loomis D. Varied forms of bias due to nondifferential error in measuring exposure. Epidemiology 1994;5: 510–17.
30. Percy C, Stanek E, Gloeckler L. Accuracy of cancer death certificates and its effect on cancer mortality statistics. Am J Public Health 1981;71:242–50.
31. Ries LAG, Hankey BF, Edwards BK, eds. Cancer statistics review: 1973–1987. Bethesda, MD: National Cancer Institute, 1990. (NIH publication no. 90–2789).
32. Myers MH, Hankey BF. Cancer patients' survival in the United States. In: Schottenfeld D, Fraumeni JF Jr, eds. Cancer epidemiology and prevention. Philadelphia: WB Saunders Company, 1982:166–78.
33. Friedman GD. Cigarette smoking, leukemia, and multiple myeloma. Ann Epidemiol 1993;3:425–8.

ACV5057

VERMONT STATE COLLEGES

0 0003 0642934 1

LIBRARY
LYNDON STATE COLLEGE
LYNDONVILLE, VT  05851

ACV5057